Unveil the Shadows. Discover the Love.

When supernatural and human worlds collide, a werewolf security chief and an ambitious witch must overcome forbidden love, unexplained visions, and secret awakenings to save themselves and their intertwined communities from the cataclysmic fall of the veil.

Beyond the boundaries of our reality lies a world teetering on the edge of revelation and ruin. In the supernatural world of the Enlightened, werewolf Noah Hernandez, second-in-command at the Larkshead Sanctuary and head of Dark Wolf Security, navigate a mysterious series of unsanctioned human awakenings into the Enlightened realm. Drawn into this perilous investigation is his magnetic but unenlightened neighbor, Emily Rollins —a resourceful witch with ambitions of transitioning her online candle business into a thriving market stall. But Emily's dreams are shrouded in haunting visions of demonic forces, strange happenings, and an irresistible pull towards Noah.

As their worlds spiral ever closer, a surprising connection between Emily's candles and the unsanctioned awakenings immerses them deeper into a world of secrets and hidden desires. With the impending fall of the veil threatening to expose and obliterate their realities, Emily and Noah must navigate the labyrinth of love and danger, fighting to protect their love and their very existence.

A thrilling supernatural saga of hidden worlds, forbidden love, and devastating secrets, 'Yule Moon' is an extraordinary journey through the uncharted territories of passion, peril, and undying loyalty.

With love from Mary

YULE MOON

FALL OF THE VEIL

SABBAT SERIES
BOOK ONE

DEANN BELL

To Rachel,

May magic find you and
guide you to your next
wonderful adventure!
Blessed Be!
DeAnn Bell

Yule Moon
Fall of the Veil
Sabbat Series Book 1
COPYRIGHT©2023
DeAnn Bell
Cover Design by Wren Taylor

Published in the United States of America by:

DLG Publishing Partners

San Antonio, TX 78217

www.DLGPublishingPartners.com

This is for my witchy mother Kismet Seddon and my gorgeous husband Rob Bell. You light the way when my path is dark.

The rules of magic are basic...so basic, in fact, that most people must make up elaborate rituals in order to convince themselves that magic really exists. – Phoebe Pearce, *Witchcraft for the Newly Awakened*

From the darkness, she called to him.

Noah Hernandez twisted in his sheets, his blood on fire with the need to find and claim his mate. He sat up slowly in bed, opening himself up to her completely, reaching back through their connected souls to welcome her. Before the sun could melt the frost from the grass, he found himself standing on his front porch, scanning the familiar outlines of the forest around his home. Cool air washed over his naked bed-warmed skin. The silver-white crescent moon centered his spirit, but only the stillness of the ebbing night greeted him. He had to find her.

Like water pouring from one glass into another, he fell

forward onto all fours and let the wolf-change take him. In the way of his people, his body lost all shape and re-formed, flesh becoming fur, arms becoming legs, thick muscles settling over solid bones to become a werewolf. There was no violence or pain in the change. It was as simple and natural to his people as breathing. Stretching his powerful muscles, he shook the cold out of his thick cinnamon-colored fur and scented the air. Like a radio suddenly dialed into the correct station, the dream-laden mind of his life-mate connected with his.

Fear, desire, excitement, determination, longing, and isolation all mixed together, flooding his mind until he could hardly tell one emotion from the other. She was moving toward him, but whether that movement was physical or emotional, he couldn't tell. All he really knew was that she was reaching blindly toward him, unable to find him. Moving into the forest, he allowed his instincts to guide his steps. His howl sliced through the silence of the approaching dawn. Senses wide open, he could feel the sun moving just under the horizon, turning the waxing moon into its shadowy self. Reaching toward her, he flooded her with reassurance.

You are not alone. I hear you. We will find each other. Tell me where you are, and I will come to you.

Moving through his territory, he tried to share with her the sounds of the first birds awakening in the dawn, the pungent smell of seawater that lapped up on the rocky shore, anything that might tempt her to stay with him. She wasn't a werewolf. He knew that for sure. The way she reached for him was unique to anything he'd experienced before. Their connection was also clearest at night.

Perhaps she was a vampire or demon? But that didn't feel right. He increased his speed without thought or direction, hoping to exhaust his body enough to quiet his mind and clear the connection between them.

There was an urgency in her call that hadn't been there before. In the morning, he would inform his mother, Alpha, in the pack. He needed to take leave of his duties to find his mate. She would no doubt shove him directly out the door if he promised to return with a wife. His heart fluttered with excitement. He had a life-mate. He howled again, shouting his pleasure and gratitude to the waning moon. The Goddess had blessed him.

She is real and ready to join her life with mine.

The mating call wasn't unique to his kind. Many of the Enlightened had ways to recognize their life partners, but werewolf mates reached out unconsciously, regardless of their species, only when they were ready to join. He hadn't realized he was ready himself until her mind had first touched his. Every thought and action after that moment was directed at preparing himself to be what she needed. Bounding through the twilight woods, tongue lulling and tail wagging, he played in the pale dappled moonlight dashing this way and then that way like an excited puppy.

The crunching sound of his paws on gravel brought him out of his thoughts, and he recognized he was standing on the driveway of his neighbor's log cabin. It was the mirror image of his own, a single-story structure built around a large stone chimney with a high-pitched roof surrounded by a wrap-around porch.

Mildred Macclesfield had lived next door to him for

the last fifteen years, but he couldn't remember the last time he'd come to visit her at home. A witch, a psychic, and a good friend of his mother's, she was also forty years older than him and preferred women, which put her firmly outside the possibility of being his life-mate. Still, he couldn't deny the urge in his body to enter Mildred's cabin. He stood quietly for a moment, his large, black-tipped ears tilting back and forth, trying to understand the instinct to go inside. *Was Mildred connected to his hunt?*

Her cabin door suddenly swung open, and she stepped out onto her front porch. Her white hair floated around her silvery nightgown in the pale light before dawn. Barefoot and in her pajamas, she walked down her driveway, then stood directly in front of him.

He came closer, noting her stiff posture and her unfocused grey eyes. She was caught in a deep and powerful vision. The hair stood on the back of his neck. Her hand drifted from her side, and she rested her palm on the top of his head. Instantly images of people and places he'd never seen crashed through his mind.

A tiny apartment filled with candles, then the cabin here in the woods, the smell of beeswax and magic, his own face beaming with love, a tall golden-haired woman floating face down in the waves of the icy ocean in a place he vaguely recognized as Red Bay. He snarled in surprise, and Mildred snapped her hand back like she'd been scalded. Her eyes blinked slowly back to focus.

For long moments his mind couldn't tell the difference between real life and the vision. Something was vitally important about it, but like an early morning nightmare slipping from the conscious mind, the urgency vanished.

4

"Noah?" she murmured, looking first at him and then around in the early dawn light. Mildred rubbed her slender hands up and down her arms to ward away the cold. "You need to run home now. Your phone is about to ring. It's important." She didn't wait for him to respond. She just turned on her heels and went back into her house.

He followed Mildred's instructions and ran for home. The forest opened to him, feeding his senses with the scents of rabbit and deer, distant hearth fires, the sounds of leaves crunching under his feet, and the underlying call for life to yield to the wheel of the year and prepare for winter.

This was his territory, and he loved every hill, mountain, tree, and gully. He loved the rugged shoreline and the fierceness of the Atlantic Sea. The thought of bringing his mate here, of showing his home to her for the first time, shook away the last of his reserve. He would pack now and leave today. The journey home was made in record time. Leaping up the three stairs of his own front porch, he transformed again, landing with ease on his human feet. If he hurried, he could pack a bag and tell his family he was leaving at breakfast. The harsh twang of his ringtone greeted him as he opened the front door. Hurrying to his bedside table, he scooped the phone off the charger, not bothering to look at the number. Only his family had the nerve to call him this early in the morning. "Make it quick, I'm heading out the door."

"Noah Hernandez?"

The formalness of his name made Noah pause in his search for clothing. "Speaking."

"This is Frank Carlos from the National Recovery Unit. I'm sorry to call so early. Are you somewhere you can talk?"

Werewolves, vampires, fey, selkie, and all the other Enlightened had only one ultimate body of law, and that was the National Recovery Unit. The Enlightened were subject to State and Federal law, just like the Unenlightened, but those rules came after individual territory laws and that of the Recovery Unit assigned to each territory. It was a complex system designed to keep the dwindling number of Enlightened safe. Noah had only ever been contacted by the nearby Augusta Recovery Unit where his sister, Selene, worked, and even that had been infrequent.

"Forgive me, Mr. Carlos. What can I do for you?"

"Larkshead is a larger territory than I would have expected for a single Alpha wolf."

Frank tried for a casual tone and might have succeeded in fooling another type of Enlightened being, but Noah's wolf hearing allowed him to interpret a larger range of pitches.

"Larkshead is a werewolf sanctuary, not a single territory."

The sanctuary was a space where new werewolves could acclimate to their powers without the threat of physical violence or worries about pack ranks. With an influx of other Enlightened looking for safe space in an increasingly vigilant world, the sanctuary size was triple what would be considered manageable by a single Alpha, but his mother, Angela, managed it without much difficulty.

Frank whistled. "Paperwork says you're second in command in this territory and first to be contacted by the Recovery Network in regards to Guides. It also says you're a partner in Dark Wolf security. Is that right?"

"Yes. I head up the Guide network in this territory. Dark Wolf gives the newly Enlightened somewhere to earn a living while they learn territory rules. Are we under some sort of investigation, Mr. Carlos?" Noah pulled open drawers throwing underwear, socks, a t-shirt, and a sweater onto his bed. He pulled the clothes on in no particular order and started looking for his overnight bag.

"Lord, no." Frank laughed, dropping the formalness from his approach. "Listen, I apologize for the questions. I was satisfying my own curiosity. Larkshead is just about the only territory functioning without additional support from National."

That information got Noah's full attention. "What's going on?"

"I'm calling because I've got an officer down here from the Recovery Unit in Millinocket. He's here regarding the Unguided situation. Are you familiar with it?"

"More than familiar. My sister, Dr. Selene Hernandez, is working with the epidemiology team in charge of tracking the outbreaks in Boston."

"Good. That saves me some talking. The outbreak is spreading fast. We've just had a report from your area of an unsanctioned awakening."

Noah sat down hard on his bed, all thoughts of

packing momentarily knocked from his thoughts. Lark-shead only had a very small population of Unenlightened people—so much so that he knew almost all the names of every individual. "Who is it?"

"Carl Wedgewood, selkie, had his Unenlightened wife, Janet, come through the Veil a couple of hours ago. He claims she was cooking breakfast, and he shifted before he came inside their home. He said it takes his eyes a little while to adjust to his human form but in the fifteen years they've been married, she's never remarked on it. He says this morning, she saw him and started screaming. He tried to reassure her, but she shut down."

Selkies, like werewolves, mated for life. When forced through the Veil, most unenlightened went immediately into shock. They fell down where they stood with their eyes open, and the majority of them never moved again. They could be medically kept alive but they never regained consciousness. He couldn't imagine the pain of losing a life-mate that way. "I'm sorry."

"Don't be. By the time he put her in bed and called the Recovery Unit, she had completed the awakening and started screaming for help. It's the damnedest thing. She came completely through the Veil in under ten minutes with no sign of further shutdown."

"That's not possible."

"I know, but it's true nonetheless. We've sent a nearby agent to take her into custody until she can get to grips with what's going on, but we'd appreciate if you could check in on Mr. Wedgewood. He was pretty shaken. We need to know what happened. Most of all, we need to know who brought her through without injuring her. I don't have to tell you, Mr. Hernandez, that there are a lot of people this information could help."

"You don't think he did it?"

"No. I've been wrong before, but he knows the consequences of an unsanctioned awakening. If she shut down permanently, he would too. We both know for a life-bonded Enlightened, the risk wouldn't be worth it. We think someone else forced her through. We need to know who and why."

Noah stood up and headed for his closet to continue packing. "I'll assign an officer and inform my Alpha. I have time to make arrangements for Janet to begin the integration process. What Recovery Center is she in?"

"Augusta, but the center is pretty overrun right now, so we're thinking about moving her."

"Keep her close to the coast. The integration will be less stressful for both of them if Carlos can easily return to the sea. This separation from her will be excruciating for both of them."

"I'll keep her in Augusta. Windham and Brunswick are already short on guides. We have Unguided cases from New Mexico to New York and some reports of cases in Canada and the UK. It's spreading fast. At this rate, the newly Enlightened will outnumber the Unenlightened by the Winter Solstice."

For the second time that morning, the hair stood on the back of his neck. The newly Enlightened were unpredictable. Learning to control their power while their whole lives changed around them was scary and frustrating, but it didn't have to be. That's why Noah had become a guide. That's why his parents had established the sanctuary. "What are the current instructions concerning the Unguided?"

"Collect and contain. We are sending units in to help with the rehabilitation, but there are not enough to go around. We might have to lean on you a little harder in the coming months." Frank sounded both tired and embarrassed. "I'd also like to keep the Millinocket Recovery agent who initially recovered Janet Wedgewood down there to make sure that all of your territory is thoroughly covered. He's new to the job but effective. By all accounts, you're the best in your territory. I've formally requested that you provide guidance for him."

Noah clenched his teeth, looking down at his half-packed bag. If he asked permission to leave to find his mate, his mom would let him go, even if it meant defying the National Recovery Unit and taking all the additional duties on herself. He would have to delay leaving at least long enough to ensure this new agent was sound. "You know I can't give that permission. Crossing territory is one thing. Giving another agent authority on our land is my Alpha's decision. She won't appreciate the outside interference, especially during the Christmas Market."

"If there was another way to do this, I would."

"What's the name of your agent?"

"Garland. We'd like you to accompany him to take the report from Mr. Wedgewood. We've asked our agent to make contact with you as soon as possible and to defer to your judgment and that of your Alpha until the situation passes."

"Sounds good." Noah rubbed the bridge of his nose. "Do you want our pack to report any further Unguided to you directly, or are we still okay to deal with the main unit in Augusta?"

Frank's laugh was humorless. "Send it to Augusta. I've got enough work of my own."

2

The trouble with witchcraft comes when a witch isn't specific enough with spell requests. Magic has no sense of human values. If you ask for money and then find a penny on the ground, then Magic feels it has done its job. – Phoebe Pearce, *Witchcraft for the Newly Awakened*

The brightly colored sign said *Larkshead Christmas Village- 10 Miles*. Emily Rollins breathed a sigh of relief and rolled her tight shoulders. She was almost there. The Larkshead Christmas Village was one of the most exclusive in New England, so exclusive in fact that it had taken her three years of applications to obtain a shared space to sell her candles. In some ways, she was lucky because the shared spaces tended to be indoors. As a Kentucky girl, she was pretty sure her entire budget would have been consumed trying to heat an outdoor stall.

Her sedan was packed to the rafters with the things she thought she'd need to survive the Larkshead

Christmas season, which started November 3rd and lasted 'till January 2nd. She'd sold just about everything she couldn't carry and had given up her apartment for this opportunity. If she had done the math right, she'd make enough money this season to open her first real-time store. *Candle Lit*, she could see the sign for her shop now. In fact, she'd had a small one made for her stall.

The trailer that she dragged behind her was full of what was left of her belongings, her merchandise for most of the season, and the ingredients she needed to re-stock her space if her candles did better than she anticipated. Her acceptance letter stated that her Larkshead dwelling for the season was sparsely furnished and to pack appropriately, which to Emily meant bring the basics but to her grandmother meant bring everything. They'd compromised, meaning Emily only needed a midsized trailer rather than a moving truck. She still couldn't believe this was actually happening.

As September moved into October and her acceptance letter had not appeared, she'd thought that she would have to wait yet another year or compromise with a smaller fair somewhere closer to home. Then she'd received a letter from Mildred Macclesfield informing her that her application had been accepted and was expected immediately. Emily read her Tarot cards, had her grandmother read her tea leaves, and even asked her grandmother to cast a little spell to get her business started on the right foot. Still, nothing stopped her heart from hammering in her chest.

Her plan was simple. Live frugally and hoard the money from her Christmas sales, see which of her products really sold in a real-time space, and save the down payment to buy a small shop in her hometown on Market Street Square. Her online sales were strong enough to convince herself that her business was a sound investment, but she doubted they would convince a bank.

She shook her head, trying to remind herself that she had all of the skills necessary to do this. She'd worked retail since she was fifteen years old, took small business classes at the local college. She knew candle-making inside and out. This was the next step in her plan. "I can do this," she whispered to the cold Maine coastline. "I will find a way to make this work."

Maine was as beautiful as she'd expected it to be. The forest around her was like something out of an old-fashioned fairy tale. The trees cradled the road in every color of red, yellow, and green imaginable. She rolled down the windows hoping the fresh air would further soothe her nerves. A cold mist gave the odd mixture of evergreen, sugar maple, and white ash that made up the forest here a hazy sheen and emphasized the earthy smell of the coming winter. She took a deep breath and then another feeling on some level that there was something familiar about the smell. That was just crazy because as far as she knew, the furthest east she'd been was Pennsylvania.

The thick forest eventually opened to reveal a narrow twisted coastal road. Her eyes were drawn again and again to the sparkling blue-grey sea filled with dozens of tiny, tree-covered islands. The sheer drop of the volcanic shorelines was interrupted every so often by a stretch of roughly pebbled beach. Little trails disappeared from the road into the dense woodland and then appeared to loop back and lead to the harbor town.

Well-kept houses appeared almost too close to the roadside, like they had crept out of the woods to catch sight of the passers-by. They became more densely packed and oddly shaped the further Emily went into town. The yards were already dotted with Christmas decorations and signs advertising everything from sleigh rides and hot chocolate to fresh seafood and winter wine tastings. The place was perfect. She'd known it immediately when she'd seen the website. This was the place to change her fate.

The road she was on went directly into the town and dumped her into a large parking lot before scattering in multiple directions amidst the strangest collection of New England businesses that she'd ever imagined. Each shop was shoved up next to the other competing with one another to see who could be more kitsch, colorful, or quirky. The sunlight and cries of seagulls around the harbor reminded Emily of summer, but that impression was quickly overridden by the stiff salty breeze coming off the bay.

She parked, making sure her trailer wasn't blocking anything and grabbed her coat out of the back seat, shrugging it on with a shiver. Other tourists wrapped in coats and hats better suited for artic exploration than Christmas shopping smiled and ate ice cream cones and sipped hot chocolate while they sat on benches or peeked through store windows.

The businesses were arranged around a large park that was being marked off by men and women in brown coats for the incoming independent stalls, which would be set up tomorrow and Saturday. On closer inspection of the shop fronts, Emily could see that each offered a unique range of homemade products, from soap and candy to wooden furniture and toys, to boutique-style clothing and housewares. What she couldn't spot was a single candle shop, corporate or otherwise. In fact, there were no chain stores in the town square at all. It was one of the selling points of the town and the reason she'd worked so hard to be here.

She walked along the outside parameter of the park, trying to locate Mildred Macclesfield and the shop they would share, The Ace of Cups. The acceptance letter was vague about the location. It did not include the address of the shop or the place Emily would be staying during the season. Along with the instructions to bring her own furnishings, it instructed her to walk the parameter of the park for luck before coming directly to The Ace of Cups.

Emily bet money her grandmother's spell was responsible for that part. Whenever Claire Rollins cast a spell, the world seemed to listen with half an ear. Claire got what she wanted but always in a roundabout way. When Emily's mom, Deja, got involved, on the other hand, the whole universe appeared to take note. Where her grandma would cast a spell for everything from parking spots to world peace, her mother concerned herself with healing and protecting natural spaces.

Emily herself was more of a dabbler where witchcraft was concerned. Blessing her scented candles and some rudimentary warding was the extent of her magical workings. The peculiar results of her grandmother's spells tended to make Emily wary of spell work in general. Unconsciously, she stroked her mother's silver pentacle. Her mother had dropped it around Emily's neck with a kiss on the brow and then walked away so they could both pretend she wasn't crying.

Walking around the parameter of the park was no hardship. A large white gazebo that would make Cinderella proud dominated the center of the park with neat footpaths in perfectly spaced rows all around it. Emily was pleased to see the grass was being covered by plastic grates to reduce foot traffic damage during the Christmas Market. Out of the corner of her eye, she caught sight of a tall, muscular man in a dark uniform and a short brown leather jacket leaping onto the rails of the white gazebo.

An even taller man in similar clothing was handing the first man a string of multi-colored Christmas lights while a very short woman with hair a color even Smurfs would envy directed the scene. Emily's attention zeroed in on the first man. In a series of visual snapshots, her eyes moved across him as her body unconsciously moved toward his. Black hair curled around the collar of his brown leather coat. Strong jaw, generous lips, wide shoulders tapering into a trim waist. Powerful arms and hands deftly wrapped a long strand of Christmas lights around the bottom edge of the structure's roof.

His movements were fast as if he'd done this a hundred times before and were on flat ground rather than balancing on a thin rail. His eyes were golden brown, a lighter shade than his skin, and framed by long black lashes. Eyes? Emily blinked realizing that the man had stopped what he was doing to look directly at her. She had his complete attention.

Pure sexual attraction unfurled in her stomach, splashing her cheeks with unexpected heat. She let out a soft, shivering breath of desire. He jumped down from the rail like a tiger coming off a branch and took a step toward her and then another, his head tilting in a questioning manner. The woman with blue hair put a hand on his arm to get his attention, and Emily broke eye contact, mortified that she'd been caught ogling. She dashed inside the nearest shop to get a hold of herself and was immediately overwhelmed by the smell of Naga Champa and Patchouli.

As a proprietor of scented candles herself, the overpowering smell of incense helped to calm her nerves, if not her heartbeat. Her attention was fixed on the door behind her, half hoping, half fearing the man she'd ogled would follow her inside. What would she say to him if he did? He was probably used to being stared at, given how beautiful he was, but that didn't give her the right to gawp like a fishwife. She took another deep breath pulling the smoky scent through her lungs and reminding herself that she was an adult who could talk to men.

Okay, it wasn't something she excelled at, but she could do it. Besides, she was only here for a couple of months. She didn't have time for a fling, no matter how tempting the offer was. Turning her back firmly on the door in an effort to appear unconcerned, she glanced around, noting the shop was designed like a series of sitting rooms rather than a retail space. There were oddly mated tables and chairs tucked around shelves that were filled with small brightly colored stones and books on every kind of divination that Emily could imagine, and some that she hadn't known existed. Not that she considered herself an expert, but her grandma used Tarot cards like some women used lipstick. Emily idly plucked a book off a shelf and let it fall open when two women came out from behind a bright green curtain that read: *Mildred Macclesfield: Professional Psychic.*

Emily read the sign again as if the words would make more sense if she read them a second time. A tall, elegant-looking woman with silver earrings shaped like crescent moons shook hands with another woman who was the very picture of an elderly tourist, complete with a Florida T-shirt and a coral fanny pack.

"I can't thank you enough, Mildred," the elegant woman said with a bright smile, "Your skills have been invaluable. Can I make another appointment before Christmas? Before the solstice, maybe?"

Mildred opened her mouth to say something but spotted Emily looking at them. "I'll have to get back to you on that, Angela." Mildred gave the woman a brief hug. "Looks like my relief just arrived." The elegant woman smiled curiously at Emily for a moment. She wore both power and authority as easily as she wore her crescent moon earrings, yet under it was an unmistakable kindness. Emily returned her smile with more than a little relief.

Mildred moved between them, plucking the book from Emily's hand. "I wondered when you'd get here." She sat the book firmly on the shelf. "You're late."

"I'm sorry. I wasn't sure where to go." Emily watched the other woman leave feeling suddenly abandoned.

"That's alright," Mildred said with a playful waggle of her brows. "Most of us have that difficulty at some point or another in our lives. Lucinda mentioned that you would have trouble finding the place. I didn't know she meant Ten months' worth of trouble, but she's a pain in the ass when it comes to specifics. Come on in, and I'll give you a tour. Then we can pop up and have a look at the cabin if you like."

"The cabin?" Emily repeated stupidly.

"Can't break the properties apart, so it's part of the sale. Lucinda said you would need a place to stay quickly. I remembered to put that in the letter, didn't I? A bit of rum, while I was writing makes everything fuzzy around the edges."

"Sale? No, there must be some sort of mistake. I'm your shop partner here for the Christmas season." Emily dug through her handbag for Mildred's letter.

"I don't make mistakes. I'm psychic, you know," Mildred said, touching her head and winking. "Lucinda said you needed a shop and somewhere to live pronto. She said you weren't going to be picky, but she's been wrong before. You aren't picky, are you?"

Emily blinked. "I'm not sure."

Mildred let out a laugh that would have impressed a donkey and slapped Emily on the shoulder. "Who is? Boiler's going to need replacing next year, which won't be cheap, but I got a feeling the price won't bother you by that time. Roofs in good shape, and taxes are paid until October next year. I expect some of that money back, mind you, but not till Lucinda and I find a place in Florida. Any other questions Noah can help you with."

Emily blinked desperately, trying to follow the conversation. "Noah?"

Mildred slapped her hands over her mouth and rolled her eyes. "Sorry. Never mind. That's later. I have the paperwork drawn up to transfer the properties, the price is non-negotiable, but if you need a little time to get the money together, that's okay just as long as I am out of here by sundown tomorrow."

Walking over to the door, she turned her sign over from Open to Closed. She rubbed her fingers fondly over her t-shirt. "I've been waiting for you for a long time. To be honest, I've had Larkshead Christmas Village up to my eyeballs. If I hear Good King Wenceslaus one more time, I might have to jingle someone's bells." She wrung her hands a moment as if worried she was putting Emily off the sale. "Don't get me wrong, the Christmas Village keeps this place open almost year-round. We get the summer tourists for seaside seafood and the camping, the leaf lookey-loos for the fall colors, and then the Christmas fanatics right up until the end of January. Business is a bit slow during the spring thaw, but I use that time to take a holiday somewhere warm. Lucinda said you don't mind the cold, but I do."

Emily felt like she'd fallen down Alice's rabbit hole. "You must be confusing me with someone else. I'm Emily Rollins. I'm just supposed to share your shop for the season, not purchase it. I don't have that kind of money even if I wanted to buy it. I don't know, Lucinda."

Mildred snorted. "Who would want to know her?

She's about as friendly as a sore-toothed badger. Between you and me, she's a better psychic than I am, but she's got a way with words that could strip paint. She said you'd be lost, but I thought she meant literally, not figuratively. Are you or are you not trying to open your own business?"

Emily opened her mouth and then closed it again. "Yes, I am, but—"

"You don't like Larkshead?" She pulled Emily behind the curtain to reveal half again as much space. Without the curtain, the shop was a rectangle with doors and display windows on the short sides facing the park on one side and the seaside on the other. It was interrupted by two offset rooms that were labeled Private Consultations and Breakroom.

"Larkshead is beautiful but—"

"Breakroom has the bathroom and kitchenette. You can keep your stock in the consultation room, I suspect. The woman before me rented out the back to a different shop owner. I use the curtain to keep the breeze out and my clients comfortable, but it depends on how much display space you need. What do you make, anyway?"

"Scented Candles," Emily said, taking in the space and trying to figure out what to do.

"Enchanted Candles? That sounds interesting. Lucinda didn't mention you were in the trade."

"Scented, not enchanted," Emily corrected, trying to decide if Mildred was serious or if this was some sort of hazing. "I mean, they are blessed, but that's different."

"That's even better. There are some rules that apply to selling enchanted objects in the town square. Otherwise, products must be homemade or locally sourced, or something like that. Bigger companies have to stay on the edges of town. If I were you, I'd keep the door of the shop on the harbor-side locked. The wind coming off the sea is wicked cold after August." Mildred pulled Emily toward the breakroom. "We'll have a cup of coffee, sign the paperwork, and then I'll take you to the cabin. Lucinda's waiting for us there."

Emily allowed herself to be pulled into the breakroom. "There is no way I can offer a fair price for this place."

"I'll decide what's fair. Are you really chasing your dreams or just looking for an excuse to give up and go back to where you came from?"

Emily shook her head as if the movement would jiggle the world back into the right order. "I am chasing my dream."

Mildred winked. "Good job, girl. Now you've caught it. What are you going to do with it?" She poured Emily a cup of coffee that could have doubled as engine oil and led her to a table that had two contracts and two pens already laid out on it. "We're going to have to move fast. Christmas season starts officially Sunday, but all the shops have to be opened for Christmas four days from now, the same day as the Christmas Market is fully set up. I've had to agree to your opening hours over the holidays because I wasn't sure when you'd get here, but you should be able to renegotiate in February for next year."

"Four days? There's no way I can get moved and set up in that time."

Mildred snorted, putting four heaping spoons of sugar into her coffee before shaking the spoon at Emily. "Can't you? Looking for that excuse to quit again? Takes a special kind of person to work in Larkshead. Lucinda said you were made for this place, and I think she's right. Don't tell her I said that. She thinks enough of herself without adding my compliments in."

Mildred sat her down in front of the contract and placed the coffee and the pen in her hands. Emily took a cautious sip and then another.

"Read it carefully. All the instructions must be followed in the letter. The cabin comes with the shop, no questions asked, but it also must remain with the shop. That's part of the deal. The next part of the deal is that when you're ready to move on out of here to something bigger, you pass both the shop and the cabin to someone just starting out. That's what I'm doing now. You pass it on for the same price I'm selling it to you for. The same price I bought it for. No more and no less. That's important."

Emily frowned. "Why?"

"Call it tradition. Call it a curse. Whatever it is, the condition is old enough that I'm not willing to find out what happens if you cross it. Five generations of owners have followed it and had a good run."

Mildred sipped her coffee quietly, watching while Emily read through the contract. There were a couple of conditions that Mildred hadn't mentioned. For the month of October, a bell would have to be installed on the shop door. On the Summer and Winter Solstice water from the sea had to be boiled in the shop and used to mop the floors, but it was the price that made Emily's heart stop. The shop and the cabin were being sold to her for one

Massachusetts Pound and ten shillings to be paid in full by the New Year.

"This can't be right," Emily whispered, taking a deep drink of coffee. "That's only about $4,500.00."

"Hmm," Mildred said with a nod. "It was cheaper when I bought it."

"It's easily worth ten times that."

Mildred shrugged, her eyes bright with humor. "Wouldn't matter if it was worth a thousand times that. I signed the contract. I agreed to sell it for what I bought it for."

"Where would I even get a Massachusetts pound or shilling?"

"The bank. They keep them for these occasions. You buy them for an outrageous fee and hand them to me for the sale, and I cash them in for a fee. Part of the rules. Think the bank wrote that part in. Best to just follow and not worry about why."

A thousand reasons why she shouldn't make this deal galloped through her mind. She wasn't even sure this woman had the right to sell the place. The cabin could be a shack in the woods. Both places could have several structural problems. According to Mildred, the store with her merchandise had to be open in four days, and at twice the floor size she had planned for. She barely had enough candles to fill the whole shop.

No shop partner meant that she would either have to stay here from open to close every day with no breaks or employ a person fast, which she also didn't have the money for. There was no place in the current layout to make her candles, and her mother was going to kill her for moving to Maine.

Each sound reason she could come up with seemed to drown in Mildred's question, was she chasing her dreams or looking for an excuse to go home? She put her hand on her mother's pentacle. If she didn't like the place, she could sell it just like she bought it and go home, right? She picked up the silver pen and signed her name on the document.

Mildred nodded her head as if she'd expected that answer. "Your Grandma said you weren't a risk taker, but I bet she's wrong. This shop has always been called The Ace of Cups—the start of a journey. Whether your journey is successful or not is up to you. If you can't make it here, the rules we agreed to still apply. Now, one more condition not on the contract, and The Ace of Cups is yours." Mildred picked up her own pen with a teasing smile.

"What's that?"

"You take this old woman and her crack-pot sister out to celebrate at The Mermaid's Song and tell me what Claire Rollins has got up to since I saw her last. I gotta special place in my heart for that woman, and I bet we could all use a drink."

Emily was being handed her dreams all neatly pack-aged. Her Grandmother's work. She should have known. Her mother was going to kill them both. She took a deep breath and then another. "It's a deal."

The lights in the shop blinked twice as Mildred signed her name to the contract.

3

Magic has a certain wildness inherent in it. Humans interpret this wildness as dangerous; a witch interprets this wildness as potential. Neither really understands that magic is neither and that they themselves are the source and the cure of that wildness. –Olivia Goldstein, *Mastering Magic*

I own a cabin. I own a shop called The Ace of Cups. I now live in Larkshead, Maine. My Mother's going to kill me when she finds out what's happened. Emily tasted the words in her mouth, trying to understand how life-changing they were. An unstoppable grin lit her face. The road to the cabin was wider than she had expected, considering that Mildred said there were only two houses on it. Her nearest neighbor was about two miles up the road. The properties shared a beach, but the series of forests and trails that stretched between the two places belonged to the Hernandez family.

Her trailer bounced around behind her as she followed Mildred deeper into the woods. The total drive should have taken about 15 minutes at a normal speed, but Mildred drove about half that speed, so Emily called her grandmother on her hands-free phone. She couldn't face her mother without a plan.

"Emily," her grandma said in a cheerful voice. "How's Maine?"

"Don't play innocent with me. What spell did you cast? And don't say you didn't because this situation has Claire Rollins written all over it."

Silence.

"Grandma?"

"My spell wasn't a spell, exactly. It was an exchange. Did you know that I used to tell fortunes down at the Missouri State Fair?"

"What does that have to do with anything? What did you exchange?"

Silence and a bit of rustling. Emily gritted her teeth, suspecting she wasn't going to like what she heard.

"It was a good deal, really. Mildred owed me a favor from years ago. I gave her a Tarot reading, a selenite crystal wand she's been after for years. You're supposed to give her money which will release her from a contract so she can move to Florida. Oh, and I promised to move with her and Lucinda to Florida."

"Grandma!"

"Don't worry, chick-a-dee. It will work itself out. Congratulations! I can't wait to come and visit you next summer. Oh, there's someone out at the door here. I'll have to talk to you later. I love you. Bye!"

Emily opened her mouth to demand answers only to be greeted by the dial tone. She rolled onto a gravel driveway behind Mildred, reeling from the information. This was a set-up. She should have known it at the shop. She got out of the car, shaking her head and looked at her new home with a critical eye.

The cabin needed work but still managed to take her breath away. From the stone chimney to the wrap-around porch, everything about it said home to Emily. There was a set of rocking chairs left of the front door, one of which contained a woman who had to be Mildred's sister, Lucinda. Emily got out of her car, following Mildred up the steps trying to take everything in.

Lucinda offered her hand. "It took you long enough to get here. Let's get this tour over with and head back to the Mermaid's Song. There's a rum with my name on it and I'm starved." She handed Emily a piece of bread, a piece of coal, a handful of change, and a heart-shaped stone. "The first things you bring into a home fill it with intention. Clear your mind of your worries. The bread is so you will never be hungry, the coal so you won't be cold, the coins so you won't be poor, and the heart so that you always find kinship here."

Emily was familiar with the ritual; her mother did it every time they moved. Was everyone prepared for this but her? She shook her head, closing her eyes and clearing her worries, focusing her intention on each item individually. Following the sisters through the front door and into the kitchen, she lay her items on the small island that separated the kitchen from the main living space. "I bring to my new home food, warmth, money, love, and an open mind."

Mildred nodded. "Good. You're going to do well here."

They moved around the cabin, listing the things that would need to be done in the future. The electricity and water were on but would need to be switched to her name. She needed oil for the heating system in January, groceries, and to talk to someone named Jessie Wilde about providing firewood for the winter. The woodshed had enough for a couple of weeks, but that wouldn't help much with the coming weather.

The place was open plan with exposed beams, a stone fireplace, a kitchen island that separated the kitchen from the living room, two bedrooms, one bathroom, no back door, and absolutely none of Mildred's furniture or personal effects. It was completely bare.

Lucinda watched her for a moment with a smirk. "We sent Millie's stuff down to my place a week ago. We have a room at the Mermaid's Song until tomorrow, and then you're on your own...sort of." She winked at Mildred, who winked back.

Emily laughed, shaking her head. "Grandmother."

Mildred laughed with her and then gave her a brief hug. "Claire Rollins is a piece of work, isn't she? That woman is and will always be the greatest love of my life. That's a story that's best left for her to tell, though. Let's get your stuff out of your car, and then we'll drive down together to celebrate."

No sooner had the last box been laid down than Mildred grabbed Emily's arm to fulfill the last part of their bargain at the only high-end restaurant in town, The

Mermaid's Song. As each sister drank her weight in spiced rum out of shell-shaped cups, they began to tell tales. From youthful exploits of reading fortunes in carnivals, including the Missouri State Fair, to their current plan to read Tarot on Siesta Key Beach, both sisters liked nothing better than to mettle in the future.

After the first couple of drinks, they'd predicted everything from Emily's happiness in her new home to her swiftly upcoming marriage. They were in complete agreement that Emily's business would be a stunning success, but they winked slyly at one another while explaining that it would not be for the reason she thought. Lucinda warned seriously that Emily should be careful when blessing fairies.

Mildred snorted with derision. "Don't listen to her." Mildred stared into Emily's wine glass as if she were reading tea leaves. "She makes up the stuff between her visions. She's got no idea how it all really connects."

Lucinda swirled her rum in her glass with a wicked smile. "At least I have real visions and don't need a deck of playing cards to know what's going on."

They glared at each other for a moment and then burst out laughing. After the celebration, Emily helped them into their hotel room with a promise to invite them to her wedding and to call on them in Florida every so often. As she headed out the door to catch her cab, Mildred handed her a tarot card. On it, a hovering hand-held a bright gold chalice with what appeared to be a dove diving in. Water flowed from the cup like a fountain and down into a turbulent sea filled with flowers. The Ace of Cups.

"To new friends and new beginnings. Keep it in the store for luck."

Lucinda patted her shoulder sympathetically. "You're going to need it."

4

Love magic is some of the most dangerous magic to work with, not because it is any more or less powerful than other types of magic, but because what a heart needs is often a mystery even to its owner. —Marie Le Glasse, *Navigating Relationships in the Enlightened World*

Noah's heart pounded in his ears, and every sense he owned was trained on the golden-haired woman retreating into Mildred Macclesfield's shop. He crossed the park, then the street, and ran directly into his mother, Angela, almost knocking her over. He had to catch her by the shoulders to keep her from falling over. She looked at him with confusion for a moment.

"Sorry, Mom. Are you okay?" he asked giving her a brief hug before stepping back.

She looked pleased rather than annoyed. "Noah. I was just thinking about you." She glanced over her shoulder. "Who are you chasing?"

Noah blushed. "No one. I was going to talk to Mildred."

They turned at the same time to see Mildred turn her door sign over from opened to closed. Angela pulled Noah to her side tucking his hand into the crook of her arm. "Looks like she doesn't want to talk to you. Walk with me. I want to talk to you about the information you got from Frank Carlos." His mother moved toward her car, fully expecting him to follow.

He hesitated a moment, torn by his interest in the woman inside the shop and the need to keep his alpha up-to-date on the situation. Deciding that he would follow her to the car and return to wait for the woman to come out of the store, he walked beside her. "It's not much to go on. The Millinocket agent still hasn't made contact, and Janet Wedgewood has already been taken to the Augusta Recovery unit. I asked Selene to check in, but Janet is refusing all visitors."

Angela looked worried. "Including her husband?"

"Especially her husband," Noah replied, looking back over his shoulder at the entrance to the shop.

"If they are bonded—"

"I know, but Selene says that it has to be Janet's choice. She's an adult and has the right to make her own decisions."

Angela gave Noah's hand a gentle squeeze. She knew without having to be told that what was happening to Janet was one of his worst fears. "The newly Awakened have so much to take in. I can't imagine what she's feeling right now."

They made their way past the last of the shops. Angela

stopped at the edge of the parking lot to look out at the sea. She knew he wasn't telling her something, so she was giving him the opportunity to correct the situation before she had to ask.

"I was lucky that your dad was already Enlightened." She patted Noah absently. "I hope your new mate is as well. For your sake and for hers." Her grin turned to tease. "Speaking of which, Mildred tells me today that you're going to be mated by Thanksgiving."

"Well, that gives me about three weeks to find my mate, woo her, and get her to declare herself as mine. Since I haven't found her yet, that doesn't give me much time." He tried for a casual tone but knew he had failed.

Angela looked him straight in the eye, her brow arched. "I told her that my reading said Christmas, but she's convinced that I'm confusing you and Selene. What aren't you telling me?"

Noah pulled her forward toward her car. "Selene, who swore last week that the world would be a better place without romantic relationships? That Selene?"

"Your sister is a genius when it comes to science but a bit hard-headed in matters of the heart." They reached his mother's car, and she dug around in her purse for keys. "Neither of you has made the first connection to your mate, so the whole conversation is a bit silly, right?"

She knew Noah didn't know how, but she knew. He cleared his throat. "I wanted to talk to you about that. My mate has made contact. I wanted to tell you sooner, but I'm having trouble locating her. After I find this Millinocket agent, I would like to formally request permission and begin my hunt."

Angela stopped digging for her keys and pulled him into her arms. "I knew it. How long until you leave?"

"The Christmas Market is a hard time for us, and then with the call from the Recovery Unit..."

A sad knowing expression crossed her features. "You aren't immediately requesting leave because you don't want to leave me shorthanded." She cupped his face like she used to when he was a boy and had done something to make her proud. "Be careful, my son. Caring for others is a wonderful thing, but you have to care for yourself as well."

"I know. When I have finished with Carlos Wedgewood and the Millinocket agent, I will request leave to find her."

"No need. You have my permission to go as soon as you can. You're a generous leader but hear me. If she calls you again, you will start your hunt immediately. That is my order as Alpha. Do you understand me?"

He leaned forward and scooped her up for a big hug. "I hear you, Mom."

"Good. Finish here and then turn your Christmas Market jobs over to Nick Wilde." She opened her door and reached into her car to pick up a box filled to the brim with Christmas Market information. "I want you to go back to Dark Wolf this afternoon with Joseph. Get a team together for the investigation. Something feels wrong here, like we're missing something obvious."

Noah took the box under his arm and kissed her on the cheek. "I've got something to do first, but I'll get right on it."

Although he'd gone back to Mildred's shop door three

times whilst, under the guise of finishing the gazebo lights, he hadn't seen any signs of Mildred or the woman he was looking for. He'd sent Joseph to Dark Wolf to get a team together and took the box of information to the mayor of Larkshead, a hobgoblin called Nick Wilde, who owned a shop not far from Mildred's. Nick was ecstatic to take over the Christmas Market paperwork. Noah looked down the street for the last time while Nick held open his shop door.

The Hobgoblin followed his gaze with a knowing grin brushing his short finger thoughtfully down his tufted beard. "If you're looking for Mildred, she's closed up early and taken that young woman with her."

Noah didn't ask how Nick knew he was looking for the woman. Hobgoblins, as a rule, loved to be in the know and to bargain with information. It was one of the reasons they made excellent politicians. The Christmas Market paperwork included the shop agreements, parking arrangements, stall maps, and who was and wasn't Enlightened. Nick's shop was a general store, but it didn't escape anyone's notice that although his shelves were always full, his pockets were never empty.

Trying not to knock over the closely laid general merchandise displays, Noah followed Nick through the main store and into the back. "Do you know who Mildred's guest was?" He tried to ask casually, but Nick was an expert at information trading.

"I might have heard something." Nick motioned for Noah to follow him up a tight staircase into his apartment over the shop.

Noah had to duck to enter Nick's apartment, but like

all hobgoblin public spaces, it adjusted quickly to his height. The room was tidy and warm, with chairs tucked around tables of various sizes, all stacked with books. He sat the box on the nearest table which adjusted itself to make space for the box while Nick poured them both a dram of hobgoblin whiskey. It was an honor he hadn't expected. The smell of the golden liquid reminded Noah of running carefree through the summer fields in his childhood. He cleared his throat. "Mildred's guest can wait. I came here to ask for a favor."

The hobgoblin's eyes turned black with anticipation as he handed Noah an exquisite crystal tumbler. "This whiskey is one hundred and eleven years old, a bit young in the tooth for most, but it's my own special blend." He took a long appreciative drink. "Are you offering a favor for a favor?"

Noah sniffed the drink, detecting a hint of magic. This was a game of trust. Nick was testing Noah to see how far they would confide in each other. He sipped the drink without questioning the magic. It was an act of complete trust.

Nick's gaze turned thoughtful. "It's good magic. Wild magic. If you trust it, the magic enhances your chances of gaining your deepest heart's desire. If you don't..." Nick laughed, tilting his tumbler back and forth and gazing through it, "Well, it's wild magic."

Allowing the magic and the warm taste of whiskey to move through his body, Noah cleared his throat. "I am offering a favor for a favor. An even exchange of information and time only."

"Deal," Nick nodded, throwing back his own drink and filling another. "What can I do for you?"

"Janet Wedgewood was forced through the Veil two days ago. I'm tracking down who did it to deliver them to justice. If you come across any information on the unguided, you come to me with it immediately without telling anyone else. I don't want this to cause a panic." Noah threw back his own drink and handed his glass to Nick for a refill.

The hobgoblin laughed appreciatively and poured a double measure for them both. He handed the tumbler back to Noah. "What about your mother?"

"You know better. If she asks, you tell. Otherwise, the information comes straight back to me."

Nick grinned slyly but without malice. "I'd have done that for you without the exchange. My daughter, April, is Unenlightened like her mother. My grandson Michael is Enlightened, like me. We have to be careful. What's happening to the Unenlightened frightens me.

It frightened Noah too. If the Unenlightened suspected what was going on, the situation would turn into a witch hunt. He took another drink, enjoying the sensation of the honeyed heat on his tongue and the wild magic moving through his body.

Nick sat back in his chair, taking another deep draft. "If April shut down, I'm not sure what I would do. The Recovery rules are there for a reason. Those who break them should be held accountable." He motioned for Noah to sit back.

Noah did as instructed, in no hurry to leave Nick's

company. Nick snapped his fingers, and a dinner table tucked in the corner of the room covered with books slid between them. Nick tapped his clawed fingers on the wood of the table a couple of times, and a feast of vegetables, fruit, and cheese appeared where the books had been.

"Will you join me? I have some information you need."

Noah nodded his stomach rumbling in appreciation. Although he preferred meat, hobgoblin meals were not only delicious but often laced with health blessings.

Handing him a plate, Nick began to divide the feast between them. "My cousin in Boston says they are finding two or three unguided individuals a week up there and aren't any closer to finding out why. The Enlightened up there think it's witchcraft, but the Enlightened witches swear that the spell must be coming from a coven of Unenlightened witches. The Enlightened think that the increase in awakenings will eventually cause the Veil to fail. My cousin thinks the Veil itself is thinning, causing the awakenings."

Witches were born half inside and half outside the Enlightened world. They rarely became fully awakened. All the Enlightened witches were registered to a territory, but Unenlightened witches only occasionally pulled magic across the Veil, making them difficult to identify and track. Noah took another long drink. In the tradition of Hobgoblins, he would be expected to eat and drink as much as he could hold. To hold back was an insult. It was going to be an interesting night. "What do you think?"

"The Unenlightened can't accept people who are a slightly different color; they certainly don't have the brain power to understand what it means to live beside a different species, never mind that they have been doing so since the start of time. If what my cousin says is true, it will be mayhem."

Noah tucked into his plate making sure to keep pace for as long as he could with Nick. The table spell was as impressive as the meal. Each dish was at just the right temperature and disappeared from the table when the food was gone, only to be replaced by a different dish.

"This table was a wedding present from my uncle, twice removed. My sweet Laura, April's mother, never did see all it could do, but I think somewhere deep inside, she knew it was magic. I think they all know we are here on some level."

He poured Noah a tall-stemmed glass of water and then a short glass of something that looked like tar. Noah swirled the dark liquid in the glass. "I talked to a man called Frank Carlos. He said the cases of the unguided are spreading fast. There aren't enough guides to go around."

"Us Enlightened are just as bad with our territories and hierarchies. If we didn't have them, we wouldn't need guides. I don't want my family divided, but to unite them means possibly upending the whole world. Either way, it's going to be messy." He tossed back his whiskey and filled the glass again. "I'll tell you what I know freely. No exchange necessary."

Noah bowed his head. "Thank you."

Rubbing his hands together, Nick popped a handful of black grapes into his mouth. "Now, if you want information on that woman…you'll have to ask someone else. I only saw the way she was looking at you. Reminded me of this lass I once knew in Wales."

Noah laughed and settled in for a story.

Emily stumbled out of the cab onto her driveway, trying to figure out which of the keys Mildred handed her to open her front door. A path leading to the beach started from just off her driveway and was short, according to Lucinda. She thought briefly of wandering down there to look at the dark water, but Mildred had told her in a mysterious voice over dinner to be careful of the sea this winter.

Emily didn't know anything about living close to the ocean and made a mental note to pick up a tide table and some information about the coast from the Larkshead Visitors Center. The evergreen woods around the place were dotted with skeletal trees that were covering the ground in a blanket of yellow and red autumn leaves. Opening the front door on her third try, she moved into the dark cabin and dropped her handbag on the floor. She gazed into the mostly empty space waiting to feel tired, but she was so excited she could hardly stand still. She could already envision her herbs drying from the exposed beams in her living room while the fire in her fireplace drove away the winter chill.

Propping the Ace of Cups in her kitchen window so she would remember to take it to work tomorrow, she began clumsily making this place her own. Right now, her furniture was limited to a bed, a tall dresser, a four-seater pine kitchen table with matching chairs, and an over-stuffed lounge chair that had seen better days. She moved from room to room with determination arranging and rearranging her meager belongings until she felt happy with them and making a list of things that she would need. By the time she found her night clothes and her toothbrush, she felt the first tendrils of sleep and a hangover begin to set into place.

She went outside to sit on the porch with the only food she had in the place, a bag of Cheetos, a diet soda, and a candy bar leftover from the long drive up here. Not really a nutritious first meal, but she'd eaten well at the Mermaid's Song. All she needed was enough to keep her hangover at a reasonable level. She settled against the porch rail near the stairs and dangled her legs over the side as she unwrapped her chocolate bar. The night sky peeked down at her through the trees and sparkled with more stars than she had ever known existed. She raised a hand as if to run her fingers through them and grinned.

Without thinking, she pointed at one and said, "Star light, star bright, first star I choose tonight, I wish I may, I wish I might have this wish I wish tonight…"

The night seemed to hold its breath waiting for her to speak. Her mother had always told her to be careful what she wished for, but her grandma's advice was to wish for the best and don't settle till you get it. Emily turned her gaze inward, rolling her desires around in her mind with the same movements of the chocolate melting in her mouth.

Sifting through a hundred crazy dreams, she looked for the one that would provide her with the most happiness. She tried to articulate the wish, but contrasting what she wanted with the endless searching and planning she'd done for the last couple of years was too much for her wine-addled brain. With a saucy toss of her head, she said, "Put me on the right path for happiness, and if it includes that incredible man from town today, all the better."

She stayed a while longer munching Cheetos, watching stars, and making lists in her head of things she had to do tomorrow. She went inside to get a pen and paper before the list got longer than her memory. When she got back outside, the biggest dog that she had ever seen in her life was lying on the porch, delicately helping itself to her Cheetos.

The dog looked a bit like pictures she'd once seen of a red malamute, but its markings were not as distinct, and it was also much larger than she'd imagined a malamute could be. The word wolf flitted through her wine-hazed mind just as the dog turned its head toward her with a snoot full of bright orange cheese and began to wag its tail. She couldn't believe that it had managed to come up her stairs and sit down without making any sounds. She took a step toward it hesitantly, looking for signs that it was wild or worse, that it was rabid, but the dog continued to wag its tail faster.

"Uh, hello there. Are you enjoying yourself?"

The dog sneezed at her and then turned back to the bag of chips, delicately helping itself to another. She came closer, holding out her hand for it to sniff. It did so briefly and then rolled over to have its stomach scratched. She reached down and rubbed his belly, noting that the dog was male. He threw his head back in doggy bliss. His cinnamon fur was coarse and thick, but he was clean and obviously well cared for. She couldn't see any collar or identification on him, but that didn't mean he was wild. She settled close to him, noting that he was easily the same sitting height as her and that he smelled a little bit like whiskey. "Are you lost?"

He sneezed again and then rolled back onto his stomach to snuggle closer to her. He reached out with one paw and brought the chips closer to him. He rooted around in the bag for another bright orange Cheeto, dropping it into her lap with a cheerful woof. She rubbed his large ears playfully and handed the soggy chip back to him. "Thanks for sharing, but you can have it."

He looked seriously at her for a moment tilting his head one way, and then the other as if what she was doing had some sort of deeper meaning to him then lapped the chip happily out of her hand, taking time to clean all of the salty powder off. Emily petted him, her fingers skipping over his fur, checking to make sure that he wasn't hurt. He had to belong to someone. He had great taste in junk food and was too nice to be wild. She'd have to ask when she went into town tomorrow if he didn't head home in the meantime.

They sat for a while, sharing warmth and watching the forest together. He finished off the chips and placed his head in her lap with a contented huff. It was late, and she needed to take her stock to the shop, unload it, and take the trailer to the depot before the streets became too crowded. The dog stood up, stretched, then used his paw to bounce the screen door open and let himself inside. With a shrug, she got up on wobbly legs, picked up their trash from the porch, and followed him in. She wouldn't have left him out in the cold anyway. While she put her can on the counter for recycling, she heard him jump up onto her bed.

"Hey!" She came into her bedroom, arms crossed over her chest. He sniffed at her and then curled himself up at the end of her bed to sleep. "Don't make yourself too comfortable. You're only an overnight guest. Understand?"

Something about his audacity was charming.

She shook her head, scratching his jaw. "Honestly, this is the weirdest day of my life, and that's saying a lot if you knew who my family were. Let's get some rest. We can decide what to do with you in the morning."

5

When telling futures for strangers, you should be aware that no one wants a bad future. Even if the future is an unmitigated disaster, you should tell the seeker that it will all work out to their advantage. That fortune is not only kind, but with enough belief, it becomes the truth. —Mildred Macclesfield, *The Art of Fortune Telling for Financial Gain*

Noah woke up naked, on top of the blankets, and at the foot of an unknown bed. For a moment, he couldn't believe what he was seeing. He was in a stripped-down version of what looked to be his own bedroom, but none of his belongings were here. Instead, there was a beat-up pine dresser, the bed he was laying on, and a stack of boxes in the corner with newspaper crumpled all around. His eyes wandered over the bed, noting that neither the quilt nor the beautiful woman wrapped in it was familiar to him. Was he dreaming?

The last thing he remembered was shifting to go home. He'd had too much whiskey to even think about driving. Hobgoblin magic had been running through his veins, and he'd felt...happy. He remembered the glowing winter moon as he shifted. He remembered moving swiftly through the woods and down the coast. After that, it was only impressions and snatches. The scent of prey on the leaves...the rumbling sound of the ocean...being called...being needed.

There was no second self when he was a wolf. Both halves of his nature were his, and he usually had complete awareness of his actions in both forms, regardless of what he drank. His thoughts and senses were different in each body as much as human's thoughts might be different in a board room as opposed to a breakfast table, so this blank-ness in his memory didn't make sense. He looked again at the woman in the bed, wondering how to proceed. He knew somewhere in his mind that he had been welcomed here and touched by her as a companion.

He looked again more carefully, recognizing the woman from town. He didn't know much about angels, but she looked like every picture he'd ever seen of one. She was lying on her side, curled around a large pillow and with her long honey-gold hair spread out behind her. Her lips were full, pale pink, and frowning as if she disliked being inspected in her sleep. She smelled of sweet bee's wax and something that was distinctly her.

That scent alone would have attracted him. She would probably only come up to his chin, but the blankets gripped in her long fingers concealed anything definite about her figure. It wasn't very cold here for November, but she had wrapped herself up like a burrito in the bright quilt. That explained why he was on the outside of the blankets. He must have been too hot underneath the quilt with her.

His brain momentarily registered that she was wearing red and green flannel pajamas that were buttoned up to her neck. His experience of sleeping overnight with partners was small, but he did know that he never went to bed with someone in pajamas. He loved the feel of skin against skin, the sensation of sharing warmth with his partner. Sitting up in bed, he looked around the house again and noticed that although her clothing was piled on the dresser, his clothes were nowhere in sight.

Like pieces of a terrible puzzle falling into place, Noah remembered her thighs, her feet, her knees, her bending over him...to scratch his ears? He'd come to her in wolf form! At once, his mind conjured a picture of her waking with a strange naked man hovering next to her bed. Even if she was Enlightened, he couldn't explain what he was doing here to himself, much less to her. He immediately began to change forms and then stopped himself. For the first time in his life, he didn't trust himself as a wolf. Without an explanation for the blank spot in his memory, he couldn't risk hurting her.

She pulled on part of the quilt he was pinning down. When the blanket didn't move, she tugged again, her frown becoming more pronounced. She mumbled something about bed hogs and settled down. Noah used every bit of his supernatural stealth to get off her bed and out of her bedroom. He stood when he got into the hall, hoping against hope that he was wrong and that his clothes were left in another room. This house was almost identical to his. It had the same stone fireplace, open plan kitchen, and living room, the same mock-marble countertops, but none of his stuff was here. His mind raced. Wasn't Mildred's house supposed to be part of the same camping grounds his house was? That would explain the similarity.

Where was Mildred and her stuff? Had he been too drunk last night to know which house was his? If he was right, and this was Mildred's place, then he was only a couple of miles from home. Wherever he was, he needed to go before the woman in the other room woke up. Spotting a pink fuzzy robe on top of a stack of women's coats hanging by the door in the living room, he picked it up and forced his arms inside. It was almost too tight, and the bottom hem only came to the top of his thighs, but it would have to do. Her bed squeaked in the other room, and he froze, waiting to see if his movements had wakened her. Nothing.

Moving quickly, he went to the door turning the knob. It opened instantly. She hadn't locked the front door. There was some intrusive wildlife in this area, himself not included, and the door couldn't be locked from the outside without the key. A thought slammed through him. If he left her now, she would be unprotected. He started to leave anyway, but his wolf nature snarled in protest.

It was like being torn into two people, one who demanded that he protect the sleeping woman and one who knew that if she caught him here in nothing but her bathrobe, he would probably go to jail. He put both hands on either side of the door frame feeling the wood give way slightly with the effort of keeping himself from going back to her. He chanted to himself internally she wouldn't understand. He would come back when he was dressed, wait for her to wake up, and make sure she was safe. He felt the intensity inside him lessen but not disappear. Before he could change his mind, he pushed open both the front door and the screen door and moved onto the porch pulling them gently closed behind him. A soft murmur of movement in the house alerted him to her waking. Without another thought, he wrapped her pink robe more firmly around himself and dashed into the woods.

Emily was still trying to figure out how the dog had managed to close the front door behind him as she walked up Larkshead's main street. She'd managed to unload all of her candles into the shop with the dolly provided with the trailer. Although she was there well before normal opening hours, she'd noticed that the Christmas Market stalls were already being constructed and some of the businesses were already open.

The drop-off location for the trailer was a gas station called The Last Stop, located on the way out of town. A lovely woman named Nadine had taken the trailer and given her a large cup of coffee to welcome her to the neighborhood. She also sold Emily a mermaid-shaped ice-scraper, a long-handled snow broom for her car, and some de-icer for locks.

"I'd talk to Noah about getting your driveway plowed first. You guys are close enough to use the same person," Nadine said, putting all of Emily's things into a paper bag.

Emily choked on the sip of coffee she was taking. "Plowed? I need a plow to get out of my driveway?"

Handing Emily the bag, Nadine grinned from ear to ear. "You're not from around, are you? I'll just say you might be okay with a shovel until next week, but then real winter comes, and you're going to need a shovel, a plow person for your drive and your road, and a set of snow shoes and yack tracks. January ice turns that Larkshead parking lot into a skating rink."

She nodded, promising herself to Google yack's tracks when she got back in her car. "I'm in trouble, aren't I?"

Nadine shook her head. "If you'd moved anywhere else, I'd say yes, but this is Larkshead. We take care of each other here." She took the receipt from the till and wrote a phone number on the back. "If you get stuck or have a question, give me a call."

Although Mildred told her that the Harborside parking was generally saved for tourists, she failed to mention where the locals parked. Swinging into the same parking spot she had yesterday, Emily arrived for her first day at her own store smiling. It was a new experience to want to go to work, and she took a moment to savor the feeling. Shoppers from across New England came to participate in the Christmas Village festivities. Horse carriage rides, Christmas tree lighting, Christmas carol singing in seven languages, and hundreds of stalls filled with exclusively homemade goodies were just some of the activities touted. Larkshead was also one of the few towns that honored Yule celebrations on the winter solstice as a regular part of their holiday calendar.

On both sides of the street, shopkeepers were turning over signs, dusting shelves, sweeping sidewalks, and getting ready for the day. Emily's frosty breaths curled in the air and the whole place smelled of ocean, coffee, and maple syrup. Her online sales would keep her fed, just barely, while she got established, but she knew that her scented candles needed to be experienced in a real shop to make the kind of sales that she needed to call herself successful.

Buying Mildred's bookshelves, cash register, and stockroom shelves had almost cost more than the sale price of the store itself but was the only way she could arrange displays before her doors had to open for business on Monday. Shaking her head, she opened the shop door and went inside. She'd have liked to give herself a little bit more time to settle in, but she couldn't do that and honor Mildred's holiday opening hours.

In a room full of boxed candles, Emily reached into her handbag and pulled out the Ace of Cups tarot card Mildred had given her. Walking to the back of the store, she leaned the card on a display shelf in a prominent place. She took out her journal from her bag and flipped to the last page that she normally dedicated to lists and wrote down Small Picture Frame. With a nod, she stored her bag in the back and began to arrange her displays.

By the time noon hit, Emily's shop was decorated with candles of every shape and size, but there was no disguising the fact that she needed to add something to the shelves to make her displays appear less clinical. She'd made three trips back to her home to fetch the remaining stock, dismayed at how little space it took up on the display shelves.

After three years of tripping over candles and boxes in her small apartment, she was determined to keep as much of her work at her business place as possible. If she stayed on top of it, she could keep her candles topped up by making smaller batches at the cabin more frequently until she could afford to put in a stove here at the shop.

Her stomach rumbled, reminding her that her lack of groceries, the time she'd spent returning the trailer and looking for the dog this morning, meant she'd missed breakfast. She got her purse and her keys and walked out into the sunshine. Her gaze briefly searched the gazebo almost by their own volition. She was looking for him. He was probably married, or a visitor, or someone who came twice a year to put up and take down the Christmas lights, but she looked for him anyway.

"Beautiful day."

Emily jumped, looking down at a slender little man who reminded her simultaneously of a Gringotts goblin and friar tuck in spite of his blue business suit and red tie.

"Yes, it is."

He offered her a hand with a politician-worthy smile. "I'm Nick Wilde. I'm the mayor and the man in charge of the shop decorations this year. You must be Emily Rollins. My shop is directly across from yours on the harbor side."

Emily shook his hand, trying to shake the goblin impression from her mind. "Have we met?"

"It's a small town," he said with a clever grin. "Everyone knows everyone, especially on the main street." He handed Emily a letter. "Your name was also on the visiting vendor's list originally and needed to be switched to the permanent vendors. This is the list of standards for permanent vendors. I'm in charge of all the vendors this year."

While Emily scanned the first letter, he handed her a second letter.

"This is the list of decorations you need to get into place by next weekend. Nothing major. Lights, baubles, some greenery. Music is up to you, but you need to make sure that it isn't loud. The Larkshead choir stall is three shops down from your front door, park side, and they don't like to compete."

"Music?"

"Seasonal stuff. It isn't required, but it sure makes the season bright." He patted the pockets of his coat. "I can bring you a suggested playlist if you want. I had a couple, but I've handed them out already."

She glanced over the decorations list. "Thank you. Mildred said something about decorations, but I wasn't sure what she meant. My shop is looking very empty at the moment."

Nick Wilde rubbed his snub nose and gave her a conspirator's wink. "I also have a good nose for a Christmas bargain. Some of the things on the list are available in my store. You don't have to get them there, but we like to support one another when we can."

His face shifted again from Friar Tuck to that of a goblin. Emily blinked a couple of times to clear her vision. "Of course. What's the name of your place, in case anyone asks where I got my decorations?"

He looked at her for a long second before rocking back on his heels. "The Goblin Market. I sell mostly Christmas decorations and homewares this time of year. You look like a woman who needs Sugar Plum Fairies, am I right?"

Emily felt a small thrill of inspiration. An image of her candles surrounded by fairies tickled her fancy. "I think you're right."

"I can make you a deal." The man's smile stretched the length of his face, and Emily would have sworn his brown eyes turned black.

"Can you?"

"My shop is a bit crowded. The fairies could come here, at no charge, to be sold with a sign indicating where my shop is. You keep a list of which fairies are sold, and we settle at the end of the season. Whatever isn't sold, you buy wholesale at the end of the season. Any disruption caused by the fairies is yours to sort out."

Emily arched a brow, pretending to think. Her mother was an expert yard sale negotiator, and Emily wasn't behind the door when it came to bargaining. "Throw in the required Christmas lights on your list and promise to cut the price of the fairies to half if their sales don't go well, and you have a bargain."

He whistled. "Fair bargain. I agree. We are going to

make very good neighbors." He glanced down at his remaining lists thoughtfully. "You know, it appears my Christmas decorations list is missing candles." He winked at her. "There's nothing like candles to make Christmas bright. I'll make sure to add them when I deliver the other letters."

She returned his wink with a teasing grin. "I appreciate that. Shall I see you tonight to collect my fairies?"

He touched the side of his nose again. "No bother. I'll have my daughter bring them over. A pleasure to meet you, Emily. If you need anything else-"

"Do you know where I can get some lunch?"

"Do I know?" Nick puffed up with pride. "Nick Wilde knows where you can get anything." He pointed to the top of the hill. "The Blue Moon. It's the best place for lunch in town. You can tell the owner, Angela, I sent you. Welcome to Larkshead, Ms. Rollins." He sauntered away whistling, "Have Yourself a Merry Little Christmas."

As she made her way through town, Emily chalked her goblin double vision up to low blood sugar, too much excitement, and not enough sleep. She reached the top of the hill and pushed open the door of a beautiful café with a little sigh of relief. The smell of bacon, pancakes, coffee, lemon cleaner, and an earthy smell that was somewhere between damp evergreen and newly turned soil wrapped around her senses.

The unusual combination of scents that made up The Blue Moon put the goblin's vision out of her mind and immediately had her imagining a new candle in her range. Everything in the Blue Moon Cafe appeared to be moon-shaped or moon related. Pictures scattered across the walls, mobile pieces hanging from the ceiling, and even the tables were various orb shapes. It was fantastic. She chose a table away from the door and picked up a menu from a full moon-shaped menu holder. She was weighing her options when her stomach rumbled.

As if summoned, a smiling woman about Emily's age came up to the table. Her black hair was chopped into a perfectly sculpted pixie style that made Emily suddenly aware that the state of her own hair might not be ideal. The woman was very tall, and she wasn't wearing a uniform. Instead, she had on dark jeans and a red cable knit sweater that complimented the bronzed color of her skin. She was also looking at Emily as if she had just discovered something wonderful. Emily smiled back.

"Hello. My name is Selene, and it sounds to me like you're ready to order."

Emily placed a self-conscious hand over her stomach. "Yes, please. Can I order some pancakes, some bacon, and a coffee if you're still serving breakfast?"

Selene put her hands on her hips, her eyes narrowing playfully. "Did Noah put you up to this? He knows that his pancakes are better than mine."

Emily tilted her head in confusion. "I'm sorry. You must have me mixed up with someone else. I've heard his name around here a couple of times but don't know anyone called Noah."

Selene inhaled deeply, the teasing smile wavering on her lips. "Are you sure?"

Emily laughed. "Absolutely. I did meet a charming man on the decorating committee, but his name was Nick." She offered her hand, "I'm Emily Rollins. I'm opening the candle shop down the street at the Ace of Cups."

Selene shook her hand. "Decorating committee? Please don't tell me Nick Wilde is starting already."

"Starting?"

"Decorating? I swear the Christmas season would start in June if he had his way. Is there a theme this year? Last year it was Christmas mermaids."

"Wow," Emily chuckled, "Is that even possible?"

"It is possible. I guess it's funny now, but it looked like Pirates of the North Pole around here." Selene rolled her eyes. "I'll go get you some coffee and then get your order started. I won't be long."

Emily nodded, looking over Nick's list for possible mermaids. The café was packed, and as she scanned the list, she had the strangest feeling that the restaurant staff were watching her. The bus boy, another waitress, and the cook behind the counter seemed to be taking deep breaths when they got close to her, exchanging glances and murmured conversations with each other. Just about the time the glances began to feel uncomfortable, Selene returned and filled an oversized mug with coffee.

"Don't mind them." She gestured with her chin toward a group huddled around the counter. "We get a lot of visitors but not a lot of neighbors if you know what I mean. Mildred's move was a surprise, and those are few and far between around here."

"Have you lived here long?"

"My whole life. This café belongs to my mom, Angela.

I'm covering for her until Tuesday while she does her annual Christmas shopping down in New York City." Selene pronounced the word Christmas like some people said the word mildew.

"You don't like Christmas?"

"I like Christmas from about the 15th of December to the 26th. Then I'm done. My mom is Christmas crazy, just like the rest of the people around here. Her tree gets bigger every year. We already have to move furniture."

Emily checked her list. "Do you know where I can get a Christmas tree and maybe some greenery for the store? I would love something fresh."

Selene shrugged. "Nick will tell you to get it from Jessie Wilde's farm, but you're better off ordering it from Rowan Martin down at the Holly & Ivy Florist. Her uncle, Ash, collects all the trees after Christmas for free. The Martins and the Wildes have a long-running feud in this town. My advice is don't get involved.

Emily wrinkled her nose. "How do I do that?"

Selene leaned over as if to whisper a secret. "Buy your tree from Rowan but order your firewood from Jessie Wilde's farm. It's kind of a checks and balances system."

"Whose side are you on?"

Selene topped up Emily's cup. "Your side, of course."

Another much younger waitress with sea-green hair and a septum piercing walked up to the table with Emily's order. Rather than reaching around Selene to set it down or introduce herself, she handed the plate as quickly as she could to Selene and headed back to the kitchen. Selene sat it down and then fetched a selection of syrups from another table.

"I guess there's a lot I need to learn about Larkshead," Emily said, watching the young lady disappear into the back.

Selene put her hands on her hips, following Emily's gaze. "Don't learn it too fast. It's only interesting the first time."

6

The most sexually promiscuous of the Enlightened are Tree Nymphs followed closely by Sirens. Tree Nymphs often give an appearance of fidelity to the newly Awakened only because the lifespan of a Tree Nymph is so long that they consider a 100-year affair to be a brief dalliance. —Marie Le Glasse, *Navigating Relationships in the Enlightened World*

It had been a stupidly long day. During the Christmas season Noah's main job was implementing multiple plans for keeping overly eager tourists from dying of exposure in the woods. This year hadn't been very cold meaning that his teams were still trying to keep the campers from leaving their trash, eating what they shouldn't, or burning the place down.

He should have at the very least been following up with the Enlightened about the Unguided situation like he'd told Frank Carlos he would, but Noah had spent most of the day staring into space wondering if the woman he'd left this morning was okay.

Had she noticed he left? Had she looked for him? He'd gone back to check on her after he was dressed but she was gone by the time he'd arrived. He was pushing a grocery shopping cart around Hannaford's trying to think of a way to introduce himself without looking creepy, and to remember what groceries he needed at home, when he spotted her at the end of the isle.

She was reading the ingredients on a can of ravioli with rapt attention. She was taller than he'd estimated. Her hair was half-twisted into some sort of messy knot that simultaneously defied gravity and suited her.

Dressed in jeans, short boots, and a close-fitting blue sweater that called attention to her curves but wouldn't do much against the cold, she looked adorably out of place. He felt his mouth go dry. He'd given her height, her hair, her choice of bed linen, her lack of door locking, and almost every other incident of this morning, thorough thought. He was half reading over her shoulder when she turned around.

She jumped away from him with incredible speed and he turned at once to defend her until he realized that she was holding her can of ravioli in front of her as a defense against him. He blinked back at her startled expression and took a courteous step back. He hadn't even been aware he was making his way toward her. Noah opened his mouth to say something clever, but no sound came out. He tried again, but nothing happened.

She gave him a wary look. "Do you need something?"

The soft southern twang in her voice caressed every

nerve in his body. Words refused to come to him, he was so lost in the details of her expression. Her eyes were like sunlight on the sea, her black pupils surrounded by gold halos which twisted into a surrounding bright green before fading into blue. Wide and framed with honey lashes, she met his gaze unflinchingly, almost in a challenge. She was no red riding hood who needed saving; she was the hunter. The thought made him grin.

She still smelled of sweet bee's wax and something that must have been a cleaning spray, but under that was the unmistakable scent of himself. His scent on her skin brought out possessiveness in him that he hadn't thought himself capable of. He watched her look at him, fully taking in his appearance, his uniform, and his expression. Unconsciously, she relaxed waiting for him to explain himself.

"I'm Noah. Noah Hernandez." She continued to stare at him incomprehensively. He tried again, this time offering her his hand. "We're neighbors."

She smiled, the expression making little wrinkles appear at the corners of her eyes. He felt inordinately pleased with himself for making her smile. She shook his hand firmly, "I'm Emily. I've been told that you make good pancakes."

"Emily." He rolled her name on his tongue to taste it. "You must have talked to my mother."

She shook her head. "Not unless she is my age."

Her grin was contagious. "My sister, Selene?"

She nodded. "I met her at The Blue Moon this morning. It's nice to finally meet you."

He took a step closer to her silently thanking his nosey

sister for interfering. Emily mirrored his action again, all but closing the distance she had put between them. He almost whooped for joy. Not all people took to werewolves. Some of them had instincts that were old enough to remind them that they had once been food. "It's nice to meet you, Emily."

She offered him the ravioli in her hand. "Do you want me to hand you a can? I can't say it's the best of the range, but it is edible." Noah grimaced and she smiled again. "I thought not. You look too healthy for this stuff." Her eyes wandered over his body again in a way that let him know without a doubt that she liked what she saw. "Is there something that I can do for you, officer?"

"Ranger," he corrected automatically. "The badge confuses people. I'm a Forest Ranger, not a police officer."

She leaned forward and squinted to read the badge. "Not much difference between the two where I come from."

"Where are you from?"

"Kentucky, for the most part."

He felt the urge to snap her up into his arms. She was so close, too close. From this distance, she didn't have a hope of getting away from him. He put his hands in his back pockets more than a little disturbed by his thoughts. "I just wanted to introduce myself and say welcome to the neighborhood."

She looked intrigued. "How did you know we were neighbors?"

"It's a small town." He could have kicked himself. Of course, he shouldn't know her on sight. He tried to reassure her. "We also share a beach and a road."

"Ahh. Now I remember." She nodded, accepting his explanation. "Nadine said to ask about a plow. Do you have a dog?"

"A dog?"

She placed the ravioli in her cart with a shrug. "Yeah, someone's dog showed up on my porch last night. He let himself in but he was gone when I got up this morning. I'm hoping that he got home safely."

"He's fine," Noah answered his eyes wandering over the contents of her shopping cart noting that everything in it could be eaten straight out of the package. "You should make sure that both your screen door and your front door are locked when you go to bed."

"Should I?" A hint of wariness was in her voice.

Noah backtracked. "I just figured if the dog could let himself out that it probably meant that the door wasn't locked. There are a lot of wild animals out by our place."

She arched a brow looking amused rather than annoyed. "I'll keep that in mind. I suppose I come from a place where door locking isn't essential. Is the dog yours?"

"Uh, no. He lives in the woods."

"He's wild?"

Noah gave her a wry smile, hedging his answers. "In a manner of speaking. He finds ways to take care of himself."

"Poor guy. What's his name?"

"Angelo." He gave her his own middle name reluctant to lie to her any more than was necessary. "Are you staying at Mildred's long?"

"Apparently. I've bought the cabin and the shop in the square."

She delivered the information as if it were the first time she'd said it aloud. Relief flowed through his body. He had time for her to get to know him. If it had been otherwise, he wasn't sure what he would have done. All he knew is that he wanted to be close to her, to know her. Instant attraction wasn't something he'd experienced before. In the past, his sexual interests had been built out of familiarity yet he could imagine her arms around his neck, the feel of her skin beneath his lips. He tried to concentrate. "What kind of shop are you opening?"

"I make aromatherapy candles."

"Would you like to have dinner with me?" He hadn't meant to say it. The silence stretched between them while she tried to figure out his intentions. Noah gave her what he hoped was an innocent smile. "I promise it will be better than canned ravioli."

"That's not much of a promise." She teased and tried to push her hair over her ear but the strands only popped immediately back to their original position. "I'd love to but I'm a little short on time right now. I have to be open in two days. I'll be lucky to be able to sleep between now and then." She took a deep breath and then shrugged. "When?"

Noah pretended to think about it. If he could get away with it, he would invite her out tonight but he acknowledged he was already pushing her level of comfort. "Sunday? It might set you on the right foot for the week. I could show you some of the trails around our houses, and maybe cook for you." He saw indecision pass over her face and recognized it for what it was. She was sensible that she could be walking into a dangerous situation. He tried to remember what Joseph had said about the differences between dating werewolves and dating Katrin. Something about being in public. "I also know a place in town that makes a mean clam chowder."

Several expressions crossed her face while she weighed her options. "What are you planning to cook?"

"Enchiladas?"

She moved toward him again, so close she had to tip her face up to maintain eye contact.

"Spicy?"

Was she flirting? He scanned her face noting the teasing tilt of her lips. He couldn't possibly be that lucky. "As hot as you can take it."

She nodded. "Enchiladas it is. If you throw in a Margarita, I could be convinced to take a walk first."

He was going to say something equally as flirty when he was interrupted by a voice from behind.

"Noah Hernandez?"

Noah cursed his luck turning to look over his shoulder. Agent Garland had finally decided to make himself known. Noah tried to save the situation by holding up a hand toward the newcomer in acknowledgement and answering Emily's question, but the unguarded expression on her face stopped him. For a moment she looked at the newcomer with complete fascination before she schooled her features into a look of casual friendliness.

Noah looked again at Agent Garland noting that he was some sort of wood nymph. You could tell because he had fashioned his clothing out of himself, meaning that occasionally the seams simply melted into his skin. In the woods, his human form would have looked very natural but the glamour was difficult to maintain in man-made areas.

The Nymph's hair, his eyes, all of his clothing, and even his shoes were in varying shades of brown and green. He was taller than Noah but not as broad. For his kind, he looked very young. He was also looking at Emily with an equal amount of fascination and friendliness.

Noah turned back to Emily, "Margaritas are included. Is 5ish, all right? It's early, but it might give us enough light to explore the beach before it gets dark and get you home for an early night. I'll come get you."

She took a step back placing her hand over the pentacle on her necklace. "Great. Sounds great."

Her nervousness caught Noah off guard. She was half watching him and half watching the nymph whose skin took on a woody texture as he gave Emily a smile. "I'm sorry I interrupted your conversation. I am Garland." He offered Emily his hand.

She accepted it, her eyes appearing fixated on the changing textures of Garland's fingers against hers. Noah's heart beat with excitement. If Emily could see Garland's skin, then she was Enlightened. Garland continued as if her interest in his texture was something both natural and flattering, "I have been looking for Noah all day. Are you part of his pack?"

Emily's eyes snapped to Noah's as she withdrew her hand but her smile didn't falter. "Pack?"

"Department," Garland corrected himself without missing a beat, "I meant department."

"No," she cast a questioning look between himself and

Garland. "I'm new here. Noah and I just met. I make candles."

Nymphs were naturally both fascinated and wary of fire. Noah could feel the discomfort radiating off Emily but her expression reflected only casual interest. Garland's smile, on the other hand, was just solicitous enough to make Noah step closer to her. He caught Garland's eye letting him know that he was making a claim. Unfortunately, Nymphs have no concept of fidelity or ownership when it comes to mating so Garland blithely ignored the display. "I'm pleased to meet you."

"It's nice to meet you too," Emily responded taking a step toward Noah, her shoulder just brushing his arm. Desire spread through him making it difficult for him to focus on Garland's words.

"I was looking for a hiking path not far from here. I was told that Noah could help me find it."

She nodded. "I'll leave you guys to it." She swung her shopping cart away from them both smiling back at Noah over her shoulder. "I'll see you Sunday?"

"Absolutely."

With a cheerful wave, she pushed her cart toward the registers. Noah let out a deep breath.

Garland's face colored a mossy green with embarrassment. "Forgive me. I did not realize she wasn't yours." Garland's voice was soft and his regret sincere.

"I'm considering making her mine, but I think I make her nervous." Noah watched her for another moment before turning to offer his hand to the nymph.

Garland grasped it for a moment as if picking up a towel from a counter. "It was I who caused her discom-

70

fort. I could have sworn for a second that she saw me. I would not have offered her the greeting otherwise."

Noah ushered Garland toward the door. "I thought so too. I think we might have read a little too much into it considering what we are supposed to be keeping an eye out for. Maybe something about the situation embarrassed her?"

Garland drew a long breath. "What would and would not embarrass a woman is forever beyond my understanding."

Noah patted him on the shoulder. "Mine too, my friend. Mine too."

So, the name of her gazebo man was Noah Hernandez. Emily smiled to herself as she unpacked her groceries in her kitchen. Since the moment she'd seen him jump down off the gazebo rail, he had haunted the unguarded corners of her mind. That he was as attracted to her as she was to him was an unexpected and welcome bonus. Even as she acknowledged that a relationship was the last thing she needed while trying to establish herself here, and getting involved with the guy next door upped the potential disaster factor exponentially, it never crossed her mind to say no to dinner.

Aware that she might be putting herself into a potentially dangerous situation, she should have declined to eat in his home without getting to know him first. His surprised smile when she'd asked what he was going to cook, the proximity to her own home and the fact that just the casual brush of her shoulder against his had sent a bolt of desire straight through her had decided the matter. If he'd asked her to go directly from the grocery store to dinner, she would have probably gone. The expression on his face when she'd said yes was adorably clueless. Like she had just magically appeared after he made a wish and now, he didn't know what to do with her.

Emily's mind flitted over Noah's companion, Garland. At first, she'd registered his earthy rugged features thinking him beautiful but his appearance had shifted like Nick's. Superstition was as natural to her as breathing and something about Larkshead was ringing warning bells in her mind. She was no stranger to the weirder ways of the world. Her grandmother claimed to talk to ghosts and her mother could make anyone like her just by saying their name, but Emily felt she'd been blessedly skipped in the weirdness department. Other than an overdeveloped sense of smell and the occasional bout of harmless déjà vu.

Pulling the dog bowls out of her shopping bag, she filled one with water and one with dog food before placing them on the porch. She didn't know what was going on in Larkshead, and she wasn't sure she wanted to know. Her momma told her most of her life looking at a blessing too close always caused doubt. Whistling "People Are Strange" by The Doors, Emily opened a can of ravioli and set about making more candles.

7

Each Enlightened species has a set of specific cultural mating rituals connected to it. They vary from continent to continent, but are for the most part, easy to learn. The Unenlightened, however, have rituals so complex that they are almost incomprehensible to a rational being. It is therefore best for the easily frustrated Enlightened to avoid romantic relationships with the Unenlightened when possible. – Marie Le Glasse, *Navigating Relationships in the Enlightened World*

Noah and Garland pulled up in front of a small home overlooking the sea just as the sun was setting. Only a short stone wall kept the place from completely blending into the landscape. Carl and Janet Wedgewood lived here. Garland said that Janet was awake and speaking, but that she was not taking the information or the situation well. Noah suspected that it was because the Recovery team continued to ask Carl to give Janet some time and space. Janet was probably suffering from separation as much as she was from shock. Selkies struggled with separation from their mates almost as much as they did from the sea. It was unusual for a Selkie to choose an Unenlightened mate for that reason.

Right now, Carl was sitting on the beach looking out at the ocean with an expression of loss that tore through Noah. They approached making sure that they could be clearly heard. Selkies were more aware of predators than any of the other Enlightened, with the possible exception of Muses.

"Mr. Wedgewood?" He looked up. His grey eyes only briefly acknowledging them before returning to the sea. Noah continued. "My name is Noah Hernandez. This is Garland. We've been sent down by the National Recovery Unit."

Carl began to get up, panic replacing his pain. "Is she okay?"

Garland nodded. "She's talking with some of the other Enlightened. They believe that her awakening was complete when she arrived at the center. We need to talk to you about what happened."

Carl settled back; his shoulders slumped in defeat. "I came in the house after a swim. She panicked when she saw me. I was so shocked myself I didn't know what to do or how to help her. Then she just shut down-fell like a cut rope on to the kitchen floor." He stopped talking his face twisting as if he were re-living the incident play-by-play. "If she hadn't come back, I would have followed her. She's my life-mate. It's my job to protect her on this side or on the other. I put her in our bed. Then she opens her eyes and looks at me like I'm a monster. I tried to touch her but she just backed away."

Noah knelt beside him. "She was surprised. Awakening is difficult."

"She says, 'You lied to me. You lied to me every day for our whole lives together.' And I can't find any words to explain cause, deep inside me, I know she's right."

Noah couldn't imagine that conversation. He'd always known that it was a possibility that his own mate would not be Enlightened. "Mr. Wedgewood, were you less phased than normal when you came inside? Is there a possibility that constant exposure to your changes might have forced her through the Veil?"

"Janet? No. She don't believe in any kind of supernatural stuff, not even when she was a child. I was only half changed the day I met her, swimming right here on this beach." He brushed the sand from his trousers. "You know, we once saw a brownie in our kitchen. I thought for sure that she would see him, but she looks straight at him in his pants and shirt and says, 'We got a mouse in the house.' No sir, something happened to her. Someone forced her through while I was at sea. I left her undefended."

"Was there a change in her habits lately? Did she mention running into anyone new?"

"No, but if I find who did this, I'll kill them myself just for putting her in danger. If she hadn't opened her eyes…"

"We don't know who or what is responsible," Garland said backing away from the violence that radiated off the older man. "May we look around your home? We might be able to spot something connected to the other cases."

Carl shrugged. "It never has been my home. It's Janet's. I belong out there." He gestured toward the cold grey sea. "I was a fool to think I was ever worthy of her."

Garland turned toward the house but Carl's hopelessness stopped Noah from leaving. "Your kind and mine only have one mate. She's angry right now, but more than that, she's awake, she's alone, and she's unguided. She needs you."

"She won't let me come near her."

Noah looked out at the sea. "But you said when she came around that she wasn't mad at you for what you are, she was mad at you for not telling her what you are. That sounds to me like she still loves you."

Carl looked at him with hope. "What can I do?"

"Apologize. Explain. Go see her. Let her yell. You and I both know, angry or not, she'll be more comfortable with you close. You both will."

"And if she doesn't want to come back?"

Noah thought about it for a moment. If they were human, he would say something like it wasn't meant to be, or that Carl could find someone else, but that wasn't true. "I guess that depends. Is she your life-mate?"

Carl held Noah's gaze and a lifetime of moments filtered through his expression; anger, joy, sickness and health but above all, love. The older man didn't acknowledge the tears running down his stern face but he nodded. "We belong together."

"Then wait for her. Trust her to come back to you."

Noah left Carl outside and went into the house. If possible, the devotion between Carl and his wife was even more apparent. Photos and paintings of seascapes in almost every state of weather were interspersed with photos of them standing on beaches, surfing, swimming, and looking at one another with complete devotion. Noah sorted through the scents in the house as easily as he scanned the photos.

There was an unmistakable scent of fresh magic. If Janet was not a witch herself, then she'd brought something magical home. He scanned the household items again looking specifically for a disturbance in the energy but all he could tell was that the item had once been on Janet's bedside table. A small circle mark in the dark varnish, like the bottom of a large coffee cup, was all that remained. Garland came up behind him.

"I also sense magic here. Whatever happened, it started here. It feels like spell craft. I found this in the garbage."

Garland handed Noah a small shipping box with a Boston label on it that read *The Craft Shop*. The feeling of magic wasn't as strong on the box but it was there. Noah took the box to Carl. The selkie was standing in the kitchen with his hands in his pockets looking as much like a visitor as Noah and Garland were.

Sitting the box on the counter, he asked his next question carefully. "You said your wife didn't do magic, but this is from The Craft Shop. It's a store for witchcraft in Boston.

Carl picked up the box turning it over slowly in his hands and then bringing it up to his nose. "It smells like one of Janet's fancy incense packs. I think they stink to high heaven but she loves them. Has tons of them."

"Has she ever had one from this shop before?" Garland asked taking the box back.

"I don't pay much attention to them. She's always got one burning."

Noah brought the box to his nose again noting the soft green earthy smell so that he could identify it. "Do you know where this one is? It was beside the bed. On the table."

"Could be any of them. She switches them out all the time. You think this has something to do with incense?"

"We're going to find out. In the meantime, I need you to find anything Janet has that's connected to this shop." Noah gestured to Garland to follow him. "We have two covens in town. We can take the box to one of them and ask about what kind of magic is here. If we go now, we might catch Rowan Martin before she leaves her shop."

Selene was cutting onions in Noah's kitchen when he got back home Sunday. He and Garland had covered a lot of ground that day talking with both the Martins and the Wildes along with most of the other Enlightened witches in the area but were no closer to understanding what happened to Janet Wedgewood.

They had discovered The Craft Shop sold incense, herbs, crystals, and just about anything else a modern witch could want. All the witches said that the shop only sold white magic items. Rowan herself said that the magic on the box was faint, but it felt like a white magic rather than a curse. It appeared to be a dead end, but Noah put a call to Frank Carlos all the same.

Carl had searched their house but found neither the

original bundle nor anything else connected to The Craft Shop. He remained adamant that Janet wasn't into witchcraft. Underneath the conversations with the magical Enlightened was fear that the awakenings were a sign of a larger problem to come. It had taken a considerable amount of time and reassurance to keep everyone calm.

As if that weren't bad enough, an unexpected tour bus had shown up at the Larkshead Visitor's Center with a large group of retirement-aged amateur wildlife photographers that had made the short Loop Hike last long enough for The Visitor's Center to radio him to check on them. Now he was rushing to make sure that he had everything ready by the time he picked up Emily.

He'd called his sister on his way around the Loop Trail and asked her to purchase the food he had left behind at the grocery store when he'd run into Garland. He had hoped she would drop it off and leave, but he should have known better. Shrugging his jacket off at the front door, he waited for the questions to start.

Selene leaned casually across the kitchen counter with a wolfish grin. "Just how long have you been sleeping with Emily Rollins?"

"What?"

Selene scraped the onions into a nearby bowl. "You know, pretty blonde girl, big hazel eyes, opening a candle shop in town, came into the restaurant the other day reeking of you."

"Her last name is Rollins?" Noah went to the kitchen sink and washed his hands.

Selene tossed the knife and chopping board into the sink narrowly missing him and crossed her arms over her chest. "You have her bathrobe in your bathroom and you don't know her last name?"

"What were you doing in my bathroom?"

"What normal people do in a bathroom," Selene said rolling her eyes. "There I was, washing my hands and I see a pretty pink robe hanging on the back of your door. I get close to it and it smells just like Emily smelled yesterday. Mom is going to flip when she finds out."

Noah opened the cabinet closest to the stove and began pulling spices out. "You didn't tell her?"

"Not yet, but just as soon as I get my money for buying your groceries, I'm making a special call."

Noah closed his eyes and counted to ten. "She'll overreact."

Selene clapped her hands together. "That she will. She'll have a place to sit at the Christmas dinner table before you can even say Happy Thanksgiving."

The look of sheer delight on Selene's face was the only reason that Noah didn't walk over and shake her. Little sisters were a nightmare. Instead, he sat the spices down by the onions and collected a bottle of red wine from the rack beside the fridge, and set about opening it. He was pleased to see that Selene had taken the time to put the groceries away and start the enchilada sauce.

"Don't scare her away. I need enough time to make sure she'll stay put before she gets a load of you guys."

Selene's teasing smile turned astonished. "Are you serious about her?"

He hadn't really thought about it logically. He knew he wanted her, and that he wanted to get to know her. He'd only had one conversation with her but had already told

Garland that he was trying to make Emily his. "Yeah, I'm serious about her."

"Oh my god! This is great! I had no idea." She came around the counter and gave him a hug. "How long have you been seeing her?"

"Our first date is tonight if I can get this meal together, vacuum, and get you out the door in time."

She gave him a get-serious look. "You can't fool me. You don't smell as much like her as she smelled of you, but she definitely smelled like you. And I did see a pink robe."

"Have you ever heard of a werewolf losing control of a shift?" He walked back into the kitchen feeling the need to put some distance between them.

"You mean like attacking someone?"

"No, I mean shifting and then not remembering what happened during the shift or shifting unwillingly."

Selene looked at him carefully. "There are cases. Old ones. I've done some research into old lycanthropy charges. Most of the accused victims say they didn't remember what they did during the change, but that is more likely that the werewolf being interviewed was trying not to reveal anything to the Unenlightened interviewer. What's going on?"

Noah shrugged. "I'm not sure. I woke up in Emily's bed the other morning, and not in the fun way. Emily said a dog showed up on her porch, let himself into her house and then out again the next morning. I remember leaving but I don't remember finding her or shifting."

Selene came up behind him putting a comforting hand on his back. "Did she see you change?"

"No, but only because I was lucky. I went to Emily's home as a wolf and should have awakened as a wolf, but I didn't and that worries me. Can you keep your mouth shut until I can figure out what's going on?"

Selene gave him another hard hug. "No, but I can help you get your dinner together and run interference when Mom makes her approach."

They both laughed. When their mother was determined to do something, there was no stopping her. Noah began to put the chopped ingredients in the pan. "If you want to help, go get the vacuum. I'm cooking."

Emily took a deep breath as she looked at herself in the mirror. She had put on just about every outfit she owned trying to decide what was appropriate. If she had been going out to a restaurant, she would have known exactly what to wear but Noah had chosen a short hike ending with dinner at his house. That ruled out a dress and heels. She finally settled on jeans, walking shoes, and a turquoise cardigan set. She'd straightened her hip-length hair and clipped the front part of it back with little turquoise clasps her mother had brought her from New Mexico. A silver locket filled with bits of yew tree for protection and decorated with filigree etchings hung delicately around her neck and she added long silver earrings to match.

Walking into her living room she picked up the list of things that she needed to get for the house. It would be too tight to afford most of it this month, but she was sure that she would be able to get the basics. Glancing at her coats hanging by the door she added a bathrobe to her list. What had happened to it was beyond her understanding. She half remembered hanging it in the living room but hadn't seen it since. Her opening day was tomorrow and she was as ready as she could be. Thankful that this date would at the very least keep her from spending her whole night worrying, she slipped her silver pentacle into her pocket.

A knock at the door right at 5 pm made her heart trip.

"Get a grip, Emily," she chided herself pulling open the door to see Noah standing on the porch looking at the dog bowls. He was sexy enough to make her feel a little self-conscious but the look of pleasure on his face when he saw her made her nervousness dissolve into something much more enjoyable.

"Wow. You look beautiful."

Suddenly Emily felt sexier than she had ever felt in high heels and a dress. "Thank you. So do you. I'll get my coat and keys, and we can go."

"Sure." He looked back at the bowls. "Are those for Angelo?"

Emily shrugged her coat on over her purse and put her keys in her pocket. She looked around her living room to see if she'd forgotten anything. "I was worried that he might not be getting enough food if he doesn't have a home."

"He's more likely to eat the animals attracted by the dogfood than the dogfood itself."

Emily came back to the door frowning down at the bowls. "I hadn't thought of that. Hopefully, he will do that out of eyesight. I thought I might see if he'd let me take him to the vet for a check-over and some shots."

Noah pulled her door shut behind her and waited for her to lock it. "You want to keep him?"

She checked her purse for her keys and then remembered they were in her pocket. It was hard to concentrate when he was so close. It took her two attempts to slide the key into the lock. "Maybe. I love animals and I can't stand the thought of him lonely or hungry."

"He's lucky you moved in. Don't worry about the shots; I'll take care of it."

The image of Noah trying to wrestle the giant dog into a car made her chuckle. "Are you sure you can get a hold of him? I can help if you want."

"Positive," he replied grinning and stepping out of her way. "But if I get stuck, I will definitely call you for backup."

Noah moved down the stairs watching Emily lock her door. He thought about offering her his hand but remembered that Joseph said humans were a little hesitant about physical contact. It was something werewolves did not understand. Joseph had concluded touching was mostly a sexual thing in the human world; in the wolf world, there were more layers. They touched to show concern, to show joy, to show fellowship. They were touched because the contact helped them to feel accepted and loved.

Emily followed him down the driveway putting her hands in the pockets of her coat but keeping close. He realized he would have to keep their walk short if she wouldn't allow him to warm her with his body. Her jacket wasn't made for this kind of climate and wouldn't keep her warm for long. Selene had been more of a hindrance than a help in getting his house in order, but he finally managed to stash Emily's robe in the back of his closet and get the place somewhere close to what he wanted.

They walked toward the trail that led down to their shared portion of the beach. The trail followed the water line along a rocky beach most of the way to his house before leading back up to his driveway. Before they turned onto the forest path, he stopped her and pointed to the road. "When you're ready to go, all you need to do is say so, and I will take you home. No explanations are necessary. My driveway and yours are mirrored. If you feel like you're ready to go home, and aren't comfortable with me driving or walking you back, just turn right at the bottom of my drive. Keep walking until you see a driveway on your left. There are no houses between us."

She looked at him surprised and pleased as if he'd given her an unexpected gift. Then she stepped forward, stood on tiptoe, put her hands on his chest, and brushed her lips lightly across his once and then again with more intensity. Noah was so stunned that he didn't dare to move. Slowly, he wrapped his arms around her and dropped his head to deepen the kiss.

Her arms wrapped deliciously around his neck as he swept his tongue across her lips to ask for entrance. She obliged, and he lifted her pulling her fully against his body. He was hyper-aware of every sound she made, the scent of her perfume, the textures of her lips and tongue, but most of all, of her desire to taste him. When she finally broke the kiss off, they were both panting.

He rested his forehead against hers trying to remember how to breathe. "If that's my reward for relaying information, we are going to have a really good time together."

She laughed breathlessly. "I'm counting on it."

He let her settle back down to her feet but before she could step away, he took her mouth again testing her acceptance of his touch. She kissed him back allowing him to press her close. His inner wolf howled in triumph. Emily had initiated their bond.

8

The rumor that Magic itself is not inclined toward being good or evil is only partly correct. Demons find it very easy to be evil and Angels find it very easy to be good. The rest of the world, both Enlightened and Unenlightened, are strung out somewhere between these two extremes. It is best to evaluate each being, even Demons and Angels, on their own individual merit. The exception to this rule is Fey who have very flexible, and in some cases erratic, ideas about what it means to be good or evil. – Phoebe Pearce, *Witchcraft for the Newly Awakened*

The path was barely discernible to Emily but Noah moved forward as if it were paved. The dark green forest closed around them and eventually the chattering of birds and insects filled the silence. In the distance, the crash of waves against a rocky shore added a counter rhythm to the gentle pace Noah was setting. He seemed more alive in the woods, his movements energetic and his eyes constantly scanning the terrain. Occasionally, he would stop and point out a plant or hidden ravine, something she would have overlooked herself in her efforts to identify the path.

Normally kissing came at the end of dates, like a green light to the next level of physical intimacy. She'd decided early in life that if she didn't like a guy well enough to kiss him at the start of a date, no amount of date time would lead to kissing at the end. She'd already decided she was going to taste him but his efforts to make her feel safe and in control had presented her with the perfect moment to let him know she wanted him. She'd been unprepared for how much he wanted her in return or how much his hunger would ramp up her own desire.

He had received the kiss as it was meant, as an invitation to touch her, and now he turned that invitation into an erotic game. He held her hand, lifted her across a fallen log, and tucked her into his arms when she began to shiver. He also brushed his fingers against her face, pressed his lips to the top of her hand, and held her loosely against him while he pointed out sites. Shaking her head, she tried to keep her attention on what Noah was saying rather than on what he was doing to her.

The dimness of the forest gave way to a stretch of rocky beach and Emily squealed in excitement rushing to the edge to dip her fingers into the sea. The water had to be cold but she dipped her hands in again and then touched the water to her tongue. She winced at the salty taste and smiled up at him. Noah felt a flutter of pleasure in his chest.

"I've always wanted to live close to the ocean. I never thought it would really happen. Do you swim here?"

"Not in November. The water is cold enough to cause hypothermia." The disappointment on her face was palpable. He squatted next to her. "You can start swimming in late May and swim all the way up to late October, longer if you get a wet suit. In November, it's better to have a dry suit. I can get you a tide table from work. If you want, in the spring, we can take a canoe to some of the coastal islands. They are some of the most beautiful places on earth."

"I would love that."

She used his thigh to push herself up and then offered him her icy hand. He didn't need it but he took it anyway.

"Do you know I was seventeen the first time I saw the ocean? My Mom and I made a nine-hour trip with only bathing suits, beach towels, and Mountain Dews. It was heaven. We got so sunburned that we had to take turns laying in a cold bath the next day. It was so worth it."

Noah watched her watching the sea. He couldn't imagine not living near the ocean. As she skipped stones, put shells in her pocket, and danced away from the water with an almost childish excitement he thought about how everything about this territory was second nature to him; tides, the places to swim, the best places to watch the sun turn the ocean orange, they felt embedded in his soul.

Traveling was not something most werewolves did

well. There were a few that could overcome their territory issues, but he wasn't one of them. He could stand to be away about a week, and then his territory would call him back.

"I've lived next to the ocean almost my whole life. Your accent says you're from the South. Where in Kentucky is it that you call home?"

"We moved to Paducah, Kentucky when I turned 18. I guess if I were going to call any place home, it would be there. My mom was born with the heart of a wanderer. She averages about three months in a place before she moves on but she tends to stick to the South. When she left Kentucky, I stayed with my grandmother. Mom can make friends anywhere but it takes me time to adjust to a place."

He smiled, relieved. "Me too. When I was younger, I thought about striking out to other territories. Went to a university in Syracuse, New York, and did some of my training in California, but I was homesick the whole time. Where's your mom now?"

"An excellent question." She laughed rubbing her hands dry on her jeans before putting them in her pocket. "Last time I checked, she was cooking on riverboats traveling up and down the Mississippi. It's hard to tell with her. The wind blows, a bell rings, and then she's off. She texts me all the time with pictures of new friends and homes and comes to see me when she's close, but I gave up keeping track of her a long time ago. My grandma was the same until I moved in with her. I honestly don't know how I'm related to them sometimes."

He hugged her kissing the top of her head not sure if he was comforting her or himself. Being alone was something he'd never had to worry about. In fact, he spent most of his time trying to get some alone time. Being part of the sanctuary meant that most of the werewolf packs were closer than they would have been anywhere else.

"I'm related, in some way, to almost everyone in town."

Emily looked at him like she didn't quite believe him. "What's your family like?"

"Have you ever seen *My Big Fat Greek Wedding*?" Emily laughed and he ushered her toward the path so that they could make their way to his place. They were losing the light, which wouldn't bother him but he didn't want to have to explain his night vision until he was sure that Emily was Enlightened. "I'm not kidding. Mom is convinced she's a matchmaker, and my dad encourages her in whatever new scheme she's cooked up to get Selene and me married. Which reminds me, when she comes to your shop feel free to tell her to mind her own business."

"When?" The humor in Emily's voice was unmistakable.

"Sure. You're laughing now. By this time tomorrow, she'll even know your shoe size."

"Is that why we are walking through the woods to your home rather than going to a restaurant in town?"

Noah tucked her under his arm again admiring the way she just seemed to take this information into stride. "There is no hiding from Mom. If you'd rather go to a restaurant when we get to my house, I'll get my keys and we can go from there." If she said yes, he'd just have to think of another reason for them to come back to his place. There was no question now that he wanted her in his home and in his bed as soon as possible.

He was watching her watch the woods when he felt Emily tense. Glancing up, he caught a glimpse of a Wil-of-the-Wisp crossing the path ahead of them. It was one of the reasons he'd brought her out this way, to check if she was Enlightened. Trouble identifying other Enlightened people was one of the problems the Veil created. Talk too much about the wrong thing to the wrong person and you could end up in a psych ward.

Wisps were common Fey who entertained themselves by creating wild goose chases. Unenlightened saw them as bright flashes of light or glowing fog, everyone else saw them as a pain in the ass. They were one of the few Enlightened that could be acknowledged by both parties without incident. Sometimes Wisps would lead the lost back home, but they were just as likely to lead you off a cliff. Noah had negotiated a truce of sorts where they could lead anyone, including him, anywhere they wanted to as long as they didn't hurt anyone. In exchange, they reported to the pack if they found anyone who was lost for more than a couple of hours or had been hurt.

The Wisp in question, Kiss-Me-Knot, must have been heading home because all she did was wave at him and continue through the forest. For reasons only she knew, she preferred to mislead married couples. Just the same, he would have to double-check the path to make sure they were going the right way.

He watched Emily noting that her eyes followed Kiss-

Me-Knot just long enough to pass the spot she'd disappeared into the undergrowth, but she didn't remark on either a light or a Whisp. She looked over her shoulder as they passed the spot where Kiss-Me-Knot disappeared and squinted for a second as if she were trying to read the underbrush.

"Did you see something?"

She smiled up at him but unlike her previous smiles, this one was the same practiced look she'd given Garland. "I'm not sure we know each other well enough for me to tell you what I've been seeing the last few days."

Noah threaded his fingers through hers. "I promise I won't laugh."

Emily shook her head. "Never mind. It's nothing a good meal and a good night's sleep won't fix.

Three times in just a few days. Emily couldn't believe it even as she watched the glowing, naked woman wave at them and then disappear into the woods. First Nick Wilde, then the tree man called Garland at the store, and now this. Noah hadn't acknowledged either Garland or the woman which meant that whatever was happening was happening only to her. She schooled her features into what she hoped was a pleasant expression and then forced her mind to focus again on Noah.

He hadn't missed a step when the glowing naked lady had come into view. Emily had watched him carefully but all he seemed to see was her distress. He was doing his utmost to let her know that she was safe with him but she was beginning to wonder if he was safe with her. She focused on him, his breath, the heat of his body coming through her light coat, the brush of her hip against his thighs. It wasn't helping her to regain the equilibrium she was looking for but it was definitely taking her mind off of things.

The twilight colors of reds and purples began to give way to dark blues just as they reached Noah's driveway. Noah had two white wicker rocking chairs on the porch with a small table between them, but other than that, it was like walking in a big circle back to her house.

"Déjà vu, right?" Noah put his hand on Emily's lower back to usher her up onto the porch.

"My mother's name is Deja. She thinks seeing the future just makes people worry about things they can't control." She went to the door and then stepped aside to allow him to open it.

"I like the idea of free will too much to believe that it's all set in stone but I do think some things are fated." He squeezed her hand coming around to the side of her. "There are four cabins all together up the coast, but apparently only ours are identical. They were the start of a camping retreat before the owner decided that it was too cold for a camping business."

"What happened to the other two cabins?"

"I own all of them but yours. The other two were in rough shape. I've demolished one of them but the other is waiting for me to get the time and the money together to do something decent with it."

"Why didn't you buy my house?"

Noah rubbed the back of his head with a grin. "I talked to Mildred about buying the cabin a couple of years back but she wasn't interested in moving yet and wouldn't consider splitting the properties up. I don't have any interest in running a store. Then the cabin was sold privately before it officially came on the market."

Emily winced. "Sold to me? You must have been disappointed."

He opened the front door and removed his hand from her back standing aside to allow her complete autonomy. By the rules of werewolf courtship, the first steps into his home had to be her choice.

"I was at first, but then I bumped into my new neighbor at the grocery store and I have a feeling we are going to get along great."

Emily stopped in the doorway looking back at him over her shoulder with her hand on the frame. It lacked the ferocity of what had happened when he left her house but not the impact. He attempted one more time to give her a choice. "If you want to eat at a restaurant, you can wait here and I'll turn off the oven and get my keys."

Emily shook her head walking confidently through the door. "And miss Enchiladas? No way. You can take me out for chowder another time."

He closed the door behind them with a wolfish grin.

The door closed with an audible click that made Emily suddenly aware of how isolated they really were. It wasn't the bachelor's home she'd imagined. Every surface was covered with brightly colored objects from the patchwork quilt thrown over the back of an overlarge brown leather sofa, to the feathery plants in lavishly decorated pots. Mismatched pictures of family and friends, each in a different kind of frame, were hung close together on the walls and all worked together in a bohemian sort of way. In the window overlooking the driveway was a little pile of oddly shaped stones and small pine cones. The objects appeared to be precisely placed, like a woodsy version of a meditation garden.

She'd expected stark and functional but Noah obviously had an artist's heart. Emily pulled one of the shells from her pocket rubbing the sand off it and sat it down in the group of stones feeling that it belonged there. She moved toward the kitchen noting that the table was already set, complete with wine glasses. Noah moved around her to light a fire already laid in the hearth. It was clear that he'd gone to a lot of trouble to have her here. She felt more than saw him watching her as he moved around the room.

"This place is beautiful."

Noah breathed a sigh of relief and took her coat. Placing it next to his own by the front door, he was secretly pleased with her little shell addition to his home. A woman leaving something at your place typically indicated that she intended to come back. It was just a shell, but it was also something that she'd intended to take home with her.

He wanted her to be comfortable here, to be comfortable with him. He wanted to make love to her in front of the fireplace, to see her hair spread out beneath her while he tasted every inch of her creamy skin. He wanted to know her favorite ice cream and how strongly she drank her coffee in the morning. In retrospect, it might have been a mistake to bring her here because he had never been a man who resisted temptation. She was standing in front of his fireplace, only a couple of feet from him, the light dancing over the high curve of her breasts and accentuating her hips. Arousal hit him so hard that he almost groaned.

"Are you hungry?" He heard the invitation in his voice as he poured them both a glass of wine and held one out to her.

She came closer, a playful smile on her lips. "Starving."

"It will be about twenty minutes." He went back into the kitchen, turned up the oven with the enchiladas inside, poured salsa into a small bowl, and then opened a bag of tortilla chips bringing both into the living room and placing them on the coffee table. She followed him back into the living room collecting their wine and bringing it through. He took the opportunity to feed her while her hands were full and dipped one of the chips in the salsa and held it out for her to try.

"My mom makes this salsa. If it's too hot, I have a milder version that Selene likes." She gently took a bite laughing as the chip disintegrated and he was forced to quickly eat the rest of it off his hand. They sat down the wine and began a game of feeding one another while trying to avoid being covered in salsa. Noah licked a bit off her fingers and she leaned forward to kiss him, sharing the slight burn of the jalapeño present on her tongue.

The chips were forgotten and Noah maneuvered her back on the couch and settled the weight of his body on top of hers pinning her beneath him while his arms kept his chest from crushing her. He spent long minutes smoothing her hair with his hands, exploring her mouth and then her neck. When his lips found the place her pulse throbbed, she moaned and leaned her head back offering him her throat. Her submission undid his intentions to move slowly with her.

He scraped his teeth across her pulse and then nipped her hard enough to mark her. Her fingers splayed through his hair and she brought his mouth more firmly to her throat. Possessiveness flared through him and he found himself gently suckling the skin, running his tongue across the bite to take some of the sting out. Another person, wolf or not, would see the mark and understand she was taken.

There was no doubt that she could feel his hardness between them and he moved to settle himself between her legs. She gasped, her hands moving along his sides and his back searching for a way under his clothing. The oven alarm started beeping and Noah dropped his forehead to hers trying to remember that this was a first date. She was marked, she was here, he didn't need to overwhelm her. He would give her the space to come to him by choice.

"You are saved by the bell, temptress." He kissed her again and then forced himself to move away from her and pull her up into a sitting position.

She looked beautifully confused and noticeably kissed. The mark on her shoulder wasn't large, but it was distinct. He headed for the kitchen before he burned their dinner. It was unfair to claim her without making her aware of the claim but his experience with Unenlightened women was non-existent.

Treating her like his when she'd only agreed to one date was another problem he hadn't considered. Intelligent women tended to be wary of instant commitment. Although another werewolf would have considered his possessiveness a flattering sign of real interest, other species felt caged in by the closeness a werewolf needed from a partner. Never above you. Never below you. Always beside you. Those were werewolf words of bonding between mated pairs but werewolves understood that always beside you was more than a metaphorical promise. Werewolves were second only to vampires in their clinginess in the Enlightened world. He pulled the enchiladas out of the oven and sat them on the counter to cool conscious of Emily's movement.

She stood feeling self-conscious again and brushed imaginary crumbs off her blouse. Her level of attraction to Noah was out of this world. Sleeping with someone on a first date did not tend to give bed partners a good impression but she found herself entertaining the idea for purely physical reasons. Rather than cooling her eagerness with some space, his politeness seemed to amplify her own sexual boldness. If it had been up to her, their dinner would be burned and they would both be pleasantly satisfied but Noah obviously came from a more conservative family. She took a large gulp of wine before moving around the end of the couch to help. "Let me help you put dinner on the table."

The cabin door swung open just as she moved around the end of the couch. Noah seemed to materialize between her and whoever was coming through the door, his hand pushing her firmly behind him. A younger version of Noah, about seventeen, strolled in with eyes so golden they seemed to glow. He was wearing torn jeans and a black T-shirt that said 'Talk Nerdy to Me.' His sudden presence was odd enough but he also wasn't wearing any shoes in November. Emily felt rather than heard a sound like a low growl come from Noah.

For a moment, the boy looked stunned. "Holy shit, is that a girl?" The boy was trying to peek around Noah oblivious to the obvious signs of his displeasure.

"Don't you know how to knock?"

The boy shrugged. "I smelled enchiladas. Mom's making spaghetti. No brainer. Since when do you have girls here?"

"Since now. That means knock."

Emily snickered.

Noah grabbed her hand and pulled her out from behind him. "Emily, this is my youngest brother, Sebastian. Sebastian, this is Emily."

"Pleased to meet you." His eyes were dark brown now and he was studying her like he'd never seen a woman before. She offered him her hand.

He shook it carefully, his eyes swinging between her

and Noah with a rouge-like smile. "Hey, Emily. Nice to meet you too." He turned to Noah. "Mom's going to flip when she hears about this."

"Sebastian." Noah's voice held a note of warning that again seemed to pass right over his brother's head.

"Sorry to ruin your date, Emily. Noah doesn't usually have dates here." He seemed to consider the statement for a minute before adding, "Actually, Noah doesn't usually have dates. He's kind of a dork."

Noah rolled his eyes. "She doesn't need to know that and he has a date here now, so go home."

"Right." Sebastian started to move toward the door then turned back. "Dad said if I helped you at the visitor center for the next couple of weekends, I could use his car for prom."

"Fine. Come to the station tomorrow and I'll get you set up. Now go home."

Sebastian laughed rubbing his hands through his hair. "Guess I'm eating spaghetti." Noah pushed him unceremoniously out the door.

"Nice to meet you, Sebastian," Emily called out after him.

Noah closed the door firmly and then leaned on it wondering how he was going to save this situation. The romantic mood that he'd been slowly cultivating had disappeared.

"Where are his shoes?"

Noah looked toward the closed door trying to come

up with a reasonable explanation. He hadn't noticed Sebastian's bare feet. As a rule, his family had clothing tucked just outside each other's houses so that they had the freedom to run in their own territory without carrying anything. Most of the time his family didn't bother to change fully until they were in the house. That Sebastian had changed and put clothes on meant that he was probably just being nosey rather than seeking food.

"He probably left them on the porch because they were muddy."

"Should we offer him a ride home? It's pretty dark out there."

In reality, Sebastian had probably shifted and was most likely halfway home by now, so even if Noah was willing to offer him a ride, it was too late. "He's been running through these woods since he learned to walk, but I'll text Dad and let him know Sabastian is heading home. Shall we eat?"

Emily's eyes darted toward the door looking a little smug. "You forgot to lock the door. You know, someone recently told me there are a lot of wild animals around here."

Noah reached behind him and turned the lock with a resounding click. "I was trying to make you feel comfortable."

"Appreciated." Her tone said she did not believe a word.

"Would you believe me if I said that this didn't happen all the time?" He gestured toward the door.

"No."

"Good, because I wouldn't want to lie to you so early

in our relationship." He walked over trapping her between the back of the couch and himself. "How about if I told you they get better once you get to know them?" He kissed her forehead and then the tip of her nose bringing her focus back to him.

She put her arms around his neck giving him a feisty look. "Not buying it."

He kissed her lips lifting her up and placing her bottom on the back of the couch so that he could stand between her legs. When he kissed her this time, he leaned over so that she had to wrap herself around him in order not to fall over allowing her to feel just how well they would fit together.

"I might be worth the hassle."

Her fingers brushed the hair on the back of his neck. "You just might be."

"Give me a chance to convince you?"

She kissed the tip of his nose playfully. "Feed me first."

Noah kept his word about Margaritas but also poured her some water to go with her dinner and set about learning the things that made Emily happy. She told him about Nick and the Christmas decorations and her plans for her shop. He told her about Dark Wolf and the challenges of keeping tourists alive during a real New England winter. He started to tell her about his plans to make the other cabin into a bigger family home but stopped.

The word family reminded him that Emily just had a real taste of what it was going to be like when they became a couple. He had to keep reminding himself that even if Emily was Enlightened, she wasn't a wolf. She wouldn't understand the intensity of his need to be close. His friend Joseph had once explained that when dating Katrin, he had to pick one of the thirty things he wanted to do with her in a week in order not to appear like a stalker. Noah wished he'd paid more attention to Joseph's other advice. Emily started to pick up the plates but he stopped her. "I'll get them later."

He meant to kiss her softly but she slid into his arms like she was helpless to resist him. He kissed her hard and deep, his hands dropping to the place where her sweater touched her jeans. Moving inside to caress her bare back, he explored the textures of her skin. She made a sexy little hissing sound at the contact as if his hands burned her. He caressed her again expertly moving her toward his bedroom. He pushed her against the wall cupping her bottom and taking advantage of his height which forced her to tilt her head up to keep contact with his mouth. He struggled not to show her his strength. He could easily hold her here while he stripped her naked. He wanted to be inside her. She ran her hands down his shoulders and her breath shuddered from her body.

"I want you, Emily, but if you don't want to do this, now is the time to say so. Otherwise, I'm going to start removing your clothes."

She stared at him a moment as if she didn't understand the question. Her passion was hot enough that he knew he could overwhelm her, but he wanted this to be her decision. He tried again gesturing toward his bedroom with his chin. "Are you staying the night with me, Emily?"

She took another shaky breath her eyes darting between him and the bedroom. The uncertain expression that crossed her beautiful features was enough of an answer for him. He wanted her to be mentally ready not just physically. Wrapping his arms around her on top of her clothing, he cradled her head to his chest. "We don't have to do this all at once. We have time, right?"

A look of mischief crossed her face and she shrugged as if she were deciding. He kissed her again allowing his inner wolf to overwhelm his senses. He tasted her, touched her, and promised her in every wicked way he knew that when he took her to bed, she was going to enjoy the hell out of it.

"We have time!" she gasped when he pulled his lips away to nibble her throat.

"How much time?" he asked continuing his erotic coaxing. "If it's only a little time I might need to take advantage." His tongue swirled over the mark he'd put on her neck. "Will you see me tomorrow, next week?"

She started to giggle. "Friday?"

"I don't know," he placed playful kisses across her face. "That's six whole days from now."

She looked at him like he was being ridiculous. "You've managed this long without me. I think you'll survive."

"Monday?" He threaded her fingers through his and held them over her head while he kissed her.

She tugged his lip with her teeth threatening to bite him before letting go. "Wednesday, that's as good as you're going to get. I have a new business, you know."

Noah let her hands down but didn't move his body

away from hers. "If I promise to moderately behave, will you watch a movie with me before I walk you home?"

She looked up at him through her lashes. "What movie?"

He kissed her forehead. "Do you care?"

9

Although most of the Enlightened are humanized by the Veil, all Enlightened have the ability to show their true form or power. Shapeshifters are the exception to this rule. Their transformations, their animal forms, and their human forms can all be observed by the Unenlightened. This makes investigations challenging in shapeshifter territories. — Frank Carlos, *Recovery Report-147*

Like teenagers, they had made out on the couch with a movie running in the background that neither of them watched. They had explored each other discovering little ways to turn the other one on. Emily was ticklish on the tops of her hips and his breath on the place where her shoulder and throat met made her nipples instantly hard. Her hands brushing over the muscles on the small of his back had a similar effect. It was a kind of power and a kind of torture. He loved every minute of it.

He walked her home after the film knowing what he

was going to do even before he did it. Erotic play aside, he needed to make sure that he knew what his wolf-self was doing when he was around her. Kissing her senseless at her front door, he got her to agree to see him on Friday as well as Wednesday, then walked back just far enough in the woods to change.

His wolf-self was so close to the surface that he barely had time to stash his clothes before his body began to contort. Putting her in danger was not an option. Inside the house he could hear her humming part of the Star Wars theme song while she got ready for bed. He tried not to linger over his remembered image of lying with her on her bed, holding onto human memories made it difficult to fully shift.

Noah was no more at home as his wolf-self than he was being human. Normally both selves were natural to him but tonight he was uncomfortable as a wolf. The self-inflicted sexual frustration took the form of mild aggression as he walked up the steps of her home. Opening his senses to their extreme, he noted the scent of the mailman and the mixed smells of the herbs and wax that he now knew she used for candle making. Underneath it all was the intoxicating scent of her. He jumped up on the door to bounce it open but it remained firmly locked. Wolves didn't smile but he felt happiness that she'd listened to him pulse through his body.

There was no internal struggle or blanks in his memory this time. He wanted the same thing in both forms, to be welcome on the other side of the door. Content that his thoughts were his own, he began walking away from the house. The clicking sound of the deadbolt made him pause. Shapeshifters were restricted from using their alternative shapes in any way that would violate another's privacy. Still, he sat down at the bottom of the stairs waiting to see if she would open the door. She peaked at him in the same plaid pajamas he'd seen her in the other morning. Belatedly, he remembered that he needed to get rid of her robe.

"Angelo? Where have you been? I've been looking for you."

She stepped aside to allow him inside but he didn't go. He was lucky that she hadn't locked him in last time. Instead, he headed over to the dog bowls she'd bought him and took a drink of water. She wrapped her arms around herself scanning the woods, presumably to check to see if his human self were close by.

"I am fresh out of Cheetos, buddy, but if you want to come inside, I might be able to find a suitable replacement."

He went back to her with his tail wagging. He wanted her to be comfortable with him as a wolf, to accept his presence. If she wouldn't allow his human self to be with her all the time, then he could use his other form to placate his need to be close to her. He felt a twinge of conscience for taking advantage of her innocence but it wasn't enough to compete with the reassurance of being beside her.

She was running her hands along his thick ears when the sudden scent of something undead drifted past. The odor was so light that he had to concentrate to find it. Even so, Emily scanned the woods as if she could smell it too. He turned toward the darkness growling.

"What do you see, Angelo?"

He couldn't see the creature, but the smell was becoming unmistakable. He lowered his body to the ground baring his teeth and snarling a warning at the same time. He used his bulk to herd Emily toward her door.

"Shhh," she said rubbing her hand between his shoulders. "Let's go inside. Come on buddy, let's go."

He bumped her again to urge her inside and then jumped off the porch heading toward the intruder. She wouldn't go in until he was gone and he couldn't follow her inside until he identified the unknown person in his territory.

"Angelo!"

He ignored her plea heading out of sight at top speed and toward the threat. The demon was standing on the edge of Emily's woods. It was easily twice his size but it was unprepared for his attack. He launched himself at it simultaneously changing into his human form to pin the winged creature against a tree by its throat. The demon struggled to push at Noah's arm, but it was unable to do more than get a couple of shallow breaths. Noah could hear Emily coming off the porch. He snarled, "You will move away from my life-mate or I will kill you here."

The demon nodded and Noah let go. It dropped to its knees taking in a couple of shaky breaths. "I'm James, from the Boston Recovery Unit. I tried to call earlier."

"Do not lie to me, demon. The agent I gave permission to be here made contact already. You have not been granted crossing in my territory."

The demon bared its teeth in challenge but did not stand up. "I'm looking for an Unguided woman."

Emily was moving in their direction. "Angelo? Come here, boy."

Her mind connected suddenly to his using the same unique pathway he'd tried to follow for months. She called for him as Angelo and him as Noah at the same time, demanding he return to her side. He almost obeyed her but his need to keep her safe won out.

"Be quiet. Come with me quickly. You will not alarm my mate. Do you understand me?"

The demon stood folding his large wings behind his back. "I understand."

Following at a respectful distance, Noah collected his clothing and his thoughts. Losing control twice shook the foundations of what he believed himself capable of. He had the right to defend his territory but he knew deep down that it wasn't his domain that had caused his rage; the demon was too close to Emily. Only with his wolf rage quieted by the demon's submission could Noah really allow the impact of what happened to run through him.

It was Emily who had called to him in the night. The familiarity of her mental connection left no doubt in his mind. He wouldn't need to seek her; his mate had found him! Joy coursed through him followed by relief and a sudden understanding that he wasn't losing control of himself. Drunk on hobgoblin whiskey, he had simply heard his mate's call and gone to her. Nick had said the magic in the whiskey was wild. That explained the transformation.

He would have to watch himself more carefully because his kind could be aggressive and jealous while they were still establishing a bond. Noah nearly had his head taken off when he'd made the mistake of accepting an invitation to play video games with Joseph's mate, Katrin, before they were fully bonded.

They reached his porch faster than he would have liked. At the moment, all he cared about was getting back to Emily as fast as possible to comfort her. He gestured for the demon, James, to sit down in one of the porch chairs while he got dressed but James perched on the porch rails folding his wings behind him. The position put him at a distinct tactical advantage over Noah, but he understood the demon's need to regain face. Noah took a seat. "Why are you here? Boston didn't send you."

"My apologies, Mr. Hernandez, for crossing your territory unannounced. I don't have clearance to be here so I thought to make contact as quickly as possible. I should have remembered that wolves bite first and ask questions later."

Noah ignored the insult. James took out his phone and showed Noah a picture of a beautiful young woman with wild red hair. She had her arm around a young werewolf.

"I'm looking for an Enlightened female called Phoebe Pearce. She's been kidnapped from Boston by a vampire called January."

"Did you call the police?" It wasn't a question. The Enlightened were bound as much by human laws as they were by the rules set by the Recovery Unit.

"No. It would be pointless. The vampire that took her

is very old and unfortunately too smart to get caught by police, Enlightened or otherwise."

Noah looked at the picture again. "She's not with a vampire in that photo."

"No, she's with a werewolf named Alex Kimbos. January is his guide. The number of newly awakened that are currently in the Boston area is unprecedented. Alex disappeared also."

"And Larkshead is the closest werewolf sanctuary," Noah finished not recognizing the werewolf in the photo. "If your wolf had applied for sanctuary, you know he would be protected here." Noah stood to look James in the eyes. It was a direct challenge. "And you are avoiding my question. Why are you here? You're outside your own Recovery zone, and as far as I can tell, unrelated to the people involved."

James sighed coming down from the rail to stand in front of Noah looking as ancient as he likely was. "I gave January my word I would keep his life-mate safe."

Noah whistled. A demon was his word. If this Phoebe were harmed, even by accident, James was as good as dead to his own kind.

"January, the kidnapper, exchanged promises with you to keep her safe? If he is willing to bargain with demons for her safety, what makes you think he would harm her?"

James looked uncomfortable. "It's complicated."

Noah crossed his arms over his chest. "Try me. I'm pretty smart." They stared at one another for a long moment, James's claws gripping the porch hard enough to make it groan. Noah moved back just enough to be able to move out of the way if the demon decided he'd given away enough information.

"January wants Phoebe by his side whether she wants to be there or not. In his mind, he gave her a choice but, she wasn't fully aware of what she was choosing. She's already a witch and a very powerful one. I believe she's one of the first Unguided. If January converts her, before I prove that Phoebe's awakening was caused by something other than January's conversion of her, January will be held accountable."

"If your vampire is that old, he would know that himself."

James clicked his wings together in irritation. The force of his anger caused the air to heat. "He does know it. I told him myself!"

Noah prepared to change. He'd managed to catch James off guard in the forest, but the demon wouldn't be easy to take down again. "You said that she came through the Veil without the vampire's help. Does she have any connection to The Craft Shop?"

James began to pace the porch. "She works there."

"I got a call from The National Recovery Unit recently to alert us about an Unguided situation spreading here. Do you know how Phoebe was awakened?"

"She says she read out a spell from a magic book intended for vampires, but I have my doubts. She's powerful, but not powerful enough to awaken herself." James stopped pacing and walked directly to Noah. "If I can keep her human for a little longer, I can prove that she was the first Unguided in Boston. I can prove January's innocence by using her to locate the person or item that brought her through the Veil."

"Making her patient zero." Noah rocked back on his heels at the potential impact of that information.

"Patient zero?"

"My sister is looking for outbreak patterns for the Unguided. If she can find the first Unguided in Boston, she can narrow down potential causes for the outbreak."

"And stop it?" James bowed formally. "Then I offer an exchange. Allow me to stay in this territory and find Phoebe Pearce so that I can stop these awakenings."

Noah thought hard about the request. Dealing with demons meant that you needed every detail spelled out clearly. Creating loopholes in a seemingly straightforward bargain was what they did best. "You will deliver Phoebe Pearce alive and unharmed to the Augusta Recovery Unit. Your stay is granted if you obey the territory rules here. The moment they're broken, your welcome is revoked."

James scowled. "You've dealt with demons before, but I am not here to take advantage of you or your promises. I just need to locate January before he converts her. Will you alert me before you alert the police if Alex Kimbos, Phoebe Pearce, or January comes through your territory?"

Noah shook his head holding his hand out to James. "I can promise that I will call you if I see either Phoebe or January in my territory. I will tell you after I have reported it to my alpha."

"But not Alex?" James said with a frown.

Noah ignored the question. "After I let you know that I've seen them, I will call the proper authorities to take care of the situation. I will also tell Boston you have permission to be here so long as you obey the laws and share your information on the Unguided. I will do this without an exchange."

James arched a brow in surprise. "Why? You could ask me to promise almost anything at this point. I need something you have. My life is on the line."

"If what you say is true, then it's more than your life at stake." Noah invited the demon into his house while the first snowstorm of the season appeared on the horizon.

10

Contrary to Unenlightened beliefs, Fairies prefer whiskey to honey and bread. When it comes to dealing with fairies the rules are very clear; feed them and tell them they are magnificent. Attempting to subvert these rules will only lead to disaster.
—Ichabod Rimmington, *Surviving Fairies*

Emily rushed out the door Monday morning cursing herself for hitting snooze on her alarm clock. This was her opening day and she'd done everything in her power to make sure that it would be perfect. Nick delivered his sugar plum fairies to the doorway of The Ace of Cups Sunday afternoon while Emily was out shipping online orders. Each one was so elegant and realistic in their details that she'd felt compelled to tell each one they were magnificent while she gently arranged them around her displays.

Rather than being glass, each was made with a flexible material Emily had never encountered before. They were so real looking she imagined they just might come to life and dance when unobserved. She told herself imagination was the reason they seemed to subtly move around her displays and why their prices came off when she turned her back on them.

With the shop clean, her candles and Christmas displays mostly arranged, and her little kitchenette stocked with enough coffee and snacks to see her through the week. She had whispered a goodnight to the fairies last night superstitiously leaving a large piece of fruitcake on the counter for them.

She'd been watching the snow come down since late last night. Keeping half an ear out for Angelo, she'd fallen asleep last night knowing that she would need to leave herself more time to get to work Monday morning. Understanding that snow was going to be a big part of her life and actually living with it were two completely different things. As it was, she had one puny ice scraper in her car, cloth gloves, no snow shovel, and she'd still not managed to order fire wood.

The northern wind made short work of her so-called winter coat and for some reason, all she wanted to do this morning was to go knock on Noah's door and see if he was okay. She had the weirdest feeling he was in danger. Shaking her head and calling herself a ninny, she put her boots on and headed to the kitchen to get some coffee to go.

Noah had texted her this morning to wish her luck and reassure her that he was looking forward to seeing her Wednesday. Then he had launched into a series of sporadic texts on what kind of shoes were best for summer vs winter hiking, what kind of coat she would need for the winter, and then where they could get hot chocolate on the Winter Solstice.

He was like playing with fire. One moment cute and playful and the next, so hot he burned. How he could find time to text and still get to work was beyond her, but his attention made her smile. Something about the completely guileless way he explored their future plans made her aware that he might be looking for reassurance. She knew what to do with men who just wanted to fool around; she had no idea how to handle someone who was looking for more.

Her previous relationships were ones of mutual convenience. Even the ones she'd classified as serious, she had always been happy to have an abundance of personal space. Shaking her head at her own ridiculousness she locked her front door and then rushed down the steps. The sound of her shoes hitting her wooden steps rather than crunching through the snow brought her back to reality. Someone had cleared the snow from her steps and her driveway. They had also knocked the snow off her car and scraped her windows clean. A yellow post-it note tucked under her windshield wiper read:

Good morning Sleeping Beauty,
  Be careful going into work. If you get stuck, call me. I'll see you soon.
  Noah

. . .

She read it twice unable to believe that she'd not heard him outside, and more, that he would go to so much effort to make sure she got out this morning. She held the note to her chest, grateful that his foresight meant that she could open her store on time.

The roads were amazingly clear considering half this amount of snow would have been a state of emergency in the South. Overnight, Larkshead had gone from a quiet fall town to a bustling Christmas paradise. The sidewalks were being cleared by both shop owners and town maintenance. The Christmas Market was fully erected with each tiny building stuffed to the rafters with merchandise and sellers bundled up for the cold. The Christmas tree lighting was taking place the Wednesday before Thanksgiving but the huge evergreen was already in place.

She slid out of her car, grabbed her coffee, and threw her bag over her shoulder at the same time. If she sprinted, she would have enough time to drink some of the coffee she was carrying before she had to open her doors. The choppy grey water contrasted sharply to the pale snow and Emily smiled at the light dancing on the tops of the waves. The cry of the gulls tickled the air, but underneath their cry, she noticed another sound.

The premonition hit her like a hammer: *Flashes of being held under icy water by strong hands. In the vision, she wanted to thrash and scream but the hands were like vices on her arms. The shock of the cold sucked the power from her body. She was brought up only long enough to gasp for air and then pushed under that water again. She couldn't get to the surface and she needed to breathe...she needed to breathe...*

Someone touched her shoulder in the parking lot and

Emily's breath rushed back into her lungs with a startled cry.

"Emily?" Nick Wilde was frowning at her wearing the bottom half of a Santa Clause suit. "Are you okay? You look like you've seen a ghost."

She focused on the sound of his words and the warmth of his hand on her arm fighting to hold onto the details of the vision. She forced a smile onto her lips. "Sorry, the cold must have knocked the breath right out of me."

He patted her sympathetically. "Gets worse before it gets better. We were lucky to have the snow so late this year. The first year I was here it snowed from October 1st to May 1st. It got to where I couldn't remember what color grass was."

Her smile came a little more natural the second time. "Are you trying to cheer me up?"

"You don't worry. We keep an eye on each other around here. Speaking of, I noticed you had to lock up the shop the other day to do your shipping. You wouldn't be looking for an extra pair of hands, would you?"

Emily blinked in surprise at the rapid change in subject. Then she noticed that Nick had come outside without a coat as if he'd hurried to catch her. She would need someone eventually because not only did she need to ship and receive products, she couldn't stand in the shop all day without eating or going to the bathroom. Somewhere in her day she also needed to make candles.

Her previous planning had included working at night and sharing the shop with someone who might be willing to watch a moment while she stepped out, but an employee was a serious commitment.

"Today is my opening day. I don't really have any idea of what the foot traffic is going to be like. I'm not sure I can afford myself, much less anyone else."

"I wouldn't worry about foot traffic this time of year. It's like the last call at a free bar for most of the season." Nick laughed at his own joke ushering Emily toward her own shop. "You don't have to make any decisions now. I know this is a big ask, but if you're looking, my daughter, April, , is available for the job. The only problem is she wants to take my grandson, Michael, everywhere she goes and that includes work."

Emily glanced down at him to see if he was kidding. "I sell candles. You know, glass, wax, and fire. It's not really a place for children."

"My point exactly." Nick shrugged into the arms of his Santa suit looking at the Christmas Market stalls rather than her. "I don't want Michael there with her. I want to watch him myself. I thought maybe, with our shops being so close together, we might be able to work something out. April managed clothing at a K-Mart before she had Michael. Before that, she used to come to help me at the store. I'd have her back in a heartbeat, but she says she's too old to work for her daddy. I thought maybe-"

Emily glanced at the front of her shop. Twelve people were looking through her windows like they had been waiting for her all night. There would be no coffee or bathroom today if she didn't get some help. "Send her over and we will see if we can work something out."

Nick looked at her like she'd spoken another language.

Then he smiled blinking away the moisture standing in his eyes. "I owe you. You won't be sorry."

Emily waved at him threading her way through the crowd. "If I am, I know where to find you. Tell her to stop by when she's ready."

Noah came into Dark Wolf and caught Joseph's eye over the top of his laptop. "Run with me."

It wasn't a request and Noah didn't wait for a response. He went outside and let the winter wind blow the frustration from his mind. Two new cases of Unguided individuals had been reported over the last two days and Alex Kimbos had officially applied for sanctuary.

Alex refused to shift or to take a guide in the sanctuary stating that he was simply here until January returned. Alex's refusal to take his wolf form would manifest itself in increased aggression and loss of control. At this rate, it wouldn't be long before Alex would have to be checked into the Recovery Center for his own safety.

Noah needed to focus today but all he was doing was worrying about whether Emily had got into work alright. She'd sent him a text telling him he was wonderful for clearing her steps and car this morning and hadn't said anything since. On a rational level, he knew it was because she was busy at work but his brain didn't seem to want to work on a rational level where she was concerned. He needed Joseph to teach him how to give her some space.

Werewolf courtship was faster and more intimate than

Unenlightened courtship. Knowing that Emily was supposed to be his, was meant to be with him, made functioning without her tedious. What was worse, it was only a matter of time and exposure before they would both find it uncomfortable to sleep separately.

Shifter bonding was emotional, physical, and involuntary. Werewolves didn't bother to make false claims about being mated because they could both feel the bonding when it was happening. He thought he might have a little more time because Emily appeared to be Unenlightened but he had laid in bed last night and burned to be next to her. The thought of unintentionally causing her the same discomfort twisted something deep in his guts. He needed some guidance.

When he felt Joseph beside him, he headed off into the wildest part of the sanctuary. They shifted together. Noah allowed his other senses to take over and began to run silently communicating turns, jumps, and potential prey to Joseph with the slightest of sounds and movements. They picked up supernatural speed until his mind could only focus on keeping his body from crashing into the trees and icy undergrowth. When his muscles trembled with exertion and he couldn't keep his feet silent, he reached the small private clearing his pack used for meetings and transformed again gasping for breath. Joseph appeared by his side a few moments later even more exhausted.

"You want to tell me what that was about?" Joseph took a deep sniff and then grinned. "Or should I say, who?"

"There is a situation regarding the Unguided."

"Bullshit." Joseph put his hands on his hips. "A run like that is either because you want to fight or you want to fuck. What's her name?"

"I'm not here to talk about a woman."

"Fight it is, then." Joseph centered his weight on the balls of his feet and dropped into an attack stance. "If you need me to beat you up, I'm game. You're the one that risks looking like a thug to your new woman. I'm married."

He came forward delivering two jabs, one directly into Noah's side the other just missing him. Joseph pulled his punches so that neither would break bones. Where Joseph had bulk, Noah had speed.

"You're distracted. If you weren't thinking about a woman there is no way I could get so close to you."

As if to prove the point he kicked Noah twice in the hip and then jumped back keeping his fists up.

"Emily," Noah said before he leapt forward hitting Joseph in the stomach, and then in the side when he curled around to protect himself. "Her name is Emily. You're holding your fists too high. It leaves your stomach unprotected."

"I have to keep my fists high. Katrin gets pissed off when I smash up my face."

They circled one another. Noah delivered a series of punches and kicks trying to stay out of Joseph's lethal reach.

"Your wife is 5 foot nothing. What could she possibly do to you?" he taunted. He took a hard knock to the chest that made him glad that he would never meet Joseph in a real fight.

"She can be mad for a really long time. No one is happy when she's mad."

Noah rolled his shoulders staying out of the path of Joseph's fists but made sure to keep him swinging. The more tired he was, the sloppier he fought. "You must be getting old if you can't charm your way back into your wife's good graces."

Joseph snorted and missed another swing. "I can't wait to rub this advice in when you find your life-mate."

"I found her."

The statement made Joseph hesitate allowing Noah to land two solid punches before moving back out of arm's reach.

"When you knew Katrin was your life-mate but she would never know this side of you," he gestured to the forest, "how did you feel?"

Joseph laughed before he attacked. He landed two kicks and a jab before Noah caught his leg and pulled him off his feet. Joseph kicked back knocking Noah on his rump. Joseph sat up holding up his hands to indicate he was done sparring. They both stood up brushing the snow from their bodies.

"The honest truth? I could give a shit. I found the one person in the world meant for me. There are sides of me I hope she never sees and times when she forces me to show her parts of myself I don't want to see. She reminds me that humans are worth protecting."

Noah rolled his shoulders checking for injuries. Joseph did the same. "You don't feel like you're lying to her?"

"I won't lie to her. I tell her what's important and leave

out what's not and what's dangerous to her. You can't lie to your life-mate, it fucks everything up."

"Did you ever wish Katrin was-"

Joseph didn't let him finish. "Nothing in my life is worth having if I don't have Katrin. End of story. She could piss off a saint and the only way she learns is by screwing things up for herself, but I need all of her, just the way she is. I don't wish she was anything else."

Noah rubbed his brow giving voice to the worry he'd been carrying all week. "I think Emily is Unenlightened." It was more than just hiding his wolf nature from her. His job meant close and constant contact with Enlightened that were still coming to terms with what they were.

Joseph came closer and clapped him on the shoulder. "She's your life-mate. You're made to fit her. It's your job to make sure that you aren't asking more from her than you're giving. Make adjustments. You'll find the right balance."

Noah ran his hands through his hair. "What if I screw it up?"

"What did you just tell me? You're not much of a life-mate if you can't charm your way back into her good graces?"

Noah was tempted to knock the smile off Joseph's face. "How do I keep from smothering her?"

Joseph shrugged. "The hell if I know. Katrin still tells me to get lost about once a week."

Joseph offered Noah a hand. His breaths were still coming rapidly from their sparring. "Bring Emily to Katrin's birthday party Saturday after next."

"Why?"

"So, I can see the woman responsible for throwing off your guard."

Noah nodded enjoying the companionship and the warmth of the other man. "I had a visit from a demon Saturday night."

Joseph growled deep in his throat. Demons had been the reason Joseph's family sought out Larkshead as a sanctuary when Joseph was a child.

Noah continued. "His name is James. He's looking for a vampire called January. Alex Kimbos knows something about it but he's not responding to my calls."

"Do you want me to find Alex?"

"Yes. I'm also looking for a vampire called January and a witch called Phoebe Pearce if you come across them. They have information connected to the Unguided cases that The National Recovery Unit needs. Steer clear of James until I'm sure why he's here."

"Demons are scum. Whatever he's looking for is for his own gain."

Noah felt the truth of Joseph's words. "I'll be careful."

"Good. Let's go. I'm freezing my balls off. I'll race you back." He shoved Noah over in the snow and shifted into a huge black wolf before he took off back toward the office. He was dressed and at his computer smirking by the time Noah walked back through the door.

11

If a psychic tells you that you change the future once you know the future, they are only partially correct. You can give a person very clear directions to a good future and they might still get lost. Don't take it personally. —Mildred Macclesfield, *The Art of Fortune Telling for Financial Gain*

Later that afternoon, Noah pulled up to the Augusta Recovery Center with Garland and Carl Wedgewood in his car. Although Janet had been in recovery for over a week, reports had come back to him that she was in decline. Carl had tried to see her every day but she'd refused to let him through the door and had also begun to refuse meals and respond only sporadically to conversation. She was shutting down. It had taken some persuasion but the Center had consented to allow Carl to try and coax his wife not to slip away.

The Recovery Center looked more like an exclusive hotel than a hospital. The door and windows locked from the inside and the sign-in desk was mostly for fire safety reasons. The newly awakened could stay here and return as many times as they needed to feel safe. Garland went to give his office a call so Noah went with Carl to Janet's room. Rather than alert Janet that Carl was here, Noah opened her door and let the selkie inside.

She sat bare foot in the picture window of her tiny well decorated room. With its paintings of lighthouses and wildflowers, it looked to Noah more like a weekend resort than a hospital. Janet was hugging her knees to her chest looking blankly out the window holding a cup of coffee that had long since gone cold. Layers of sandy hair streaked with silver shimmered brightly against her long Christmas sweater dress and magnified her pale fragility. Like a woman standing on the edge of a cliff, she appeared to Noah like a woman on the wrong edge of a life altering choice.

In that moment, he felt Carl's rage that someone's callousness had done this to her. Carl moved with purpose until he was standing beside her. When she didn't turn toward him, he scooted her forward and joined her in the window seat. He settled her back against his chest wrapping his arms around her and kissing first her shoulders then her cheek. Like he was warming her from the cold, he rubbed his hands back and forth across her folded arms.

"I'm here, my love. I'm not going to go away. I love you and I'm sorry, sweetheart. I'm so sorry."

Her eyes held some unknown horizon but she began to tremble all over and without a word. Carl took the cup from her hands and set it aside. Tears slid down her face, slowly at first, and then with more strength. She relaxed into his embrace leaning her head back against his chest holding his arms around her like he was the only reality she understood. He rocked her gently murmuring nonsense until she turned in his arms and began to kiss him. Noah excused himself quietly but neither Carl or Janet noticed.

In the hall Garland met his eye over a nurse's shoulder and gestured for him to come over but Noah couldn't breathe. In his mind the woman in the window was Emily but she couldn't recover from her awakening because they weren't yet bonded. There was fury in him that someone had risked Janet and Carl's life, but another darker part of him remembered the demon's words. He had said that January would keep Phoebe by his side at any cost. Noah understood that need all the way down to the core of his being. He knew that if someone threatened Emily, tried to take her from him, that he would grab her and run. He drug air into his lungs trying to control his wild feelings.

"There are others," Garland said solemnly. "Three total, none with a clear connection to one another. They are from all over the area. The Recovery agents are struggling to cope with the numbers and the Enlightened are getting nervous." Garland looked down the hall and shook his head. "The nurse says there's a new wolf from your territory here. His name is Alex. He wants to talk to you."

Emily was trying to figure out how to watch the register and hang Christmas lights and sugar plum fairies without making thumbtack holes in her paint when a dark-eyed young woman appeared behind her. The woman was an odd mixture of professional and casual. Her red sneakers peaked out from beneath black slacks; her cream silk top sat demurely against the most brightly knit autumn cardigan that Emily had ever seen. Her brown hair was slicked back into a sleek low ponytail that perfectly showed off the woman's Thanksgiving turkey-themed earrings.

"Can I help you find something?"

The young woman handed her a sheet of paper with an almost frantic look. "I'm April Wilde. My Dad said that you were looking for help."

Emily glanced down at the sheet of paper realizing that it was a resume. "April. Of course. I'm Emily. Thank you for coming."

April smoothed her sweater self-consciously. "I would have called to make an appointment but the shop isn't in the directory yet." April clasped her purse between her hands and stood perfectly still. It took Emily a moment to realize that she was expecting to be interviewed. She scanned the resume wondering what it was you asked a future employee.

"Your resume shows that you have considerable retail experience. Why do you want to work here?"

April considered the question for a long moment. "I feel like this opportunity might give me a chance to broaden my range of retail skills."

Emily looked at April's resume again noting she had extensive management and retail experience. Experience-wise, April was more qualified to run a shop than Emily was. She tucked the resume under her arm and ushered April to the back of the store trying to talk to her and watch the customers who appeared compelled to wander around the shop holding both candles and the fairies. Sometimes they simply sat the fairies down in random places and paid for the candles, and sometimes they carried the fairies and the candles to the till and paid for them. She was supposed to be keeping a list of what sold but she needed eyes in the back of her head to keep track of them.

"I feel like you are massively over-qualified for the position."

April smiled looking around the shop with a critical eye. "Your shop website is brilliant. The product range isn't so extensive that you need to farm out your work, and not so limited as to become boring. Your online sales ratings are high, meaning you already know the basics and intend to be in business long-term. It also means that you know how to do your taxes well enough to stay in business."

Emily looked at April again appreciating her candidness. "Wow. You've obviously done some research."

"I wanted to make sure that we would be a good fit for each other."

Emily laughed liking April immediately. "Fair enough. I need you and your experience, but I'm just starting out so the pay isn't going to be anywhere near what you could make in a bigger store. So, level with me, and I promise not to be offended. Why do you really want to work here?"

"My son, Michael, has a lot of problems in daycare.

He's three going on thirty and I wish he were disruptive, but the honest truth is that he's too quiet. My doctor says that he's fine but the last time I dropped him off at daycare, I got a call to pick him up a couple of hours later. The woman on the phone said that he refused to leave the spot where I'd taken off his coat and told him I'd pick him up. Refused to the point where he wet the floor. I had to leave work."

April looked at her shoes. Emily felt like her heart was breaking.

"I tried again in a different place and he cried the entire three hours that I was gone, so much so that the daycare itself said they didn't want him back. I need to find a way to take care of my son and feed us. I need this job."

"You've got it. Welcome to the team." Emily gestured for April to follow her back to the stock room. "My turn to level up. I've had exactly three minutes of alone time since I opened the doors. I still have Christmas decorations to put up, and if I don't find some time to make stock soon, we'll be out before Thanksgiving."

The door opened with a jaunty jingle and ten women spilled into the shop. Emily patted April on the shoulder. "Prices are on the bottom of the candles. Fairies are $9.00 each. Shipping prices are on our website. We won't ship the fairies. The Wi-Fi password is Angelo. I'm using a mobile debit card machine but it's not consistently talking to the internet unless you stand next to the window."

April laughed. "Sounds like an adventure." She spotted the now framed Ace of Cups tucked amongst the decorations at the back of the store. "I'm supposed to be here," she whispered. "Mildred said I would know when I saw the card."

"If that's the case, I've only got one more question."

"Okay?"

Emily held up a package of Christmas lights. "How can we hang these without messing up our paint?"

April gave Emily the first real smile of their budding friendship.

Alex Kimbos was an accident waiting to happen. Born werewolves were educated from an early age on how to manage emotions and control their shifting. They were taught to hunt in both forms by a parent or a guide who helped them understand that their inner wolf was always a part of their human self. Alex, on the other hand, was ruthlessly repressing the wolf part of his nature. His wolf-self skimmed the edges of his human form creating a feeling in the room of barely restrained wildness.

Noah entered the room to question the man and establish pack rank but as he watched Alex's form tremble and his face tighten with fear, he felt sympathy for the young wolf. Rather than jumping to his feet to acknowledge Noah, Alex stayed in his seat gripping the arms of his chair like a drowning man.

Alex met Noah's gaze unflinchingly, almost defiantly. Noah was high in pack rank in this territory, which would normally cause a less established wolf to glance away but instead, a low rumbling growl tore from Alex's throat.

Noah smiled relaxing his shoulders and turning his palms face out toward Alex.

"My name is Noah Hernandez. I am the primary guide in this territory and next in line as Alpha. Do we need to square off or are you happy to acknowledge my dominance in this space?"

His question threw the younger wolf off and all at once the tension drained from Alex's face and was replaced by a sheepish grin.

"Sorry. I've never been great with authority figures and the wolf in me doesn't check before making an appearance."

"You are the wolf and the wolf is you," Noah replied coming fully into the room. "Trying to separate yourself into little parts leads to some severe Jekyll/Hyde identity issues later in life. When you feel the shift coming on, take a deep breath and look around to see what is triggering the reaction."

Alex looked Noah straight in the eye again. "And if you're my trigger?"

Noah shrugged moving deliberately closer, crowding Alex, to watch how he moderated his own behavior. Alex clenched his teeth and gripped the chair again.

Noah shrugged keeping direct eye contact. "I wouldn't be surprised. My records say your previous Alpha violated your trust. It stands to reason that you would feel defensive when confronted with authority."

Stopping just in front of Alex's seat, Noah loomed over him so that he was forced to tip his head back and expose his throat to keep eye contact. Alex's form wavered like disturbed water. His mouth distorted and he bared his teeth like a frightened dog.

"Please." His voice rumbled almost unintelligibly from his throat. "I can't control it."

"You don't have to. You just need to communicate with yourself." Noah crouched down in front of the young wolf and plucked his hands from the seat arms to lay them gently in his lap. "Breathe. Close your eyes and trust me. I am not here to piss on your shoes or tell you who is in charge. I am your pack-mate in this territory. We will hunt and fight as a team. Let us greet one another as friends."

Alex forced his eyes shut but tears fell from the corners anyway. "I can't do this."

Noah cupped the young man's face gently smoothing away his tears. "Let yourself feel the change like current under your skin. Give your mind a chance to understand the sensations and to give you awareness of the shift. Then shift. Give over to your other form for a few seconds and then come back."

Alex's eyes flew open. "What if I get lost and I can't get back?"

"Just think of your favorite song. Then try to sing it. Your mouth moves differently as a man than it does as a wolf. Your body will come back to make the shape of the words."

"It can't be that simple," Alex bit out.

Noah shrugged moving back to stand up. "Try it. If I'm wrong, I owe you a beer."

Alex nodded closing his eyes and letting himself go.

Rather than transforming into a wolf, his human self solidified. He opened his eyes laughing nervously.

"What am I doing wrong?"

"You probably tried to remember what song you were going to sing right as you shifted. It helps if you concentrate on a sensation that you have only when you are using your wolf senses. Scent is the easiest for me but my sister, Selene, uses different sounds for both forms. My mother uses her taste buds. You'll have to find the combination that works for you." Noah moved back to give Alex room to change.

"If I change, I can get out of here?"

Noah shook his head wondering why Alex was so determined to leave. "You're guide will come get you. You stay with them until you get the hang of transformation. Where you go after that is up to you."

Alex's hopeful expression fell. "You're not my guide?"

"I'm afraid not. I'm here to introduce myself and ask you some questions about the Unenlightened situation in Boston."

"If you're asking about Phoebe, I've got nothing to say."

"Was January's mate unguided?"

"Her name is Phoebe," Alex said standing up to loom over Noah. "She loves Falafel, coffee, and she has the worst taste in music ever, but she's not dangerous."

Noah stood slowly. "I am looking for a connection between the sudden surge in the Unguided in my territory. The only connection I have right now is you, a demon, a vampire, and this Phoebe. If you have information that can help me stop this, I want it."

Alex ran his hands through his perfectly sculpted blonde hair. "It's not just this territory, it's everywhere. The Veil is thinning, blinking, and failing in places. People are just falling through."

"That's impossible. Everything has a cause."

Alex began pacing the room, his wolf-self again pushing the edges of his human form. "Call it evolution if you want to. I don't know what it is. All I know is that it was happening before Phoebe came through."

"How do you know this?"

"Because my previous alpha forced my change so that she could start building an army to protect herself when the Veil finally falls."

Noah watched the young wolf fight himself. "Why didn't you inform the National Recovery Unit?"

"I did. So did January. They didn't believe us and we don't have enough information to prove it. Phoebe is a witch and they believe she's the cause. They won't even look at the wider picture. January wasn't about to let them persecute her. He picked us up before we could be collected and told me to stay here."

"Why Larkshead?"

Alex looked away. "He figures when the Veil fails, a werewolf sanctuary is the only place that can be protected from a Boston werewolf army. You don't have to worry, though. I'll leave before that happens."

"To keep us safe?"

Alex nodded. Noah walked up to him folding the young wolf into his arms holding him close. "Thank you for trying to protect my pack. We are brothers of the moon. We will not abandon you. You are safe here. Shift and allow yourself the freedom of knowing who you are."

Alex and Noah shifted together their clothing falling through their shifting bodies into piles on the floor. A smaller sandy wolf met the eyes of his large cinnamon pack-mate and then glanced away in deference lowering himself to the ground with his ears tucked close to his skull.

Noah let out a sharp playful yip acknowledging the deference. Alex leapt to his feet rubbing his body along Noah's. The scent marking would help the younger wolf be more comfortable. Alex rolled onto his back briefly showing his belly, his tail wagging in joy. Then he rolled to his feet shifting back into his human self. Noah followed suit. They faced one another for a moment before Noah bent down to grab his own clothing.

"Welcome to the pack, Alex. We don't tolerate bullying and rank is established through pack duties not fighting. If you're unhappy with the guide your alpha assigns, come find me. In the meantime, practice moving between your forms until you feel like the shift is entirely your choice."

Alex nodded picking his clothing up with embarrassment. "Thank you."

Noah offered the young man his hand. "If you hear from Phoebe or January. Please let them know we aren't here to hurt them. All I need is some information. Can you do that?"

Alex nodded again. "Don't trust James. I don't know why he wants Phoebe so badly, but I don't think it's to ask her questions. He gives me the creeps."

Noah nodded giving the young man another brief hug. "Me too. Take care of yourself. I'll see you later."

He turned and walked out the door fishing his phone out of his pocket. Dialing his mother's number, he waited for her to pick up. On the second ring, she answered. He didn't bother with a greeting. "We have a problem in Boston."

12

A number of things considered unlucky by the Unenlightened are lucky for witches. Black cats make excellent familiars, the number 13 is linked to Judas Iscariot, a Christian figure who has nothing at all to do with witchcraft, and breaking mirrors often occurs when a mirror is blocking an unwanted presence. In fact, the unluckiest thing for a witch to do is to believe that something is unlucky. – Olivia Goldstein, *Mastering Magic*

Noah had sent Emily a text to say that he would be late for their Wednesday date. Emily was grateful because she was running late. She had dropped into bed utterly exhausted Monday and Tuesday and wishing she'd taken Noah up on his offer to come over. Even with April's help, the sheer number of people visiting the Christmas Market and her shop were incredible. Today, however, she finally felt like she was really getting the hang of this new life.

Angelo was waiting on her porch when she pulled into

her driveway. She felt the knot of unease she'd been holding onto since he disappeared Sunday night give way a little. She gave him a good rub and a quick scolding for scaring her. He wagged his tail with such an innocent expression on his face that she couldn't stay mad at him. He also managed to appear the exact moment her sofa was being delivered.

Emily greeted them from the top of the stairs. "Hi. I wasn't sure you'd make it because of the snow on Monday."

The older of the two delivery men snorted. "This is Larkshead, ma'am. If you don't work in the snow, then you don't work. Where do you want us to put it?"

"In front of the fireplace, please." She motioned them to come inside and propped open the doors.

Angelo made a point of keeping himself between her and the men doing the delivery, so much so, that she had to practically stand on top of him to sign the delivery receipt. She'd ordered the sofa online her second night in town and was amused to realize that other than some minor differences in color, it was almost the same one Noah had at his house.

Satisfied that the delivery men meant no harm, Angelo inspected every room in her house, rubbed his body lengthwise down her new sofa and generally did what he could to put his mark on the place.

"Is he a wolf-cross?" The younger of the two delivery men asked, offering his hand for Angelo to sniff which Angelo very rudely ignored. He was sitting on Emily's feet leaning against her legs so hard she wasn't sure he wasn't attempting to knock her over.

"I'm not sure. I thought he was some sort of red Malamute."

The younger man laughed. "No way. He's way too big and bulky to be a Malamute. That's a wolf if I've ever seen one."

The older man offered his hand to Angelo who sniffed it politely allowing his head to be stroked. "He looks like he was crossed with a pony, if you ask me. How do you afford to feed him?"

Emily laughed. "Believe it or not, he's not mine." As if to make a point, Angelo walked over to one of his bowls and took a drink.

"You feed them, you keep them," the older driver said making his way down the stairs and to the driveway to close the van doors. "That's what my wife says."

The younger man winked at her. "Our number is on the top of the invoice if you have any problems with the sofa." He took a pen out of his pocket and scrolled another number on the document. "This one's mine in case you're looking to re-home the dog, or if you need anything else."

There was no mistaking what anything else might be. The smile on the young man's face said clearly that he was used to being desired. Angelo growled low in his throat making his stance on ownership of any kind clear.

"Thanks for the offer, but we're okay. You guys have a great day."

No sooner had the delivery van cleared the driveway then a beat-up truck pulling a trailer full of wood backed into it. The woman delivering the wood had to be some-where in her 80's and it looked like the bulk of her body was made up of wildly colored scarfs and long white hair. She shivered glancing up at the greying sky.

"Nor'easter coming. Looks like I got here just in time."

She smiled at Emily like they'd known each other their whole lives and pulled a silver pentacle suspended from a long chain from between her scarfs. "Merry meet. Been a long time since I met a witch I didn't know or wasn't related to." She offered her hand. "I'm Jessie Wilde."

"Emily Rollins." A jolt of static jumped between them as their hands touched. "I haven't had a chance to order any wood, yet. I was just going to call you."

Jessie shook her hand firmly and then turned it over to look at her palm for a moment before giving it a pat and letting it go. "My nephew must have beat you to it." She laughed at her own joke. "Your house is humming with energy. I use mine to keep my wood lots growing nicely. What do you grow?"

Emily glanced back at her cabin not quite sure what they were talking about. Like the gentleman that had been looking for Noah in the grocery store, she felt like Jessie was referring to something other than what she was talking about.

"I'm a candle maker. I own The Ace of Cups."

Jessie's smile grew even wider. "April's new boss. Explains the call today. Nick says I should get down here quick as a flash and treat you like family. Thought he meant because of April, didn't expect he meant it because you are one of us." She tucked her pentacle between her scarfs and came around the wood trailer. "Lift the back of that trailer while I unhook it, would you honey?"

Emily went to the back of the trailer and lifted it while

Jessie unhooked it from the truck. It teetered a bit on its wheels.

"One of us?"

"Witch," Jessie said putting her hand on the tow bar. "Okay. You hold onto this and I'll open the back of the trailer. We can just tip the wood out on the driveway and then stack it."

Emily moved to help Jessie dump the wood looking around to make sure Angelo was out of the way and spotted Noah trotting up the path. He was looking at the pair of them with a mixture of disbelief and amusement. He hugged the older lady like she was his grandma. "Hey Jessie. Where's Jim?"

She shrugged casually without meeting his eyes. "Late as usual. This young lady and I were getting the job done."

Noah walked to Emily's side and grabbed hold of the trailer hitch. "I can see that. Let me help."

Jessie smirked putting both hands on her hips. "It's like that, is it?" She unhooked the trailer gate and came around the truck to elbow Emily in the ribs. "You watch out for that one. A man who volunteers for house work has his cap set."

Noah didn't deny it. Instead, he guided Emily to tip the wood out of the trailer and then hooked it back up to Jessie's truck. "You're all set, Jessie. Tell Jim I need to see him."

Jessie patted him on the back without responding then turned back to Emily. "You're welcome to come to our rituals, if you'd like. Bring Noah too. We could use some new blood."

"Thank you. What do I owe you for the wood?"

Jessie climbed in her truck with great effort. "Nick has got the bill with him. If I were you, I'd let him pay it for not asking before he ordered it." She looked at the sky touching her pentacle again. "You guys don't get too far from the house. This storm's going to be a doozey."

They had stacked wood together, mostly because Emily had told him she would either work with him or by herself. *Always beside you.* The words ran through Noah's mind as he showed her how to turn and stack the wood in her lean-to so that it would remain dry. He could carry twice what she could in one go without using any of his extra strength and yet she went back to the log pile again and again until the job was complete.

Her eyes were bright, her brow was damp, her cheeks were pink, and a halo of golden hair had escaped her impossible bun. Noah wasn't sure if he'd ever really known what a beautiful woman was until today. Hands on her thighs, she smiled proudly at the stacked wood when the work was done. Wiping her hand over her brow, she smeared a large portion of wood dust and dirt across her forehead.

"I think that's the worst start to a date ever. If I add pizza, beer, and an apology do you think I might be able to rescue it?"

Noah gave her a quick kiss wiping some of the grime from her face. "It's a distinct possibility. We'll have to hurry. Those clouds don't look like they're going to wait for us."

The grey sky was slowly turning purple with the weight of the snow. Emily gave it an uneasy glance. "That doesn't look good. Should we reschedule?"

"Not a chance. I'm already here and I want to add more dates to our schedule, not shift the ones I have around."

"You have today and Friday." Pulling the clasp from her hair, she tried and failed to shake out the wood dust. "How many more dates could you fit in?"

"No comment. I don't want to prove my brother correct and sound like a dork." He offered her his hand so that they could go into the house. "So, you ordered wood delivered on date night?" He watched in amusement as Emily looked down at her rumpled clothing and dirty tennis shoes.

"I didn't order anything. Nick Wilde ordered that wood. I ordered a couch." Emily led him through the door kicking the boxes she'd used to wedge them open out of the way as she walked past. "Give me five minutes and I can be ready to go."

"It's a very nice couch," he shouted after her.

She snorted. "How would you know? You haven't even seen it yet."

With her back turned to him, she missed the look of embarrassment that crossed his face. He kept his mouth shut and made his way across the living room. She gestured toward the couch in a tah-dah motion kicking off her shoes before heading toward her bedroom. Noah listened to her remove her clothes while he gave the couch a little shove with his thigh placing it in the exact position his own couch was. "It's a very nice couch."

She called through the half-closed door. "Looks like yours. Can you believe I ordered it before I met you?"

"Great minds?"

"Something like that." She came out of her room still pulling a brush through her hair until it hung in a shimmering cape all around her. Picking up earrings off her fireplace mantel and setting her brush down there, she stepped into short boots that were hanging out beside the kitchen table. With this kind of routine, he imagined that it was rare that the things she needed would ever be found in a regular place. Right at five minutes she picked up her coat and a handbag with a triumphant smile.

"Better?"

He stepped forward and wiped the remainder of the dirt off her face. "Perfect."

Beacon Pizzeria told them that they were doing take-away orders only because of the storm leaving him little option but to take Emily back to his house for their 2nd date. Emily had allowed him to purchase the pizza but had whipped out her debit card at the grocery store to pay for the beer faster than a leprechaun snatching gold.

The snow held off until he pulled into the drive and then fat flakes fluttered to the ground in droves. Emily carried the pizza in, trying to catch a couple of the snowflakes on her tongue as she went up the steps. He followed loving the way she enjoyed everything that was natural in his world. Although Noah would have happily set the table, Emily took the pizza to the living room coffee table. He built a fire and sat crossed-legged with her listening to music, eating pizza directly out of the box, and sipping beer from the bottle as if they'd been doing it all their lives.

The radio was on just loud enough to disturb the profound silence in the air. The calm before the storm, Noah thought standing to put what remained of the pizza in the kitchen. He plucked up a present leaning against the couch. It was wrapped simply in white paper that had red squirrels wearing Santa hats all over it. He sat it in front of her feeling suddenly apprehensive. "Well, this is too early to be a Christmas present, so how about we call it a welcome to the neighborhood present?"

She sat back against the couch facing the fire smoothing her hands over the wrapping. "I think helping to stack my firewood, not to mention clearing my car, porch, and driveway the other morning more than counts for that."

"Nope, those things are what I had to do so I didn't step on your obvious independence and insist on driving you to work." He sat down on the floor beside her.

She pushed him playfully with her shoulder. "You have some serious caveman tendencies underneath that laid-back exterior, don't you?"

He kissed her shoulder. "I know. I'm working on it. Open the gift?"

She gently began to pull the tape but Noah reached around her and ripped the paper open right down the middle making grunting caveman sounds. Laughing they opened the box in a frenzy of paper. At the bottom was a red knitted hat and scarf that would have made red riding hood proud. Thick red leather gloves lay beside them. Noah took the hat out of the box and placed it gently on her head using his fingers to brush her hair out of her face and tuck it behind her ears.

She waited for him to stop fiddling and arched a brow. "What do you think?"

"Beautiful," he said and then yanked the cap down over her eyes.

Emily launched herself at him in a blind giggling attack. Although he could have easily moved out of her way, he let the weight of her body hit him and rolled back with her sprawled across his chest. She wrapped her legs tightly around his hips laughing and, in a moment, pushed her hat out of her way and pinned their hands between him. Pleasure raced through his veins as she crouched over him triumphantly. She kissed him whispering against his lips, "Thank you."

He rolled her under him spreading her legs around him. "You're welcome."

She didn't look defeated by their change in position, she looked sensual. Undulating her body in a serpentine movement, she made contact with him everywhere so that her physical invitation couldn't be mistaken.

Noah smiled down at her. "That is not fighting fair."

She leaned up and kissed him. "I never fight fair."

He worked her shirt off over her head stopping to kiss the skin he exposed. She leaned forward to do the same for him, her lips brushing his chest, his collarbones, and their joined hands. The contrast of her soft reverent hands against his skin drove him wild. As their clothing fell away. He felt like she was peeling back layers of civilization, of manners, of codes.

"I want you," he murmured against her skin.

She captured his face between her palms and kissed him. "I want you too."

Kisses turned into playful nips until something wild and dangerous was unleashed. He maneuvered them to their feet unbuttoning her jeans and pushing them and her underwear down over her hips. Using him to keep her balance, she picked up one foot and then the other so that he could strip her naked. He settled her back on the couch and then knelt between her thighs. The fire illuminated her like some powerful and forgotten goddess. He kissed between her breasts, and then her stomach letting her know exactly what he intended. She watched him through lidded eyes as he first opened her legs wide and then used his fingers to open her completely.

Emily was lost. The fire light on his skin, his hands spreading her like a feast. His tongue took the place of his fingers and explored her folds with such thoroughness that she could only lay lost in a storm of sensation. She buried her hands in his hair not sure if she was trying to bring him closer or push him away.

He pushed her right to the edge of orgasm again and again, retreating in the last moments until she growled in frustration raking her nails down his arms. He scooped her up in his arms to lay her down on the floor recreating their previous position. He reached for his pants pulling out a condom and she watched him roll it down his long length.

Spreading her legs so that he could position himself against her entrance, he held her down with one hand and rubbed himself against her without going inside, sucking first one nipple and then the other into his mouth while he teased her.

"Noah, please…" She couldn't stand this much longer.

"Tell me what you want."

"I want you inside me. Please."

It was the permission he needed. He shoved himself fully into her capturing the first gasp of their joining with his mouth. He wanted to be gentle but his intentions were lost in the feeling of having himself sheathed deep inside the woman he intended to spend the rest of his life with. He rocked his hips roughly into her claiming her body with the same ruthlessness he intended to claim her heart. She responded with needy breaths and by meeting each of his thrusts with a demand of her own.

He felt her nails on his back and her teeth nip his shoulder to mark him as he had her. He wanted her to acknowledge their connection, to demand she recognize that they were life-mates. On the edge of wildness, she hugged him close gentling their movements, running her fingers through his short dark hair. Bringing her mouth close to his ear she murmured a single command to him.

Come with me.

They shattered together, holding each other tightly.

He rolled over so that he wouldn't crush her but couldn't bring himself to let her go. Pulling her across his chest, he smoothed her long hair down her back with his eyes closed and listened to the fire crackle. Their breaths eventually calmed into an easy rhythm. He felt her chin on his chest and knew that she was looking at him.

She tucked her hand under her chin and gave him a sexy smile. "It's getting late. I need to go."

He continued to stroke her hair, twisting little bits of it around his fingers. "You aren't going home tonight."

She kissed the place her chin had been resting. "Lucky for me I wasn't asking your permission to leave."

"I'm not done with you, yet. I'll return you to your house in time for you to go to work if the weather allows it."

Emily licked his nipple and he felt his cock stirring to life again.

"I don't think I like your tone." She delivered a quick sharp bite.

Noah grabbed hold of her hair at the nape of her neck. He pulled forcing her to meet his eyes. "Stay the night with me."

Caught like a cat by the nape, she laughed, undeterred. "Say please."

He kissed her and then let go of her hair. "Please stay the night with me."

She leaned back. "I'm warning you. I am not a nice person in the morning."

Noah rolled to his feet carrying Emily up with him forgetting for a moment that as a human, the strength to do so would be considered exceptional. Her eyes widened in surprise and he wrapped her legs firmly around him.

"I'll take my chances."

Her body lay motionless, like a crumpled and forgotten bedsheet, a little ways from an operating table. Face down, her cheek pressed against a sterile tile floor. She watched shadows disturb the bluish light from the operating table above. Although she could hear people talking around her, she could neither communicate nor move. A man's arm hung from the operating table just out of her line of sight but because she could not move her neck, she could only get an impression of his figure.

The sound of operating tools crashing against a metal surface alerted her to a problem on the table. Blood from above splashed to the floor like water thrown from a glass. The arm above her began to contort and grow, stretching to inhuman portions and reaching toward her. She needed to move away from it, she knew somehow that she couldn't let the blood or the hand touch her, but her body remained immobile. She felt the air around her shift as the arm made a lunge for her. She screamed for help but nothing but the smallest puff of air escaped her lips.

The hand and arm turned a burnt red color and grew great blackened claws. The clicking scraping sound of operating tools against metal continued as the arm pulled the body on the operating table through the blood toward her. She tried again to scream for help but the hand had reached her. It covered her mouth and nose strangling even the smallest breath. She wanted to struggle but her body lay like lead refusing to obey her commands. She was suffocating.

The dream shifted and Emily was being held under ice water, the red hands covering her mouth and nose. A rough voice demanded she answer a question she didn't understand. When the hands drew her to the surface she screamed.

"Noah!"

Noah was jerked from his sleep by Emily's scream. In a moment before he was fully alert, he'd gathered her to his body and stood snarling into the darkness ready to defend her. His hands had transformed into claws and his jaw filled with the teeth of his half-wolf form. Emily struggled against him shouting for help and it took him a moment to realize her eyes were closed. He thanked whatever gods were listening that she was still sleeping. He shifted again laying her back down on the bed.

"Emily? Em?" He shook her gently, "Wake up, mi alma. I've got you."

Her terrified eyes flew open. "Noah!"

"I'm here. Right here. It's just a dream."

She wrapped her arms around him burying her face against his throat, her breath coming in gasping hiccups. He smoothed her hair back tilting her face toward him and wiping the moisture from her lashes.

"What did you see?"

She looked up at him and opened her mouth to speak but before she formed a sentence, she swallowed whatever she was going to say shaking her head. He could see her shutting him out, but he wouldn't force her to share more. He cradled her close stroking her hair, her face, her body, anything he could touch.

"It's okay. You can tell me when you're ready. You don't have to say anything right now. I'm here."

He brought her back inside the covers spooning, tucking her close to him. He kissed the back of her neck and stroked his hand up and down her arms to soothe her. She relaxed slowly catching his hand and tucked it under her chin scooting back fully into his embrace.

In the darkness, he damned his carelessness. Eight large scratches were etched along her bare hips where he'd grasped her in his half-form. Had she been awake, his transformation would have forced her through the Veil. The soft mocking scent of Emily's blood moved through his mind parading a thousand everyday scenarios from his life that could put her in danger.

Control was finite and he'd counselled more than one new werewolf on ways to avoid hurting their loved ones with their strength. Her cry had broken through his training. Resting his forehead between her shoulders in a plea for forgiveness, he promised himself that if he couldn't keep her safe beside him, then he would make her safe without him.

He woke up hungry for her again but managed to get up, start coffee, and get back into bed without disturbing her. Unlike the first morning he'd awoken in her bed, he explored her sleeping body with his eyes and his hands gently trying to coax her to life. That she was in his bed and already naked only made him hungrier. Her mascara was smudged under her eyes and she was surrounded by a mess of tangled blonde hair. He touched her smudged makeup loving how disheveled she looked. She swatted his hand away with a grumpy murmur and turned her back to him. He moved forward to pull her backside toward him and uncover her shoulder and press a kiss to it.

"AM." She said the word like it was something disgusting, the implication under the word was clearly not amorous.

He tried not to chuckle. "Good morning, my sleeping beauty. What do you want in your coffee?"

She looked at him blearily over her shoulder. "Go away, morning person."

He rubbed his cheek against hers and whispered in her ear. "You can have coffee or you can have sex. Your choice."

She dropped her head to the pillow with a sigh laying so still that Noah thought she might have gone back to sleep. Just when he thought to gently shake her awake again, she wiggled her backside suggestively against him. "Why can't I have coffee and sex?"

"We don't have time for both." He pulled her to her knees and she leaned forward opening her legs so that he could enter her from behind. He reached into his bedside table for a condom. Grasping her hips, he seated her firmly on his erection.

On all fours, she threw her head back and hissed her approval. He recognized the position for what it was, a claiming position. She pushed back into him demanding more her breaths coming in demanding little mews of pleasure. He let her control the pace while he stroked her clit. When her movements became frantic, he sheathed himself to the hilt again and again, allowing her no quarter until they both found release. They collapsed together in a breathless heap. He would never get enough of her. He kissed the place he'd marked her their first night running his tongue over the slightly bruised skin and then marking her again. She made a sound like a purr that went straight through him. "Now temptress, what do you want in your coffee?"

He was dressed before Emily had really made it out of his bed. She stumbled into her clothing and took the coffee he was drinking with nothing more than a grunt of approval. He'd delivered her to her own house and made her a second pot of coffee and she was still growling like a demon. She walked zombie-like through her home looking for the hairbrush she'd left on the mantle. If he laughed one more time, he was sure she'd kill him.

"I'm going to be late," she grumbled.

"You've got time." He poured her another cup of coffee and handed it to her. "Do you want breakfast?"

She pulled a brush through her hair with enough violence that Noah wondered how she had any hair left. "How do you have energy to make breakfast? I can barely walk."

He knew better than to respond. Instead, he searched

her home for something breakfast like. He made toast for both of them and poured some of the coffee into the flask on the counter.

She picked up her toast as if it might be poisoned and asked nonchalantly, "Are we still seeing each other on Friday?"

He understood the question. What she was really asking was hiding in the words she'd spoken only because she'd chosen that moment to not make eye contact. The getting-to-know-you period in some human relationships didn't include sex. To be honest, he was more worried that she'd be the one to put some distance between them. That she wanted assurance that he would come back meant that he'd not made himself clear.

"You're going to have a really hard time getting rid of me now. I'm over here trying to be cool with the fact that you have to go to work. The caveman in me really wants to just throw you over my shoulder and go back to bed."

She wrangled her hair into a braid in between bites of toast and smirked at him. "You need to go to work too."

"Trust me, work is very low on my need scale right now." He leaned over and kissed her. "Can I come see you at work today for legitimate reasons?"

"Sure? What reasons are those?" She went to the fridge and put enough jam on her remaining toast to make it unrecognizable.

"My friend Katrin's birthday is coming up and I want to get her something from your shop. Her husband, Joseph, is throwing a party for her at Jack Frost's. It's the only bar in town worth drinking at, and Katrin loves to dance."

Emily's smile brightened. "Does she like bergamot?"

"I have no idea, but she always has a dozen candles lit at her house."

Emily popped the last of her toast in her mouth and went into her spare room returning with a large green candle in the most intricately carved wooden holder that Noah had ever seen. Along with it were three smaller candles in pink, yellow, and blue.

Unceremoniously, she plunked the green candle and holder into his hands and he felt his wolf form surge to the surface. It was everything he could do to retain his human shape. He trembled trying to keep his thoughts together but Emily was looking at the candle rather than him. He turned the green candle over to read the name on the bottom. He needed his human senses to read but for a moment, the symbols swam meaningless in front of his gaze. The candle was called Enlightenment.

His eyes shot to hers. "Are you Enlightened, Emily?"

She brushed her fingers over the label with a smile. "I like to think of myself as aware, but I haven't quite found enlightenment yet. This is the first meditation-themed candle I ever made. The scent isn't as complex as my other candles, but it's still one of my favorites. The grandiose name helped to sell it online but it is a total pain in the ass to make. That's why I'm making it available only in the shop from now on."

Her answer hit him like a truck. Neither the question nor the insinuation was familiar to her. She was fully Unenlightened. When he bound their lives together, a part of him would always be dangerous for her.

She frowned mistaking his realization for reluctance. "If you don't like them, you can pick something else."

Her words brought images to his mind of a life without her. First pictures of him running alone in his pack, and then alone at his job, at his table, and in his bed. His mind conjured an image of a different mate for her. Someone who could share his whole life with her, but even as he thought it, he knew that he wouldn't let her go. The thought of her waking up in someone else's bed trampled the last of his reservations. He hugged her trapping the candles between them.

"They're perfect. You're perfect. Will you come with me to Katrin's party?"

She shoved him away grousing, "Yes. Let go. You're making me late and crushing our gift, caveman."

13

There is speculation in the Enlightened world that there is a third Veil that divides the living from the dead. Like the Veil between the Enlightened and Unenlightened, crossing between these Veils is dangerous and once crossed, there is no going back.
-- Olivia Goldstein, *Mastering Magic*

Noah checked his watch for the third time during the meeting. Cicero stopped in the middle of his speech and folded his hands in front of him. "Am I keeping you from something, boss?"

Joseph snickered and Noah kicked him under the table.

Noah picked up the report they were supposed to be reviewing. "No, please continue."

"He and I are going to be late to get ready for his date at my wife's birthday party if you don't wrap it up quickly," Joseph cut in.

Cicero threw his report over his shoulder and grinned. "Who is he dating?"

Joseph leaned forward. "A woman called Emily Rollins."

Cicero whistled between his teeth. "She's the smoking hot blonde that opened the candle shop in town, right?"

"How do you know that?" Noah growled.

Cicero leaned back in his chair with his hands behind his head. "It's part of my job to know who comes in and who comes out of the territory. Went to check on her the other day to see if she was Enlightened."

Joseph patted Noah's shoulder with a wicked grin. "Condolences buddy. Looks like you're with me in the Unenlightened life-mate department. Better start brushing up that charm of yours."

Cicero's eyebrows disappeared into his hairline. "She's your mate? How can you know that? She's been here less than a month?"

Joseph crossed his arms over his chest. "Werewolves are superior beings to necromancers."

Cicero sat forward and flipped Joseph off. "You wish."

Noah tossed the Unguided report on the table. "How do you know Emily's Unenlightened? There are no decisive ways of knowing for sure without asking."

"Sure, there are, just most people ain't willing to take 'em."

"He took Kiss-Me-Knot with him to town. I don't want to know what he promised her to get her to agree to that." Joseph leaned forward, "Care to elaborate?"

"Kiss-Me-Knot walked right up to her in the parking lot outside her shop and the girl didn't blink an eye. I approached and asked when she'd be opening meanwhile Kiss-Me-Knot stood there naked as a Jay-bird and twinkling like a star. No reaction. So, I ask her point blank if she's seen any odd flashes of light around the place and she says she hasn't.

Most people would at least acknowledge or explain the floating light as a glint of something, but your girl was oblivious. I was half tempted to have Kiss-Me-Knot try and touch her-."

Noah bared his teeth in warning.

Cicero threw his hands up. "But I know that's against the rules. She's either the best liar I've ever seen or she isn't Enlightened."

Noah shrugged tense shoulders and let out a breath he hadn't realized he was holding. "I know. She told me as much two days ago."

Joseph snickered. "I can teach you the Unenlightened relationship ropes. I'll even make room for you on our couch when you screw it up."

Noah flipped him off too. "Let's make this quick. How many more Unguided cases have there been in our territory?"

Joseph flipped through some papers. "None since the initial outbreak, but we're still making the rounds."

Noah checked his watch and stood up to go. "How is Alex? He was released from the Recovery Center two days ago. Do we have a report from his guide yet?"

Joseph cleared his throat. "No. I've sent word out in the other patrols and none of the other werewolves have come across his scent. His Boston guide, January, couldn't finish the job because of some kind of vampire politics. If

Alex left this territory without a guide, even in ignorance-"

Noah felt the blood drain from his face.

Cicero snorted snatching the papers from Joseph's hands. "Boston Recovery needs their heads examined. Why would they assign a vampire to guide a new were-wolf? Don't they have any packs in their territory?"

Joseph snatched the paperwork back. "If you'd read the report this morning you know that Alex Kimbos doesn't want anything to do with the local Boston pack. Their alpha personally requested to guide him but apparently, she's the reason for his first full adult trans-formation."

Cicero gaped in disgust. "She forced him through the Veil?"

"Nope. He was already Enlightened, and a werewolf, but he'd chosen to abstain from transformation."

"Why would he do that?" Cicero said not bothering to retrieve the report this time.

Noah rubbed his brow. "In some territories, when a new wolf joins a pack, there's a reshuffle for dominance. Alex was probably trying to avoid a fight."

Cicero shook his head. "You're not making any sense."

Joseph continued. "The alpha wanted him but until Alex took wolf form, he was considered outside of her pack. He most likely shifted for the first time to defend himself against her, and in all likelihood, lost the fight."

"Son of a bitch," Cicero snarled. "She either owns him through another pack member or he consents to be guided by her as newly awakened. Either way, she gets him."

"Not all packs work that way," Joseph said meeting Noah's eye. "The ones that don't have much in the way of real loyalty. His only choices after that would be to submit to her or leave the territory."

Noah stood and started gathering the reports. "He didn't do either. He requested a specific guide, a vampire. That way she can't challenge Alex until he finishes learning the ropes, she can't challenge the vampire without bringing her pack into the fight and risking her status, if she kills the vampire guide, Alex goes as property to the next vampire in his line."

Cicero stood up scooping his report from the floor and handing it to Noah. "Vampire politics. Brilliant. Why did Angela grant him sanctuary?"

"There is nothing my mother hates worse than a bully, but Alex came here because his guide requested it."

"Yes," Joseph stated looking extremely uncomfortable. "Angela's also...umm...assigned him a new guide in this territory."

"Selene." Noah closed his eyes feeling enraged on his sister's behalf. "Does my mother realize that Alex probably wants nothing to do with female werewolves?"

Joseph cleared his throat. "I'm not really in the position to question her decisions." Noah stood up and handed the paperwork to Cicero and walked out the door.

"Noah, wait." Joseph followed him out. "Katrin and I are having dinner at The Blue Moon before we go to Jack Frost's. Why don't you and Emily join us?"

"I'm not leaving my sister in the hands of an angry werewolf."

"Selene is invited to Katrin's birthday party too. If she

brings Alex, you can find a reason to talk to him alone. If she doesn't, then you can warn her."

Cicero turned the stack of reports into a burning ball hovering in the middle of the room. "Whatever you're doing, you need to do it fast."

Joseph narrowed his eyes. "Why is that?"

"Because I don't know a woman alive who likes to be standing around all dressed up and waiting to go to a party."

They headed toward the door when Joseph's phone rang. "Dark Wolf Security."

Joseph's smile turns into a deep frown. "I understand. If it can't wait till tomorrow, I can come now."

Noah took Joseph's phone from his hand. "This is Noah, Joseph isn't available tonight. What can I do for you?"

"Noah? Thank God. This is Nadine Little down at the Last Stop. I got a girl here and I think she's one of your Unguided. Never seen her before in my life. She asked me for the bathroom key and I gave it to her but I think to myself, she's sure looking at me funny. Then I think, she's either been in there a long time or she's driven away with the key. I knocked on the door, but there was no response. I got the spare and opened it. She's just sitting in a corner leaning against a wall with her knees to her chest with her eyes wide open. I can't get her to respond to me." Nadine started to cry. "She's just a baby. She can't be more than 16. I moved her to my office and got her a blanket but I didn't know what else to do."

"I'm on my way. When you hang up, I want you to call the hospital and talk to Dr Cheng. Tell her what you told me but leave out the Unenlightened part. She knows what to do."

Nadine sniffled. "She's just a little girl."

"I know. I'll be right there."

He handed the phone back to Joseph. "Go to your wife's party. I'll be there as soon as I can. Before you go, call my sister, and tell her to pick up Emily. I will text her and let her know I'm going to be late and that Selene is coming to get her."

Noah put his coat on and picked up his wallet, keys, and phone.

"Cicero, you come with me. Nadine thinks she's got an Unguided woman down at The Last Stop. We need to get there quick."

Cicero nodded motioning for the ash to go to the trash can and picking up his coat. "Are we driving or flying?"

Noah thought about it for a second. "Are you strong enough to teleport both of us? I don't have time to end up in some in-between world."

Cicero rubbed his hands together with a cocky smirk. "I'm strong enough to take this whole building if I wanted to."

"Can you do it without being seen?"

"No guarantees on that. Necromancy, I can do, scrying is a gift beyond my talents."

Noah sighed, "Then we'll have to take the car."

Emily got a text from Noah asking her to go ahead to the party and take their gift because he'd been held up at work. She would have rather waited for him but in the next moment, she got an ecstatic call from Selene talking about finally having some time alone together. Her enthusiasm had cut through the potential awkwardness of the situation.

Selene had also mentioned that the party invitation had specified cocktail dresses and for once, Emily felt like she was finally in her element. The flared skirt of the dark red dress was wide enough to make her waist look small and short enough to make her legs look long. A sweetheart neck and capped sleeves kept it from being too brazen but the dress never failed to give Emily confidence. She felt a little overdressed until she opened the door and saw Selene's version of a little black dress. Even though there was snow on the ground, Selene's feet were bare. It appeared that Noah's whole family was oblivious to the cold.

Emily pulled the door shut behind her. "You look great. Where are your shoes?"

"In the truck," Selene said smoothing her immaculate hair. "They aren't the kind of shoes you drive in. Let's go. If we hurry, we can sneak in an order of cheese fries before the place gets packed."

Emily climbed up into Selene's truck carrying her dancing shoes. Although the pick-up must have been every bit as old as Selene was, it was immaculate. She couldn't have been any more different from her brother if she tried. Other than the truck, there wasn't a rugged or outdoorsy thing about her.

"Thanks for picking me up."

"I'm happy to do so. It gives me five minutes to quiz you about your intentions with my brother."

They stared at each other for a moment across the bench seat. The snow gave the night a half light and Emily felt like she could hear the beating of her own heart.

Selene's face split into a silly grin. "I'm sorry. That probably wasn't funny. Honestly, the last thing I want to know anything about is my brother's love life. I've been dying to ask you to hang out with me since you came into the restaurant but I'm trying not to step on Noah's toes."

Emily laughed. "I have room in my social schedule for Noah and friends."

"Well, I know for a fact we Hernandez's can be pretty time-consuming. Alone time is hard to come by in this family. It's part of the reason I live in Augusta." She clicked her seatbelt, started the truck, and pulled out of the drive carefully.

"Not a fan of Larkshead?" Emily asked clicking her own seatbelt into place.

"In my opinion, it's both an academic and social dead spot. I would much rather be closer to New York." She glanced over at Emily with an apologetic expression. "Don't get me wrong, it's a close community with a lot of traditions, but when I tell someone around here that I'm an Epidemiologist, they try to schedule an appointment for skin tests."

"I think everyone feels that way about their hometown." Emily took off her red gloves and held her hands up to the heater.

Selene leaned forward and turned the heat up a couple of notches. "Mom hates the idea of me moving, but I feel like I am starving to death for something to do that doesn't involve bug spray."

Selene's entire attention was on the road. Even when the road looked icy, she drove with complete control. Something about the way Selene spoke about Larkshead made her wonder if some of what Selene said was habit. There was affection when she talked about the town and the people.

"I can't say I've done much outdoor stuff. My mom and I lived in a cabin by Kentucky Lake for a year or so, and I lived a whole summer swimming in the lake. She said I was going feral but I think she secretly loved it. After that, we lived mostly in cities."

"Noah won't live in a city. I swear he was born outside. When he was seven, my dad painted a giant mural of the woods in his room just to get him to sleep inside."

Emily leaned forward to get the inside scoop on Noah. Somehow, she felt like he wore his heart on his sleeve and played his hand close to his chest at the same time. "So, Forestry chose him at an early age?"

"Not really. He went to forestry school but when he got back from university, he and Joseph started a small-time security firm called Dark Wolf. I think he would have stayed there forever but when the job opportunity came open for a Larkshead Forest Ranger, Mom convinced him to combine his talents."

In Emily's experience, she'd never seen Noah so much as raise his voice. "I can't imagine Noah in security. He just seems too nice."

Selene gave her a wry look. "You haven't been on the wrong side of him, then. Joseph might look like the badass of the bunch but I'd cross him ten times before I'd think about crossing my brother. In his world, there is the way he was going to do it and the wrong way."

"Noted," Emily said wrinkling her nose.

Selene smirked. "I have a feeling you're not much fun to cross either."

They pulled into the parking lot of a bar called Jack Frost's, the only place in town without a single Christmas decoration. Selene said that it was the place to go when the fa-la-la got to be too much for the locals. It was a small place by city standards, but it gave the impression that everything was clean and in just the right place. Hundreds of small paintings of cocktails that Emily had never heard of hung around the place in simple black frames giving a crisp professional appearance to the warm golden walls. The place was split-level with the bar and a selection of tables on a raised dais in the front and a polished wood dance floor complete with a DJ in the back. The speakers were pointing toward the back of the place rather than the front keeping the dance floor flooded with music and allowing the bar staff to hold a conversation without shouting.

In heels high enough to make a statement, Selene led Emily to the bar. "You just point to the cocktail picture you want and the bartender will make it for you. Be careful, the drinks are stout."

Emily clutched Katrin's birthday gifts to her chest boggled by the sheer number of her options. Selene leaned forward to order them a drink when someone shrieked from the dance floor.

"Selene!"

That was all the warning they got before Katrin launched herself into Selene's arms. She seemed to be expecting the attack because she turned immediately to scoop Katrin up and gave her a big hug before returning her to the floor. "Happy birthday, beautiful."

"Do you like my dress?"

Katrin did a couple of little twirls grinning coquettishly over her shoulder each time. Her pinstriped cocktail dress came straight out of a Tim Burton film, and she completed the look with the ends of her pitch-black hair dyed white.

"You guys look great. I'm so glad you're here." She offered her hand to Emily. "I'm Katrin. You must be Emily."

Emily suddenly recognized her as the woman with the Smurf- colored hair. "Thank you for inviting me."

"I'm glad you're here. It's just us girls to start with. Joseph said he would give us an hour to flirt outrageously while he tried to get Noah not to look like a dork."

"I haven't noticed he ever looks like a dork," Emily replied surprised.

Katrin pursed her lips. "In the interest of prolonging your relationship with him in hopes of extending our friendship past the point where he is necessary, I decline to comment. I will say that he looks like a god when he's swimming but his formal dressing up skills need work." She turned to Selene. "Sometimes I wonder how you two are related at all."

"You're not the only one," Selene waved down the bartender.

Emily held out Katrin's birthday gift. "Happy birthday from both of us."

"Ahh, Thank you. I can tell you wrapped it."

"How?" Emily asked simultaneously trying to watch Katrin open the gift and pay attention to potential drinks that Selene was pointing at.

"Noah only owns Christmas wrapping paper," Katrin replied reaching into the gift bag and pulling out the Enlightened candle. She read the label, took the lid off, and sniffed it, her eyes rolling back in pleasure. "I love scented candles. Smell this, Selene."

Katrin held the candle out. Selene leaned forward taking a deep breath. Emily watched intently wondering what she would think. Selene shuddered as if she'd caught a sudden chill and opened her eyes to stare directly at Emily. There was no doubt in her mind that Selene's eyes flashed gold like Sebastian's had when he'd come into Noah's cabin. There was something primal underneath the color that tugged at the edges of Emily's memory.

Katrin didn't appear to notice the change.

"That's right. I remember now. You're the new Ace of Cups lady. I've been trying to get to your store all week but Joseph's being a weirdo about crowding you and Noah." She pulled the smaller candles out of the bag smelling each one like a wine connoisseur before returning them to their package. "I needed you in my life."

Selene clapped her hands breaking the link between them. "Enough mushy stuff. Let's celebrate new friend-ships with cheese fries."

"Lots of cheese fries," Katrin added, "and three of

those." She pointed to a picture of a cocktail in a glass the size of a soup bowl with fruit, umbrellas, and ice.

"And whatever they're having."

Emily's mouth fell open.

Katrin shrugged. "My party, my rules."

14

Once a mirror tastes magic, it will always crave it. Signs that a mirror has been used for spell craft include a darkening around the mirror's edges and shadows moving in the mirror scape. To keep a magic mirror happy, consider enchanting it to show inner beauty. It will keep both the mirror and the witch out of mischief. —Valerie Black, *Everyday Solutions to Magic Problems*

The Last Stop was three miles outside the edge of town. It was one of the last places to get fuel before the long trek back to the main highway. Wearing an apron with a Santa face on it and antlers holding back her curling silver hair, Nadine looked just like Mrs. Clause. She was one of the rarest Enlightened, someone who was born Enlightened in a completely Unenlightened family.

She'd told Noah's mom once, that before she'd found a guide, she'd suffered depression, nightmares, and unexplained anxiety. The confirmation that there were

Enlightened and supernatural creatures in the world had felt much more real and natural to her than a world where they didn't exist. Both her anxiety and her nightmares were connected to the fact that she could see the Enlightened but no one else could.

Before Noah and Cicero could park the car, Nadine was outside wringing her hands.

"Thank you for coming. Dr Cheng told me to tell you she'd contact the Recovery Unit and send an ambulance."

Cicero looked around the parking lot with a frown. "Where's her car?"

Nadine studied the parking lot like it was the first time she'd ever seen it. "I didn't see what car she came here in. Customers always seem to arrive all at the same time. I can't even rightly tell you how long she was in the restroom before I went to check. I just noticed the key hadn't been returned and then I found her."

"If her car is gone it means she was either dropped off here or walked here. Do you guys have any security cameras set up?"

"Only in the shop. The gas pumps won't turn on without a credit card and Dewayne is sure that will keep most people out of mischief. I keep telling him that the world is changing, and we should use Dark Wolf, but the man is so tight he squeaks when he walks." She pursed her lips and motioned for them to come inside.

The shop was a standard convenience store except that everything in the store was mermaid themed. Dewayne Crosson loved two things in life, his wife, and mermaids. That his wife was a mermaid was what he called the luckiest accident in the world. It had been his idea to have a mermaid-themed Christmas last year. There was a mermaid tale-shaped sign indicating the offices. Nadine opened the door revealing a young lady in jeans and a sweatshirt that was three sizes too big for her. She sat behind the computer desk staring forward as if lost in thought. Cicero went to the desk and touched her gently on the shoulder. She fell forward, the chair slipping out from beneath her. He caught her, guiding her gently to the floor. Cicero felt for her pulse, his mouth thinning.

"We need to call the police. She's dead."

Noah's heart sank heavy in his chest and all he could do was think about the experiences she would never have. Sabastian was preparing for prom and worrying about graduation, worrying about affording college, still imagining the dreams he would chase when the world was ready to call him an adult. This girl would never have any of those chances.

Nadine burst into tears. "She was walking and breathing when I sat her down in the office. I should have called an ambulance right away. I didn't know. I thought-"

Noah interrupted her. "You followed the procedure and did the right thing. Did she have anything on her when you found her? A purse maybe?"

He escorted Nadine out of the room. Over his shoulder, he caught Cicero's eye and nodded. As a necromancer, Cicero could talk to the dead. The longer someone was dead, the harder it was to get the right person back in the body. They needed to move quickly before the ambulance arrived.

Nadine shook her head. "There wasn't anything with her in the bathroom when I opened the door."

"Are you sure it was locked?"

"I used the spare key to open it but I didn't check. I'm sorry. I didn't expect anyone to be in there."

"It's okay. I want you to lock up the store and call Dewayne. Let him know what's going on. I'll update the Recovery Unit and let them direct the police. Until they get here, I want you to sit down behind the till and write down everything you can remember about what happened. Can you do that for me?"

Nadine nodded, tears still streaming down her face. By the time Noah got back into the office, Cicero was already talking to the dead girl. She couldn't move except to speak but her eyes wandered restlessly around the room. Cicero had made sure to immobilize her in case whatever came back into her body wasn't really her. The normal lines of frustration around Cicero's eyes had smoothed into an expression that was close to pleasure.

"Shawna?" Cicero said softly, almost lovingly.

"I'm still here," the dead girl said but her voice was not quite contained by her physical body. Every hair stood on Noah's body as his wolf-self surged to the surface of his mind.

Cicero continued like they were talking over coffee. "You went to the bathroom at The Last Stop. Was anyone in there with you?"

The voice split into two voices, one deep and outside of the body, one soft and inside it. They answered yes and no at the same time.

Her body jerked as if it had been shocked with electricity and Cicero moved his hands over her chest in a complex pattern. Her eyes rolled back into her head. The jerking meant that another spirit was attempting to take over the body. If it managed to displace Shawna, her spirit could become lost between the living and the dead. Noah knew that Cicero could bind her spirit to an object allowing the other spirit to displace her but there was still a risk that she would become lost. The next spirit, if willing, could relay Shawna's most recent memories, but doing so might destroy both spirits. Noah shook his head. He wasn't willing to risk losing her soul.

Cicero continued to trace patterns over the body. "Stay with me Shawna, just a second longer. Tell me where you were before the bathroom."

"I can't," she whispered, her eyes jerked to the side staring at something only she could see. Noah followed her gaze and felt his hackles rise higher. Something was here.

"I won't let anyone hurt you," Cicero murmured not bothering to look at whatever lurked close by. "I will make sure you don't get lost but I need you to tell me where you were."

"The beach." The double voice said. "He said to meet him on the beach and he would show me a secret."

"I want to speak only to Shawna."

Her body jerked again twice, each time more violently than the last time. Cicero put his hand over her eyes looking at Noah for direction. Noah nodded.

His voice became soft again but more urgent. "Shawna, do you know about the Unguided-"

"I don't know! Please, I don't know. It's cold. Too cold to be in the water. He won't let me come out." She made a choking noise like she was drowning. "Please," the girl shrieked, "I was wrong. I don't want to see it! I don't want to know!

Noah made a slashing motion with his hand. Cicero leaned forward taking a ceremonial knife out of a holster in his pocket. He made several graceful slashing movements over the body as if he were cutting something free of a net. "You will not rest here, Shawna Marie Carlin. You aren't safe here. Let go of this memory." He chanted softly making sounds deep in his throat that most humans were incapable of. "Let go of this body. It's a shell you don't need anymore. Allow yourself to be wrapped up in the energy around you. Let it fill all the spaces ahead, inside, and behind you. You will be safe there."

The body relaxed completely; the eyes remaining wide open. Noah felt tears sting the back of his own eyes as he smelled the sea salt that matted Shawna's hair into messy black waves.

Cicero waited an extra moment and then drove the knife into the carpet. "I pin the other here and now you are bound to me, you are bound to this blade."

Noah bared his teeth his elongated canines pushing his jaws forward but did not interrupt. To interrupt was more dangerous than letting Cicero finish. The lights in the room flashed twice, the blade of the knife quivering back and forth as if something alive were tacked to the floor. The body moved again but the pupils expanded until each eye was completely black.

"Tell me your name, wanderer."

"Never to a necromancer," a deep hissing voice replied from the jaws of the dead girl. The movements of the mouth were slower than the sounds, like a film with the voice track out-of-sync.

"Why are you here, traveller?" The lights blinked fast on and off in the room.

"My price." The head of the body lulled to the side and Cicero grabbed the knife handle to keep it pinned to the floor.

"You were promised this body?"

"Yesss," the voice answered becoming more distinct.

Cicero leaned away from the body in disgust. "Who promised you?"

"I will not speak his name, damned one."

Cicero gritted his teeth leaning forward over the knife. "Tell me what you know, wanderer, and I will help you move to the other side. Deny me and I will bind you forever to this blade with or without your real name."

The blade flashed red like it was super-heated and rocked violently back and forth. Cicero merely put his hand on the top of it.

"This is your last chance."

"I cannot say it, spirit thief. It is beyond my tongue," the voice spat out, this time from the closed mouth of the dead girl. Her eyes cleared and the body relaxed again as the spirit trying to enter her began to lose its grip. Cicero sat motionless watching the spirit begin to lose its way.

"Lured us separately to the beach with a promise. She to see and me to be found." The voice began to sound weak and afraid.

Cicero spoke gently again, the way he had to Shawna. "The unnamed cannot give you what isn't his. I can't give it to you either. Let me help you."

"Unnamed...demon...twice damned," The outer voice said turning threadbare. "Help me."

Noah's head jerked up. The only demon in this territory was the one whom he'd given permission to be here. Cicero pulled the knife up swiftly making more and more complex slashing movements over the body. When he'd finished, he said, "You are not safe here, wanderer. Allow yourself to be wrapped up in the energy around you. Let it fill all the spaces in front of you, inside of you, behind you. You will be safe there."

He repeated the words he said to Shawna but Noah noted that the pitch of each word was slightly higher and sharper. The strain of the spells was taking its toll. The lights flickered again and then the air cleared. The tension he sensed in Cicero moved out of his shoulders even though he knew that he and Cicero were far from done with this.

Noah looked at the body again noting the bluish color now on Shawna's lips. With the other spirit gone, she retained none of the appearances of life. Noah smelled the brackish salty water all over her. "She was in the sea, recently, maybe no more than a couple of hours ago. The clothes on her are probably not hers. Someone forced her through the Veil and then abandoned her and I want to know who. What did she say before I came in?"

Cicero kissed the blade of his ceremonial knife and returned it to its sheath before standing up to back away from the body. "She gave me her name. She remembers the bathroom but not Nadine or how she got here. Honestly, she might have already been dead before she got here. She remembers seeing herself on the bathroom floor and that's normally a result of remote viewing."

"Nadine remembers her asking for the bathroom key."

"But Shawna doesn't," Cicero added. "The spirit brought her here but couldn't take possession of her body because she hadn't given permission and she wouldn't leave. She didn't know she was dead. If that wanderer had been stronger, or Shawna had moved on immediately after she died, the soul exchange would have taken place with no one the wiser."

Noah curled his lips in disgust. "Is there any chance of us getting to her last memories without bringing another spirit in?"

Cicero shrugged. "Maybe, but only if I take some of her hair."

"A forensic team will know you took it. We're already going to have a tough time explaining what we've done here."

Cicero shrugged. "I can clean up after myself."

"I don't want you to disturb evidence that might lead to an arrest later. If you take the hair, the Recovery team will think the death is related to Necromancy."

"That's exactly what we'll think."

Noah and Cicero turned around to see a smartly dressed but otherwise unremarkable woman. In fact, she was so unremarkable that this in itself was remarkable. Whenever Noah tried to focus on a detail of her face or hair, he found that he couldn't quite remember the exact details.

"You're a Daudrych," Cicero said with interest. He offered his hand. "Cicero Blackwater."

Her eyes flashed like light off a mirror. "I'm called a Mirrorlect in this country, but you can call me Agent Boyce. You are a Necromancer. Granted sanctuary four years ago. Wanted in your own territory for Soul crimes."

Cicero's hand dropped. "I saved a woman's life with that spell."

"Why you break the law doesn't concern me," Agent Boyce said before turning to Noah. "Noah Hernandez, pack enforcer for Larkshead Sanctuary, favored as Alpha replacement, of mixed blood." She let her gaze move up and down Cicero and then Noah. "Explain to me what you and your security agent are doing here. We're supposed to be informed immediately."

Noah gave her a hard look. He didn't often find himself questioned in his own territory. "I don't have to explain anything to you. This is my pack's territory. Myself and my agent were asked by the National Recovery Unit to investigate anything that had connections to the unsanctioned awakenings in this area. The only reason you're here is because I called for you."

"The update said she was dead, not Unguided."

Cicero pointed to the body. "She is."

"Then this is now my job. Let's get this started." Agent Boyce replied walking across the room to squat next to the body.

"Don't you want to know what we found out?" Cicero demanded putting his hands on his hips.

"Not my job. All I can do from here is to make sure your meddling won't be discovered when the Unenlightened police show up. Please give me your hand."

Cicero backed away from her. "Forget it. I can clean up my own mess."

She pressed her lips together in irritation. "Can you do it in five minutes? Because that's how much time you have before the police get here."

"What about Nadine?" Noah asked coming to stand next to Cicero.

"I'll take care of it. I need to see what happened so I know what to obscure." She held her hand out to Cicero.

He scowled. "Why can't Noah do it?"

"He didn't talk to the dead."

She reached for him again and Cicero reluctantly took her hand. She barely closed her fingers around his before she let go looking at Cicero. "Leave the body where it is. You two go outside, pick up a snack or a cold drink, and head toward the cashier. Pay for them. Don't say anything until I get there."

Noah motioned for Cicero to follow him. He picked up the first two items that caught his attention. As he set the tide table and picture frame surrounded by tiny white shells on the counter, he understood that he was reaching out for Emily. Moments later Cicero added a carton of chocolate milk to the pile. Nadine looked confused.

Agent Boyce walked up to Nadine with a smile and touched her arm. Nadine blinked and then began ringing up the sale like there was nothing wrong. Agent Boyce set down the cash to pay for the items on the counter with one hand and with the other slid the written statement out from under Nadine's hand. There was no blinking lights or theatrics. Nadine's confused expression turned into a genuine smile as she placed the items in the bag holding it out to Cicero as if she could no longer see Agent Boyce.

"Thanks for the tip, Noah. You guys have a nice night." She looked at the pen she was holding and then glanced toward the bathroom with a frown. Agent Boyce motioned for Cicero and Noah to follow her out of the store.

"Wave at the cashier and then get into the car. Drive until you get to the layby, then pull over."

Agent Boyce got into the passenger seat and waited while Noah and Cicero got seated and buckled their safety belts.

What did you do?" Cicero asked, shifting through the bag to retrieve the chocolate milk.

"Nothing difficult, Soul Binder," Agent Boyce replied thoughtfully watching Cicero through the rear-view mirror. "When the police arrive, the cashier will remember clearly your arrival, your purchases, checking the bathroom, finding the girl and escorting her to the office, the phone call to the police, and going to the office with you for pen and paper to write down something Noah mentioned, but everything will look jumbled and out of sequence to her. The police will think it's shock. When they've finalized their report, I'll go back to her home and set things straight."

Noah pulled into the layby just as the police rushed past with their lights flashing. "What about the camera?" Cicero asked sounding awed.

"I took care of it before I came into the office. It's blank. You bought some things from the store which explains your presence and any physical evidence you left behind. The police will probably question you later, but as long as you keep quiet, it will wash over."

Cicero growled sounding more wolf-like than Noah himself. "Now hold on just a minute. You didn't do us any favors. Now instead of being able to properly investigate the situation, no one's going to be sure exactly what's going on. If this isn't a case of the Unguided, then we have a fatal unsanctioned awakening in this territory."

Agent Boyce frowned turning to look squarely at Cicero. "You are not a Recovery Agent, I am. We know what we're doing. What you did back there was stupid and potentially dangerous. You got exactly what a forensic team would have got except you risked a young girl's soul to do it. I will report your behavior to the territory Alpha. I expect a full report of the incident by tomorrow."

"You can request the report from the proper authorities after my mother reads it and after she's decided to submit it to those authorities. If anyone is at fault here, it's me. Cicero was following orders," Noah said between gritted teeth, tired of being dragged out, pushed around, and shouted at when all he really wanted to do was find Emily. He added calmly, "After all, you've done your job, right?"

Agent Boyce looked over him again her mouth bending into a grudging smile. "You're going to make one hell of an Alpha, half-breed." She touched her index finger to the rear-view mirror and vanished. She didn't leave a fingerprint.

Cicero sat glaring at the empty seat a moment before getting out of the car and climbing back into the front seat chocolate milk in tow. "I'll go home and start working on that report."

"Not so fast, cowboy," Noah said with a tired smile. "We're in my territory. We need to get dressed and get to Jack Frost's pronto. Do your thing. We don't want to be any later for Katrin's party then we already are. We'll get to that report in the morning."

Cicero relaxed placing one hand on the console of the car. "Right, you are, boss. Where do we need to be first?"

15

When it comes to spell craft, correct timing is much more important than correct ingredients. The only ingredient a witch really needs is a desire to make a change. Everything else can be substituted. --Olivia Goldstein, *Mastering Magic*

Noah allowed Cicero to teleport his car to his house where they could both clean up and get dressed, and then take them both to a back road behind Jack Frost's. He'd arranged for Selene to take them home but he suspected by some of the photos Joseph had sent that they were all going to have to call a cab.

Even with Cicero's help, Noah managed to be about an hour late. He wasn't in the party mood, but he put a smile on his face anyway. What he'd seen today couldn't be shared while Katrin and Emily were present, and ruining Katrin's party was the last thing he wanted to do.

Jack Frost's was jammed with young winter tourists. Noah spotted Emily in the center of a dance floor as he came through the door. It was hard to miss her. Dressed in a red dress that would have stopped traffic, she hopped, writhed, twirled, and laughed moving in perfect sync with the music through a crowd of men who were attempting to capture both her body and attention. Her gold hair clung to her temples with her exertion and her face was lit up with intense pleasure. A man close to her held a hand out to invite her into his arms. Jealousy flared through him but before he could move forward and rip the man's arms from the sockets, Joseph stepped in front of him.

"Look at me, not her."

Noah growled deep in his throat. "Get out of my way."

"She's dancing with Selene and Katrin, and they are having a good time. Take a deep breath and look again. If you go charging in there, you're going to look like an asshole and ruin my wife's party."

Noah took a deep breath and looked again this time registering Selene and Katrin swirling and weaving with Emily. Any time a guy reached for Emily, she stepped back a little with a smile and an almost imperceptible shake of her head. It was enough to warn someone off, but not enough to kill the fun. Joseph was right. Noah still felt the urge to rip the man's arms off and recognized that his experience at The Last Stop had shaken him more than he wanted to admit. "How did you keep from tearing the world apart?"

Joseph steered Noah toward the bar. "First rule of having a life-mate, Enlightened or not, is to trust her. The first couple of times I didn't have someone to stop me from doing the douche thing and it almost caused Katrin to walk right out of my life. It gets easier after you start sharing the same bed, even better when you share a house. Until then, it's a little like roulette, some situations will cause nothing to happen and in others you'll just blow up."

Noah picked up a green drink in a martini glass. "What's this?"

"Mostly Tequila. Be gentle."

Noah slammed the drink down in one gulp and shivered as the familiar heat crawled up his spine. The bartender scowled and Joseph winced.

"That's alcohol abuse, you know."

Noah pointed at another picture and waited for the bartender to hand it over. The upbeat music shifted to a sultry ballad and all three women began to make their way off the dance floor.

"That's our cue." Joseph said leading Noah onto the dance floor. "Let's show those young bloods who they're dealing with."

Noah followed Joseph through the crowd. Emily was avoiding eye contact in an effort not to encourage any of the gentlemen she'd been previously dancing with to invite her for a slow dance. He caught her hand and pulled her into his arms just as she was making her way off the dance floor. She resisted him at first until she realized who it was, then she moved close enough to press the entire length of her body to his and wrap her arms around his neck. "Hey, you're late. This place is great." She wobbled a bit on her high heels.

"You're beautiful." He kissed the tip of her nose. "And a little drunk?"

She put her head against his shoulder. "Your friends

are lethal. So are these cocktails." She leaned back to look at him, her eyes taking in his tousled dark hair, jeans, and green button-down shirt rolled up to his elbows. "You don't look like a dork at all."

"Thank you, I think."

Emily closed her eyes swaying gently to the music. "Selene said this was supposed to be a cocktail party. Where's your suit?"

"Selene probably told Katrin that too so that she wasn't the only one in a fancy dress." Noah smoothed his hands over Emily's short red dress. "You look beautiful."

She chuckled returning her head to his shoulder. "Ooh, she's clever. I knew I liked that woman for a reason."

He held her close and rocked her to the music allowing the feeling of belonging to push away the lingering darkness in his thoughts. She molded herself to him capturing the soft beat of the music with her hips and transferring it to him unaltered through subtle moves of hands and shoulders. He kissed her shoulder reverently and she responded by humming along to the music more than a little off key. Just as the music began to wind down in promises of forever, he heard a voice from behind him.

"Selene Hernandez?" Noah and Emily both turned toward the voice and saw an impeccably dressed Alex Kimbos who would not have looked out of place in a Calvin Klein add. The sophisticated cut of both his clothing and manners contradicted the raw irritation in his face as he approached Selene and her dance partner. He might have been considered boyish were it not for the power and directness with which he moved. Noah let go of Emily and moved forward to block his access to Selene.

"I'm pleased to see you safe, Alex. I was worried."

Alex blinked as if he just realized Noah was there and then looked genuinely apologetic. "I'm sorry. This wasn't my choice."

Selene thanked her partner and stepped around Noah greeting the stranger with an appreciative smile. "I'm Selene."

Alex gave her a slight bow. "Your mother sent me. Is there somewhere we can talk?"

The momentary compression of her lips was the only indication of Selene's anger but the stranger still had the sense to look embarrassed. "I know I'm interrupting you both. I'm sorry. We can do this later."

"Too late for that, now. If you'll give me a moment, I'll make my apologies and go get my drink," Selene replied pointing to a table at the back of the bar.

Alex looked at Noah. "I need to talk to you."

Noah felt Emily move beside him threading her fingers through his. "Your mother's sending blind dates to the bar?"

Noah tried to think of a reply that didn't have to do with Werewolf hierarchy. "Yep. This is why I needed you to save me." He wrapped an arm around her and kissed her playfully on the top of the head trying to distract her.

Katrin's excited squeal sounded from behind him as another dance song blared from the sound system. He stepped back with a playful bow.

"Go party. I'll make sure Selene is okay and be right with you."

She didn't get a chance to reply before Katrin caught her arm and dragged her to the middle of the dance floor.

❦

Alex waited for Noah and Selene to be seated before he started. "I know you don't owe me anything but I need help. James showed up. He said he was a Recovery Agent. One minute they were just talking and the next he grabbed Phoebe and started to burn her with his hands. He kept shrieking at her to tell him who was bringing down the Veil. One minute I was trying to get him off her and the next, she was just gone. Like she never existed. James tore my place apart looking for her. So did January." Alex's face began to contort, his grief calling his wolf to the surface. He clenched his teeth hissing in anger.

"James took Phoebe?" Noah asked.

Alex nodded. "I think so. I wasn't honest the other day. She's been with me this whole time. January told her to stay here with me until he could come to get us. Everything was fine. I didn't want to get your pack involved, Noah. She and I were just having so much fun and I was learning control..." Alex's eyes began to change shape, tears running from the corners of them.

Selene put her hand on top of his. "Listen to the music and try to follow the lyrics."

"Phoebe and January are looking for a woman called Emily Rollins. They have to find her or January's dead." Faces in the bar started turning toward them. Selene came around the table to block their view and grabbed the edges of Alex's shirt.

"Look at me," she demanded. Alex was losing shape. "My favorite Christmas song is 'All I Want for Christmas is My Two Front Teeth.'"

Noah was poised to pull her away but Selene started singing the song stopping halfway through the chorus.

Alex's form solidified into his human form, his face a picture of disbelief. "That's the worst Christmas song ever written."

She grinned patting his hand. "No, 'Grandma got Run Over by a Reindeer' is the worst Christmas song ever written. Come outside and let's go for a run. Then we can check out your place and see if we can't track your Phoebe down. Noah can check in with us tomorrow."

He nodded allowing Selene to pull him away from the crowd and out the back doors of the club. Noah walked back toward the table watching Emily the whole time. Her soft southern accent blended with Cicero's in a song of cadences that he'd never really noticed from either of them. Like having the lights suddenly turned on, he recognized that she might be his but he didn't know her. Not where she came from, what she was looking for, what she might be doing here.

Selfishly, he'd considered how to best fit her into his life without considering what he might be asking her to give up. Katrin was sitting in Joseph's lap and everyone, including Emily, was laughing at a story Cicero was finishing.

"I swear it," Cicero's voice took on an elongated drawl that Noah hadn't heard him use since he came to the sanctuary.

Emily shook her head. "You'd call an alligator a lizard, I bet."

Cicero put his hand dramatically over his heart. "Ma'am, I am deeply offended."

"You are deeply disturbed, is what you are," she chuckled reaching up without looking to grab Noah's hand and pull him down beside her. "What happened to Selene?"

Noah pulled her close. "She had to leave to go yell at my mother. What did I miss?"

"Cicero was telling us how a Louisiana boy ended up here in the frozen North."

"That question is mighty funny coming from you," Cicero replied with a wink. "How'd you get down here, country girl?"

She put her head on Noah's shoulder. "I have no idea. I'm lost as an Easter egg at Christmas, to be honest. One minute I'm driving to set up a stall for a season, and the next I've bought a place in Larkshead." Emily sat up and took a big drink from a glass full of blue liquid. "No offense to the locals, but this place is weird."

Katrin laughed. "It's weird to the locals too. Do you know once, I swear I saw big foot out behind our house?"

Joseph blushed frowning down at his wife. "She was drunk then and she's drunk now."

Emily ignored him leaning forward to whisper to Katrin. "I think I'd rather see Big Foot. I swear there's a ghost of a naked woman that walks around here. Sometimes I see her around my house, but no one else sees her. I feel like I'm losing my mind. And Nick Wilde sometimes reminds me of a goblin."

Katrin clinked Emily's glass. "I know, right? It's like he has two faces and I don't mean in a double-crossing way."

Cicero looked thoughtfully between Emily and Katrin. "When you next see that naked woman, you send her my way."

Emily laughed. "I also have a dog named Angelo only, the guy that delivered my couch said that he's a wolf. I've been trying to show him to Noah but it's like Angelo knows when Noah's coming and just leaves." Emily snapped her fingers and then turned to look at Noah. "What did the vet say when you updated his shots?"

Joseph arched a questioning brow. "What did the vet say, Noah? Did she say that Angelo was a dirty dog? Because I think he is."

Noah threw back his drink and held up the empty glass. "You'll have to ask Big Foot what she said. Are we talking or are we drinking?"

Cicero hooted. "Next round is mine."

16

A newly awakened witch should spend some time with each of the elements they intend to draw into their circle before they cast. Elements like witches but do not necessarily enjoy spending time with each other. They can become overly attached and jealous so it's important to set clear boundaries when working with them. —Phoebe Pearce, *Witchcraft for the Newly Awakened*

The store was jam packed Sunday. No sooner had Emily rung one customer up then another one was asking about ingredients. While she was answering the question about ingredients, she noticed that she was running low on stock. Even with April's help, she felt like she was bailing water in a sinking boat. So far, she'd counted sixteen different episodes of seeing people who were and were not people and they just kept coming.

Flashes of wings, horns, extended canine teeth and every other kind of physical oddity that could be named appeared and then disappeared so fast during normal conversation that Emily couldn't decide if she was having a nervous breakdown, or her drinks had been spiked at Katrin's party. April, like Noah, hadn't acknowledged any of the flashes and the muscles in Emily's face felt frozen in a false smile. What she really wanted was a cup of coffee, some lunch, and five minutes to quietly go insane.

The door bells jingled and Selene came through the door looking bright and happy. "Hey. How are you doing?" Selene asked giving her an awkward hug around the box she was carrying to the front. "Have you recovered from last night?"

"Barely," Emily answered. "My hangover is retched and the store is wild today."

"Sorry I'm interrupting. Mom sent me to see if you had time to have lunch with us before I head back to Augusta, but I told her you were busy." Selene looked around at the packed store. "Guess that's an understatement." She took two of the candles from the box that Emily was holding and inhaled. "Are these like the one you gave Katrin?" Emily nodded and Selene tucked them into her arms. "I'll have to go back to the restaurant to get my purse, but my second reason for coming was to get a couple of these."

Emily hoisted the box more firmly on her hip beaming. "Keep them. My treat. I don't think I paid for a single drink last night. Or the cheese fries."

She winked. "Neither did I."

Emily instantly felt a little normality seep back into her day.

"Let me bring lunch to you and April before I go back

to Augusta. I might not be the best pancake maker, but I make a mean club sandwich."

April nodded enthusiastically from behind the counter. "Please."

"What do you guys want to drink?"

"Coffee for me, please. As strong as you can get it," April said causing Emily to marvel again at what a perfect fit they were.

"Same here. I really appreciate it."

"My pleasure." Selene started to go and then turned around and came back. "You know, I also have a hellion teenage cousin at the café called, Kayleigh. She can't manage to take a correct order to save her life, but she can put your stock on the shelves and help field some questions if you don't mind that she has metal in her nose."

Emily looked around at the waiting customers. "Metal in her nose, three arms, whatever. We could use the help till things calm down."

"I'll send her over with your lunch," Selene said tucking her contraband more firmly under her arm and called over her shoulder. "See you at Thanksgiving."

Twenty minutes later Emily was still trying to figure out what Selene meant when a large formidable looking woman in her late fifties came through the door with a stiff anxious look and a flask. It took Emily a split second to recognize her as the woman Mildred had spoken to on Emily's first day here.

She was still meticulously put together in a way that made her seem both professional and approachable. She looked around the shop holding a large brown paper bag to her chest like a shield. It didn't take a rocket scientist to figure out that this was Noah's mother. Emily smiled feeling all at once embarrassed and pleased. She came around the counter to welcome the older woman.

"Mrs. Hernandez. Thank you so much for bringing our lunch. You didn't have to come yourself."

She looked around the shop with a smile of approval on her face. "Please call me Angela. Selene said you were busy. I didn't believe her."

She held out both paper bag and flask. There was something in the gesture that made Emily aware that she was offering more than just a sandwich. Emily accepted both, inviting Angela to follow her to the kitchenette. She felt more than saw Angela inspecting her. From the small set of cabinets over the sink, she retrieved a couple of coffee cups that were still so new she had to peel the labels off.

"Can I pour you some? I'm really sorry not to get a chance to eat with you today."

Angela looked around. "We can do it another time. I'm just being nosey. Yours is the first new shop that's opened in the main square in the last ten years."

Emily took a quick sip of the coffee. "Really?"

Angela looked back toward April and frowned. "Are you both going to get a chance to eat? I can help if you want. You don't want Kayleigh ringing up customers."

She was serious. The offer took Emily's breath away. "Thanks, but we normally take lunch in turns. This is more than I deserve for not getting up early enough to make my own lunch." Emily opened the brown bag and saw not only sandwiches, but french fries, salad, pie, cookies, and what appeared to be some kind of Christmas candy.

"Wow. This is amazing. What do I owe you?"

Angela looked down into the bag with pride. "We can call it a trade since my daughter came back with candles but not a receipt." She handed Emily a chocolate cookie. "I made these myself."

Emily took a bite. The soft gooey sweetness almost took her breath away. "This is perfect. I can see where Noah gets his cooking skills from."

Emily could have slapped her hands over her mouth. The mention of Noah's name seemed to instantly make his mother nervous. She glanced over her shoulder as if she expected him to come through the door.

"He is going to strangle me when he finds out I'm here but it's worth it. I'm the kind of woman who would rather beg forgiveness than ask permission."

Emily cleared her throat. "You're welcome here anytime."

Angela's smile widened. "Do you like fudge? I make the best peanut butter fudge in town."

Even if Emily hadn't liked fudge, Angela was so pleased to offer it the Southern part of her upbringing would have insisted she eat it. "I think fudge is amazing. I've tried to make it a couple of times but all I've managed to make was a mess."

A girl dressed completely in black with long sea green hair came into the back room. She hung back as if she expected to be rejected on sight. Angela touched the younger girl on the shoulder bringing her forward. Emily could have sworn that they were communicating somehow, but what instructions were being given she couldn't tell.

"Just in time. This is my sister's youngest daughter, Kayleigh. She can bring the thermos back to the restaurant when you're through with it."

Emily called out to her, "Hello Kayleigh? I'm Emily. Thank you for helping me out today."

The girl shoved her hands in her pockets. "What can I do?"

The question came out of her mouth with a wealth of failures behind it. "Can you refill the shelves? The stock is supposed to be labelled in the back and there should be matching labels on the shelves in the main room. I sometimes forget to put the prices on them, but there is a list on the wall and somewhere in this mess there is a pricing gun."

Kayleigh gave Emily a shy smile and nodded heading back to the shop floor. Angela stood to leave. "You're busy. I've taken up enough of your time. Come to Thanksgiving dinner. We can get a better chance to talk then."

Emily started to say yes and then thought about what she was doing. This was Noah's family and a major holiday dinner. Where she came from that was a big commitment. "That sounds great but I'll have to check with Noah."

"I don't need his permission to come here; you don't need his permission to eat at my house, right?"

Emily held her hands up in surrender. "Touché."

Angela tossed her hair over her shoulder and headed toward the door. "I'll let him know you're coming."

She didn't wait for Emily to answer.

17

Sensuality is a part of witchcraft whether a witch is Enlightened or Unenlightened. The feeling isn't about sex; it is about the connection between mind, body, spirit, and life. Sensuality is never in opposition to purity or to spirituality, only to outdated religious ideas. –Olivia Goldstein, *Mastering Magic*

Noah had first texted an apology for his mother's invasion and then called her to ask her to come to Thanksgiving himself. He'd sounded hopeful and fearful at the same time.

"I know it's a little fast. I wanted to ask you myself. You don't have to come if you're not ready, but I would love to have you there."

She'd agreed acknowledging to herself that the Hernandez family were a force to be reckoned with.

The Maine cold sliced through Emily's coat and multiple layers of clothing as she turned the lock on the shop door. Large white puffs of snow dipped and twirled through the air landing and clinging on surfaces like the sugar plum fairies that decorated her shop. The store should have felt close with three people working inside but April manned the till and answered the phone, Kayleigh stocked the shelves and priced items, which left Emily time to package and ship online orders, order supplies, and plan out some critical candle making time.

An unexpected double order for Enlightenment candles from The Craft Shop meant that Emily would make her December outgoings without needing to starve or borrow against future earnings, but it also meant that eating dinner with Noah the day after tomorrow was out of the question. She felt a small smile tug her lips. If she could just eat with him and then go home, that would be alright, but she was getting into a bad habit of spending the night every time they saw one another.

He was currently checking trails for the horse carriage rides and had peppered his text messages today with breath taking photos of horses in the snow, big red and green carriages, and snow-covered evergreens. Most of the surrounding businesses had closed for the night but the park in the square where the outside stalls were set up, and the Christmas tree lighting would take place in a couple of days, was still brightly lit and bustling. Every branch of a huge evergreen tree was being covered in lights and decorations.

The Christmas Market stalls were identical on the outside but inside, they were like the most elaborate shadow boxes Emily had ever seen. The grounds were patrolled regularly, and after 8 pm, only the food stalls were allowed to be open till 10 pm. Nick had delivered his suggested list of Christmas music, some advice for saving on her heating bill, and then unceremoniously dumped a ton of perfectly sized winter themed boxes he'd "found" for Emily's large candles. He had refused to take any money for them stating that they had been clogging up his shop. With the shine still on the cellophane wrapping, Emily very much doubted that. He was thanking her for hiring April, but the truth was she'd have been over-whelmed in a week without April's help.

Stepping out into the darkness she tilted her face to the sky feeling the light wet kiss of the snowflakes. Was it possible to find a spot where you fit in perfectly? Fitting in at other places had always been a matter of hedging, hoping, and compromise, but in every way imaginable she just clicked into place here. It was like giving up a favorite pair of shoes and then suddenly finding a more perfectly sized pair to replace them. She missed her grandma desperately, but she hadn't realized how pinched and uncomfortable she'd been as a person in her old life until now.

If it wasn't for seeing ghosts and goblins everywhere she looked, she'd be perfectly happy. Unfortunately, strangers with monstrous faces smiled at her on every corner and she could absolutely swear now that Nick's fairies not only moved around the shop, but some also came back to her after they had been sold. She'd only taken about thirty to begin with and her register indicated she'd sold them all twice. It was enough to make a woman think she was losing her mind.

Add her recent run of nightmares and visions about being drowned in the sea by red hands and it was almost enough to make her want to check herself in somewhere. The situation was so unnerving that she hadn't been brave enough to discuss it with her mother, who she normally told everything to.

Up and down the street, the shops were decked out in decorations ranging from modest stars and garlands to Santa villages so intricate that Emily half expected the miniature figures to come alive with her fairies in the darkness. That thought gave her a shiver that had nothing to do with the cold. Without warning, she slipped into a premonition.

She was submerged in water. A pair of black-tipped red hands held her under. In her mind, she screamed for help but knew she was alone with the monster. Then she was drowning. The clawed hands held her face just below the water. The red hands were connected to powerful arms and there was an angry clicking sound that penetrated the water. Rather than pull herself out of the vision, she stilled her panicking mind and focused. If you faced your fear in a dream, you could figure out what it was in real life. She began to make out a face.

A solid hand grasped her shoulder and shook her.

"Emily?"

She yelped coming up from the vision and gasping for breath. Blinking her eyes rapidly she discovered April and an earnest-looking little bundle regarding her with concern.

"April. What are you still doing here?"

"Michael and I were helping Dad." She hugged the little bundle closer to her leaning forward to brush snow off Emily. "Why are you standing outside in the cold? You look like a snow angel."

Emily became aware that the snow was still coming down in big puffy flakes but that they had gone from slowly drifting to pouring from the sky. She was covered. "What time is it?"

"Nearly 7 pm."

Shaking her head, Emily sent snow showering in all directions. She heard a delighted laugh come from the bundle who she could now see had a cherub face and eyes so dark they were almost black. April kissed his head.

"Michael this is mommy's boss, Emily."

"Hello, Michael. I think Mommy is really my boss, but I better not argue, huh?" Emily reached her hand out to him. He studied her for a moment before reluctantly offering her his hand. She clasped it murmuring, "You are beautiful."

He smiled suddenly leaning out from his mom's arms and reaching out for Emily to hold him. She scooped him up settling him on her hip without thought.

"What a big, wonderful boy you are." Bouncing him gently with her hip, he wrapped both of his chubby fists in her hair and stuffed them into his mouth. "How old is he?"

"He's two. He's usually so shy. I can't believe he came right to you."

He gave a good yank on Emily's hair making mmma mmma mmma sounds.

"Emily," April repeated unwrapping Emily's hair from his fists and then taking him back. "Let go of her hair." He let go instantly staring at Emily with a look that she would have sworn was apologetic.

She reached out and tickled his chin. "Don't worry about it, sweetie. I have enough hair to go around."

"He should be talking by now. That's what all my books say but that mmma sound is the best we can do right now, isn't it honey." She kissed his head again. "If I were you, I'd consider heading home. You look cold and your road won't be plowed until early tomorrow."

"How do you know that?"

Michael made a lunge for Emily but April swung him around with a laugh. "I saw the plowmen, Olly, at my dad's shop. Apparently, he's been sampling the mulled wine while checking out the vendor stalls. Noah told him it would be in his best interest to sleep it off at The Mermaid's Song."

"Noah was here?"

"Anywhere there is potential trouble in this town, Noah appears to nip it in the bud before it can happen. He's got a real sixth sense."

"He sent you back to check on me, didn't he?" Emily asked trying to decide if she was irritated by the fact.

"It was my idea. You seemed a little off this morning. Like you'd seen a ghost."

Emily thought about sharing her visions with April but she didn't want to scare the baby.

"If Michael and I can talk you into having a quick hot chocolate at Dad's shop before you go, Noah promised both of our cars would be cleared of snow before we head home."

"Sounds fantastic." Emily offered April her arm. Michael leaned forward excitedly and grabbed another chunk of Emily's hair.

Janet Wedgewood had made a full recovery and consented to allow her husband to act as her guide. She'd sent Noah a small gift basket filled with flavored maple syrups and an invite to have dinner at their home if he was in the neighborhood. Shawna's parents had been informed of her death and the short investigation that followed revealed only that she was well-loved and would be deeply missed.

Sebastian told him that she'd been one of the artists selected to paint the prom mural. He also confirmed that she'd been strange with some of the Enlightened at school recently, but no one thought to report her as Unguided because she seemed happy. No one in her acquaintance, Enlightened or otherwise, could give any explanation as to why she might have agreed to follow a stranger to the sea or to The Last Stop. Something about her death hit Cicero especially hard. He spent most of his time off investigating the murder.

The invitation to Emily for Thanksgiving dinner by his mother had been the highlight of Noah's day, and even that had come with some awkwardness. His mom had asked more than once if Emily was coming and had finally taken matters into her own hands. What Noah really wanted was for things to go back to normal where the only thing he needed to do was sing Christmas carols, woo the woman of his dreams, and count the days until hard winter brought Larkshead tourism to a standstill so that he could spend his nights making love to his life-mate.

He rubbed his brow and looked ruefully at the clock on his desk a little after 11:00 pm. He had to be in town tomorrow by 8 am to speak to the visiting Enlightened who had booked Christmas stalls this year. He'd seen Emily the night before last, and she'd said gently that she needed some time to make candles. He was trying to give her some space, but it was pure hell. Grabbing his coat, he headed home.

The roads were heavy with thick snow, and he made a mental note to call Olly and make sure he cleared Emily's drive when he plowed in the morning. On autopilot, he parked his truck and was not surprised to find himself parked in her driveway.

He tried to think of a reason to be here but the best he could come up with was that he'd had a hard day and he missed her. He growled at himself. She'd asked for time to work, and he needed to give it to her. As his hand touched his key, she opened the door like she'd been expecting him, her face a picture of amusement.

"Are you coming in or not?"

Noah got out of the truck and made his way quickly to the porch. He hugged Emily close feeling the tightness in his chest loosen and recognizing it for what it really was. The mate bond was forming. He could feel the heat of her body seeping out into the cold winter air and began to maneuver her inside. "I was trying to give you some space to work."

Emily allowed him to walk her backward through the door and close it behind him. "From my driveway?" She chuckled letting go of him long enough for him to take off his coat and let him kick off his shoes.

"I'm sorry."

She grabbed both of his hands threading her fingers through his and stood on tip-toe to kiss him gently. "I'm glad you're here. I'm just wrapping up. I would like to say in my defense, I tried to put her off but she's a lot trickier than I thought."

Noah blinked trying to figure out what she was talking about. "Is she?"

"She came into the shop with my lunch today. You did warn me, but I really thought you were kidding." She settled him down on one of her kitchen chairs in front of rows and rows of cooling red candles. The kitchen was filled with the heavy scent of mulled wine and just the right hint of orange. Christmas music played softly and was forgotten in the background.

"If you don't want me to go with you, you're going to have to be the one to tell her because I don't think I have the heart."

She held up her glass of wine to ask Noah if he wanted one. He nodded searching his memory for the conversation that Emily was referring to. She refilled her wine glass and handed it to him to drink before opening her dishwasher to pull a glass out to wash for herself.

"She wanted me to go to lunch with her and Selene, but the shop was so full today that there was no chance of leaving. Even with your cousin, Kayleigh, helping it took everything I had to keep up today."

"Kayleigh?"

Emily returned to him with her new glass of wine leaning over to touch his forehead with the back of her hand. "Are you feeling okay? You seem a little out of it tonight."

"It was a long day." He captured her wrist and pressed a kiss to the palm of her hand. "Start again from the beginning and I'll try to keep up."

She laughed putting her wine down beside his and hiking her pajamas up her thighs so that she could straddle him in the chair. His breath left his lungs in a long woosh while she threaded her fingers through his hair trailing her fingertips up and down the back of his neck. "I had an extremely busy day today. I sold more candles in a single day in the store than I sold last month online."

Noah hugged her. "Congratulations. I knew your store would do well. I should have taken you to dinner tonight to celebrate. You were probably exhausted and hungry after work."

She placed a series of teasing kisses on his lips. "Two good reasons why I didn't want to go out with you tonight. Hangry Emily is even less fun than morning Emily." She laughed holding him close. "And not to ruin the mood that I am hoping to create, but your mom brought over enough food to feed six people. Is your whole family obsessed with feeding people?"

He caressed her face tucking her long hair behind her ears as the realization of what she was talking about finally dawned on him. "Mom brought you lunch, then bullied you into coming to Thanksgiving, that's why you think I'm here? To apologize again?"

Emily unbuttoned his shirt and slid it off his shoulders. "Oh, I know why you're here. I recognize a booty call when I see one. Besides, you already apologized for Thanksgiving on the phone." She bent down to take one of his nipples into her mouth and then the other. His hands moved under her nightgown to cup her bare backside.

"A booty call?" Noah set her back from him trapping her hands behind her back with one hand. "I do not make booty calls."

She scooted forward and nipped his shoulder. "Really? That's too bad. I thought you were here to prove to me you were worth the effort?"

She wriggled her wrists and he let go watching as she grabbed the hem of her gown lifting it over her head. She sat completely naked on his lap. Her eyes were smoky with a little playfulness and a lot of desire.

"You look a little overdressed for what I have in mind."

He stood swinging her up into his arms. The movement tipped over the chair and made Emily laugh wickedly. She wrapped her arms around him and allowed him to carry her to bed. He sat her down in the middle of the quilt watching her move back toward the pillows so that she could lay back with her thighs spread in blatant invitation. He unbuttoned his pants sliding both the jeans and his underwear over his hips. She watched him hungrily as he crawled up the bed pressing kisses from her ankles to the juncture of her thighs stopping to dip his tongue into her folds.

She tasted like fire. Noah wrapped his arms through the crook of her knees and pinned her legs firmly apart. He feasted between her legs until Emily's breaths were coming in ragged pants and he was sure she was wet. The want to be gentle with her warred with his need to take her roughly cementing the physical bond between them. He wanted her to crave him as he did her. When she screamed her pleasure, he lapped the juices of her completion from her folds and moved up until he could rub the tip of his hardened cock against the opening of her body. He kissed her deeply loving the way she moved against him.

"I need a condom."

"Bedside table. Top drawer."

He gave her an impish look. "Be sure, now. If you say yes, this time, I'm going to be very hard to get rid of tonight."

She laughed struggling out from under him to get the condom herself. She pushed him onto his back and rolled the condom into place. She mounted him again positioning herself on top of him and then sat down on his length. Her core sheathed him so tight he thought he might explode then and there.

She trapped his hands above his head. "Who says I want rid of you?"

She rose and sank down on him again. He let her take control reveling in her undulating movements and the flex of muscles in her thighs as she slid up and down his length. He wanted to let her set the pace for her pleasure but the sight of her breasts and hips gently swaying and the feel of her long golden hair against his thighs was more than he could take.

He rolled her underneath him and pushed quickly forward holding her hips so that she now had to take him at his pace. She murmured in pleasure wrapping her legs around him to keep him firmly inside her. He moved again watching her face to learn her pleasures. She urged him forward harder and faster until he was almost locked in the heaven of her arms. Clutching him close she climaxed hard enough to bring him over the edge with her. He lay panting on top of her for a moment trying to remember not to crush her. She kissed his shoulder running her fingers lightly up and down his back.

When their breathing quieted, he rolled to his side so that he could see her. He brushed her rumpled hair away from her face and gently touched her smiling lips. Goosebumps appeared all over her pale skin as the heat of their passion subsided. She stretched luxuriously and then got off the bed to pull back the blankets. Noah followed her throwing away the condom and feeling suddenly awkward. He wanted to stay with her, but he was aware that this was her space to make rules. She slid naked under the covers and began to get comfortable. When she noticed his hesitation, she tilted her head for a moment. "Are you done with me, caveman?"

He smiled. "Not even a little bit."

She held the blankets open. "Come on, then."

Emily was sipping coffee sitting in the chair that she'd seduced him in when Noah joined her from the shower. The undrunk glasses of red wine sat in front of her removing any real excuse for her wanton behavior last night. Noah brought out a primal side to her lovemaking that she hadn't known existed. She'd snuck out of bed and showered ahead of him in hopes of being prepared for the conversation she needed to have.

He said that he was going to be hard to get rid of, and she didn't want him gone, but between her jumping on top of him and his mom arranging play dates, the man was practically being herded into a serious relationship. She'd asked him last night whether he wanted her to come with him to his family Thanksgiving but hadn't really given him an opportunity to answer. Nope. Instead, she'd taken him to bed and made love to him until they both fell into an exhausted slumber.

He padded across her kitchen in his bare feet as if this was second nature to him. Dressed only in his work pants, she watched the play of muscles across his back and chest remembering the feel of them on her breasts and under her hands. She took a drink knowing that she would take him to bed again and again if he'd let her. The man was made for sex. He spotted the coffee cup she left for him and poured a half cup of coffee before filling the rest of the glass with milk. She made a face.

"Good morning to you too." He kissed the top of her head sitting down in the chair opposite her.

"There is enough coffee to have a whole cup."

His smile was roguish as he gazed at her over the cooled candles on the table. "That coffee smells strong enough to take the enamel off my teeth. Besides, it looks like you could use another cup before you explain to me why you held me all night and then snuck out of bed this morning."

Her jaw dropped open. "I did not sneak out."

"Are you sure?" He looked at her over the rim of his

coffee cup and took a drink. "Sure looked like sneaking to me."

"You were asleep."

"The minute you moved out of my arms, I was awake." He put his elbows on the table. "You don't have to explain anything to me. There is a huge amount of physical attraction between us, but if I'm moving too fast for you, all you need to do is say so."

Emily set her coffee down on the table. "Moving too fast? I've made the first move every time."

"Believe me, if it had been up to me alone, we would have burned enchiladas. Right now, I would like nothing better than to peel your clothes off and make love to you until you don't have the strength to move away from me, but not if you feel like you have to sneak out afterward."

Emily felt her face flame with heat, not all of it was embarrassment. "We've seen a lot of each other recently. With your mom inviting me to Thanksgiving and everything, I felt like you were being rushed."

He arched a brow taking an unnecessarily long sip of coffee. "So, sneaking out of bed is because you don't want to rush me, not because I'm rushing you?"

"I wasn't sneaking," Emily mumbled into her cup.

"Good, because I'm willing to just skip to the part of our relationship where we have the same house and last name, but I'm politely waiting for you to catch up."

She choked on her coffee looking at him in horror.

Noah laughed. "See. That's what I thought. I am way more committed to this than you are." He got up to pat her playfully on the back before gathering his shirt off the kitchen floor. "Can I see you tonight?"

Her brain and her tongue refused to work together because they were stuck on separate parts of what Noah had just said. Nodding seemed to be the only response she could manage. He looked at his watch.

"You'd better hurry. I'm already late for work but you still have a chance of getting there before April does."

He headed off with his coffee to put on his shoes whistling 'Have Yourself a Merry Little Christmas.'

18

When in doubt about your relationship with an Enlightened being, invite them to eat with you. If you are friends they will be delighted, and if you are not, they will remember that you once fed them when they were hungry. It goes a long way toward making a good relationship. --Valerie Black, *Everyday Solutions to Magic Problems*

Noah pulled up in front of his childhood home with Emily beside him feeling like Yule had come early for him. The two-story traditional New England home was the social heart of the pack and the pride of his mother's heart. She had declared it as a sanctuary inside the sanctuary. A space where the Enlightened could go to work out their problems with themselves and with one another, where transformation was encouraged but fighting was forbidden.

He ran his fingers over the shell of Emily's ear taking the moment in as fully as he could. Emily knew, in a human way, that this dinner formalized their bond, but she wasn't aware of how much. To werewolves, sharing food was a declaration of alliance. Although his mom was determined to get him and his sister married, she was a stickler for protocol. Her invitation to Emily to eat with them without his request was an honor for both.

For all her bravado, his life-mate was now looking out of the window of his truck at his childhood home as if it were full of hungry bears. He brushed his hands through her thick hair a little more amused than he probably should have been. "Are you going to be okay, Goldilocks?"

"How did your mom talk us into this? What is this, like our tenth date?"

Noah caressed her thigh and looked thoughtful. "I suppose it depends on whether we're counting overnight dates as one or two dates."

"You're not funny. Do I look as nervous as I feel?"

"You look beautiful."

She rolled her eyes and pulled the door handle. "I'll take that as a yes, then."

He came around the truck to help her gather up the wine, a casserole dish full of sweet potato pie, Devilled eggs in a dish that was specifically designed to hold them, chips, dip, and what Emily said was her Thanksgiving specialty, Bourbon pecan pie. It smelled delicious. He told her that this was unnecessary, but Emily had informed him tartly that a Southern woman did not show up to a family dinner without food.

Again, he knew he should have tried harder to dissuade her, but he hadn't. His mother would interpret Emily's offering as a contribution to the hunt; an offer to feed the larger family as part of her own. Because the invitation had come from the Alpha, when his mom accepted the food, Emily would officially be considered part of the Hernandez pack by her own merit rather than Noah's. He couldn't wait to see his mother's face.

Every window of the house was decorated with a wreath and a big red bow. The covered front porch had an arrangement of holly, ivy, and enough colored baubles to make the Macy's Day Parade look like amateurs. Noah's family celebrated both Yule and Christmas with equal fervor. Around the bows and ribbons, Noah could spot the silver and gold pentacles hanging prominently on tree and wreath branches. His father Malachi's influence. Malachi was Wild Fey and like all the Fair Folk, he honored the turn of the Wheel of the Year.

Emily followed his gaze and then gasped. "Those are beautiful. My grandmother would love those."

"My dad makes them. Tell him you like them and he'll make you a dozen before you can say thank you."

Noah led her up the steps trying to ease the anxiety that was written all over her face. Before he opened the door, he leaned over and gave her a kiss. "This is going to be the worst date in history. I'm apologizing in advance. If you get uncomfortable or my family starts to be a headache, say the word and we are out of here."

She moved closer to him with a sexy smile. "That's a hefty promise."

"Next date, if you're still talking to me after this one, will be somewhere normal, public, and romantic."

"I don't think I believe you," Emily said looking up at

the large oak door. "Lucky for you, I am still trying to make up for the wood stacking date."

"Thank God," he chuckled and led her through the front door. They were immediately surrounded by family members. He handed dishes to Selene over the top of Emily's head. "Sorry, we're late."

His mother's nostrils flared as she took pecan pie from Selene's hands looking first at Noah and then at Emily. "Are these for us?"

He felt Emily tremble and then watched her square her shoulders.

"Bourbon pecan pie. It's homemade. I wasn't sure what to bring. There's sweet potato pie if you don't like bourbon or Devilled eggs if you don't like pie."

Angela waved off her apology overcome with emotion. "I like all three. They're perfect. Come inside."

Selene gave Noah a knowing smile. "Dad's outside, he wants you to look at his car. Emily, want to come hang with the women folk in the kitchen?"

He put his hands over Emily's ears. "I'm warning you guys, take it easy on her. She's new."

Emily laughed pulling his hands away and was swept into the kitchen by Selene and Angela. One hugged her and the other put the food they'd brought onto the counter and handed her a glass of wine. Selene began cutting up stuff for a salad while Angela opened the chips and put the dip in bowls.

It was obvious from the ease they worked together

that they had cooked together many times before. Emily offered to help and was pleasantly surprised to be handed a cloth to dry the silverware from the dishwasher. Angela barely waited for the kitchen door to close before she pounced.

"So, Emily, are you coming here for Christmas or will you and Noah go to your mother's?"

Emily choked on the wine she was sipping, and Selene patted her on the back.

"Subtle, Mom, real subtle. You don't have to answer her."

Angela nodded sprinkling sesame seeds onto the salad like a pro. "I just want to make sure I have the things Emily likes for Christmas. Anyway, I'm a hundred percent proven matchmaker. It runs in our family. I knew you were coming and here you are. I'll have to tell Mildred her timing was off, but I'm sure not by much."

"Don't let her suck you in. She doesn't have second sight; neither does Mildred. They are just busy bodies."

Angela sent her daughter a long-suffering look. "Not everyone has your aversion to happiness."

Emily sat her wine down to dry silverware trying desperately not to laugh. "How did you know I was coming?"

Angela took a long sip of cola from her wine glass. "I was setting the table the week before you arrived. I put down extra place settings before I even knew you were in town. I sat one next to Noah and one next to Selene. Now you're here." She gave Selene a pointed glance.

Selene rolled her eyes. "That just proves you can't count, not that you can predict the future."

"I'm right, you'll see." Angela headed toward the stove.

Selene ignored her pouring herself another glass of wine. "On a different note. How is Kayleigh working out? Her Mom said that every other word out of her mouth is Emily."

"She's perfect. Quick, polite, and detail-oriented. Michael loves her and April says that she's a natural salesman." Emily cast a worried look toward Angela. "I know she's on loan from the restaurant, but I wondered if you'd mind me offering her a part-time position."

Angela came back into the kitchen with a rueful grin. "I was going to offer to pay you to keep her. She's my sister's daughter and I love her dearly-"

"But she's a menace in the restaurant," Selene finished with a laugh. "I'm starting to think it was active sabotage. She's on conditional employment with Mom. She needs to maintain a B average at school in order to work."

Emily opened her mouth to reply but Sebastian popped his head in. "Dad wants to know if you want a fire. Hi Emily. Can Marcel eat with us?"

Angela crossed her arms over her chest. "Is Marcel standing outside the door waiting for my answer?"

Another boy about the same age as Sebastian poked his head into the kitchen. He was smaller than Sebastian by quite a bit with sandy-colored hair. He also had two different colored eyes, one brown and one blue.

"Hello Mrs. H."

"Hello Marcel," Angela said turning to strategically place cherry tomatoes on the salad. "Why aren't you eating dinner with your family?"

Marcel put his hands in his pockets and scuffed his

feet against the ground. "Uh, me and Sebastian ate with them at my house earlier."

Angela shook her head. "You guys are bottomless pits. Yes, you can eat with us but you both clear the table when we're done. Yes, tell your Dad I would like to have a fire, and then please let the table out so we can all fit."

Selene whispered into Emily's ear, "They are only getting away with this because you're here."

Angela handed them plates and cutlery. "Get napkins out of the laundry room. Selene, can you get the bread rolls out before they burn? Emily, will you see if Noah and Malachi want wine or soda with dinner?"

Selene winked. "Whatever Noah's answer is, say wine. Then we can have a sleepover."

Emily walked into the hall trying to decide what direction Noah and Malachi might be in. The inside of the house was larger than all the apartments Emily had ever lived in combined. Stairs and hallways popped out and disappeared at every turn. The furnishings were a mixture of well-preserved and well-used pieces. Like Noah's house, each surface had an arrangement of stones, plants, decorations, and figurines.

She came around the corner of what appeared to be an actual study and found a wall dedicated to clusters of family photos. The center was obviously Noah's immediate family and judging by the clusters outside, one of which contained Kayleigh and Marcel, was his extended family. The family extended from floor to ceiling on the most beautiful tree she'd ever seen painted. She drew her hands slowly over the lines amazed. Her mother and her grandmother were the only family Emily had ever known. Deja never lied. When Emily asked about her own father her mom said he wasn't worth keeping track of.

As the clusters of relatives in Noah's family expanded further from the center, the pictures became older and the family resemblance less pronounced until they ended with paintings of stern-faced ladies and gentlemen in top hats and feathers.

"Dinner is in ten minutes," Angela shouted from the kitchen.

Emily shook her head trying to get her thoughts back on track. She felt the brush of a hand on her shoulder. Turning, she found herself face to face with a tall man with a lion's mane of black hair that didn't quite cover his pointed ears. Although he was dressed in jeans and a sweater, his sharp features and clever eyes were so striking that he looked like he should be hanging out with Frodo Baggins somewhere. Emily stared open-mouthed. Noah came around the study corner holding a dirty metal disk.

"You tinkered with it, didn't you? At least read the manual before you start moving things around." He stopped behind the man and followed his gaze. "Great, you found Emily. Dad this is Emily Rollins. Emily, this is my dad, Malachi."

Malachi bowed his head to her and then asked, "An *gcreideann tú sna sióga?*"

The words were both musical and familiar. Like a half-remembered song but Emily couldn't recall where she'd heard them before. Both Malachi and Noah looked at her as if they expected her to answer.

"I'm sorry. I'm not sure what you're asking?"

They both breathed a deep sigh and Malachi shook his head. "It is me who should apologize. For a moment you looked so much like...a friend of mine; I forgot where I was in time." He put his hand out. "It's nice to meet you, Emily."

Meeting the parents of someone you were in a relationship with was, in Emily's opinion, one of the more awkward parts of relationship integration. She took his hand firmly. "Thank you for inviting me." Malachi's grey eyes seemed to take in everything about her, her doubts, fears, joys, and hopes for this relationship and this place. She felt intensely vulnerable, but no sooner had she begun to question her position when she sensed Noah coming to stand closer behind her. Malachi beamed at them. "Go *maire sibh bhur saol nua.*"

Noah leaned down to whisper in her ear, "Now he's showing off. He speaks several languages and never lets anyone forget it."

Emily nodded. "Nor should he. What does it mean?"

Malachi arched a brow in such a silly and playful way that Emily couldn't help but grin back. "First, I asked if you believe in Fairies."

Emily pretended to think about it. "Well, I'm not sure about the Loch Ness Monster, but I definitely believe in fairies."

Malachi nodded solemnly. "A sensible choice."

"What else did you say?"

Noah wrapped an arm around her. "He said, 'May you enjoy your new life.'"

"Thank you. I am enjoying it so far. Angela wants to know if you guys want wine or soda with dinner."

"I'm driving, so soda," Noah replied kissing the top of her head.

Malachi looked genuinely upset by this answer. "Stay here for the night. Your bed's big enough for Emily."

Noah shook his head. "We didn't bring any clothes and Emily has to work in the morning."

Malachi turned a pleading look to Emily. "Your clothes are big enough for Emily to sleep in. I'm sure Selene or your mother has something she can wear."

Emily put her hand on Noah's chest to stop him from protesting further. "If you don't mind us leaving early tomorrow, we'd be happy to stay with you."

Malachi yelled toward the kitchen, "Emily and Noah are staying the night."

Angela stuck her head out of the door. "That's great. Does he want wine or soda with dinner?"

Noah rubbed his cheek against Emily's before he moved toward the living room. "Whatever Emily's having. I'll take this back outside and go wash my hands."

There were Santa and turkey-shaped plates, Holly and Evergreen branches scattered around the table, and even little snowman salt and pepper shakers. A Christmas tree covered in stars and moons of every shape and color dominated the wall opposite the fireplace. Noah's Mom didn't just like Christmas decorations, she liked all decorations. Noah added that the cheesier they were the better she liked them. The number of people combined with the large fire crackling in the background made the room almost too cozy. There was no formality to their feast. Fingers dipped into sauces and pieces of food were popped into mouths as dishes went past. What struck Emily was how close everyone was. There was no real bickering or competition.

"So, what's the main dish at your family's Thanksgiving?" Selene asked eyeing up another dinner roll.

"Peking Duck," Emily said watching Noah pull the walnuts out of his sweet potato pie with a frown. "My Mom's not much on traditions but for some reason, she always finds a place that serves Peking Duck on Thanksgiving Day." She leaned forward and picked up the walnuts from Noah's plate and put them on her own. She felt Noah's lips brush across her shoulder in approval. He'd been slowly trying to encourage her to eat from his plate, but she was still reluctant to take something he might want.

Selene watched them with an expression that bordered pain. "You eat out on Thanksgiving Day?"

Emily shrugged used to the reaction. "And Christmas too. Mom says it saves doing the dishes, but I think she avoids cooking whenever possible."

Noah leaned over to whisper in her ear, "That explains your eating habits."

"There is nothing wrong with my eating habits."

Marcel jumped into the conversation, although how

he heard from the other end of the table was beyond Emily. "What's wrong with Emily's eating habits?"

Sebastian answered from around a mouth full of Turkey. "Noah says she eats everything out of a packet."

"Not everything is from a packet," Emily quipped giving Noah a superior look. "Sometimes I use the microwave.

Noah laughed leaning forward again to rub his cheek against hers. "Mom, tell her the microwave doesn't count as cooking."

Selene jumped in. "The microwave totally counts. Personally, I think it's the way forward."

Angela snorted pouring herself another soda. "If you're cooking for one, it's an option but not a healthy one. Not that I would know. I haven't ever cooked for one."

"Mom comes from a big family," Noah said reaching over to eat a piece of stuffing from Emily's plate that she'd pushed aside. "Mom likes cooking. She makes all the menu choices for The Blue Moon."

Angela shrugged with a smile. "Not that you can make many choices. The locals pick their favorites and then won't eat anything else."

Noah and Malachi began to gather the plates from the table and take them back to the kitchen. Emily picked up her plate intending to help but Noah took it deftly from her hands. "You helped put it on the table, we will clear it up."

Malachi avoided asking any questions about Emily while he and Noah did dishes but there was no mistaking the pleased look that his parents shared with him. Marcel and Sebastian retreated upstairs after cleaning up to play computer games while the adults put the world to rights through friendly debates around the fire.

Noah had squeezed into his favorite two-person lounge chair with Emily despite her protests that they would not both fit. He managed to settle her between his legs so that she could back against his chest. She'd cast a questioning look between him and sat stiffly in his arms as if she expected to be asked to leave at any moment. Noah couldn't imagine what was making her uncomfortable, in his own house, they sat together all the time.

That sitting together here rather than at home was a declaration of intimacy that meant something different in her world than it did in his didn't sit well with him. For him, it was just soothing to have her close, to be able to stroke her arm or thread his fingers through hers. He was slowly making progress in acclimating her to his physical presence. They ate together and slept together more often than they didn't, but she maintained an emotional distance that he hadn't been able to break through.

Granted, for a human relationship she was moving at an incredible speed, but it felt glacial to Noah. He had secretly hoped that eating with his family would reassure her that he wanted to be a permanent part of her life and she would give up that last barrier between them, but now he saw just how much further he had to go. More than once he found himself looking down at her while she discussed plans for her shop, and some personal discoveries she'd made about living in Maine, wondering how he could really earn her trust.

Conscious that she had to work in the morning, he made their excuses early and led her upstairs. His heart ached as she followed him quietly like a shadow. After they entered his bedroom, he reached behind her to push the door closed and took the opportunity to capture her mouth for a kiss. A blind man could read her body language. Hesitant, shy, closed, nothing at all like her normally fiery self. "What's the matter?"

"Your parents must think I'm some kind of floozy."

Noah stepped back trying to gauge if she was kidding but her disappointed expression was heart-breaking. "You're wonderful. They love you. Why in the world would you think that?"

Emily shrugged looking around his bedroom. "They didn't offer me a separate room. We haven't been seeing each other that long."

She tried to move away from him, and Noah gave her some space. His parents wouldn't have thought to offer her a separate room knowing he wouldn't be comfortable without her. Even if he hadn't told Selene he was serious about her, bringing her here, sharing food at dinner, and holding her after dinner, was as much a declaration of his intentions as an engagement ring would have been. He moved toward her and wrapped his arms around her trying to understand what she was asking for.

"Do you want your own room? They didn't offer because they know we sleep together normally."

"No, I don't want my own room." She still didn't look comfortable. "We're not quiet when we have sex, and I am not facing your parents over breakfast after…" She trailed off causing him to laugh. "They'll hear us."

"I don't know about you, but I ate too much to even think about sex."

He grabbed the hem of Emily's shirt and pulled it over her head tossing it dramatically to the side. Werewolves learned discretion at an early age because of their very developed sense of hearing. Continuing to strip her he considered his options. He hadn't taken into account that Emily had a conservative side, or he would have never agreed to stay the night here.

Moving toward his dresser, he stripped off the remainder of his clothes shaking his hips dramatically and batting his eyes over his shoulder. "Well, if you are sure I can't tempt you. I guess I'll have to wait until we are alone."

Emily snickered at his clumsy moves.

He threw her a T-shirt and laid two pairs of PJ pants on the end of the bed. "In case you need the bathroom." He slid naked beneath the sheets and pulled her under the covers and against him. "Just so we're clear. I'm glad you're here. My parents are glad you're here. My sister might trade me for you if it comes down to it."

He felt Emily laugh.

"Thank you for bringing me."

Her hands drifted gently across his arms ceasing their movements when her breath began to steady. Noah squeezed her close and drifted off to sleep.

19

*For newly awakened witches it is important to give your belief system time to adjust to being Enlightened. Ask yourself important questions. Does any part of this information intimidate me? If so, why am I frightened? What reasonable steps can I take to make it less frightening? In most cases, you will find a way to resolve what you once knew to be true with the new information. --*Phoebe Pearce, *Witchcraft for the Newly Awakened*

Emily was leaning against Noah's chest reading over an invoice list while he dozed on the couch. The house smelled of cinnamon and cloves and Christmas music played from her streaming device in the corner. There were a dozen things he needed to do at home, but he was unwilling to go without Emily, and she was emphatic about needing to balance her books here in her home. It amused Noah that although her home often looked like it had been rummaged by goblins, her accounts and her store were immaculate.

The number of nights they slept apart was now less than the nights they slept together. Soon it would no longer be a question of if they stayed the night together, only a question of where, and for that he was grateful. The word Love hovered around their relationship like a moth bouncing frantically off a lighted window, but the best Noah could get Emily to admit was that she wanted him close.

The separation for both was getting harder which was why she was leaning against him with her computer in her lap rather than at the table which would have been more practical. When she committed to something, she gave a hundred percent. When she finally committed to him, there would be no need for the words she was avoiding now. He stroked his fingers gently down her arm feeling a smile tug his lips. He couldn't wait for the moment when he could freely tell her he loved her.

The cases of the Unguided just kept getting worse and worse. Noah had rushed out of Emily's house last night to help the Recovery Unit calm a young man hiding from his lover in the kitchen of an all-night restaurant. He'd responded to Emily's questions about what he was doing with as much honesty as he could. He hated keeping things from her. His role at Dark Wolf helped to make his increasingly frequent absences plausible but he could feel her frustration when he skirted around an explanation.

On the radio, reports of unusual sightings were coming in with enough frequency to be termed "Twilight Zone Moments." Vlogs, blogs, and several social media sites were tracking the Enlightened better than any police force could. Like Katrin's affirmation of Emily's sightings here in town, the Twilight Zone confessions had stirred several other confirmations from the Unenlightened.

The National Recovery Unit was tracking hotspots in an effort to get to the Unguided before they could be swallowed by the mental health care system, but the strain on the Enlightened was visible. When the shrill ringing of the phone shattered their bonding time for the third night running, Noah reached over to Emily to inform whoever was calling that they would have to take care of the situation without him. He pulled Emily close for a moment and she looked at him with compassion. As he put the phone to his ear, he realized it was Emily's phone ringing, not his. She sat up and looked at the screen.

"It's April." She put the phone to her ear. "Hello?"

"Emily? I am so sorry. I didn't know who else to call."

Both April and her son were crying. "What's wrong?"

"I-I need you to come over. Something happened. Something's wrong with me."

"Do you need me to call an ambulance?"

"No! Please. I can't explain. Oh God, I don't know how to explain it. Please."

"I'll be right there. Where do you live?"

"The end of Easton Street. Number 17."

Noah was already getting their coats. "Tell her we'll be there in twenty minutes. I have a first aid kit in the truck, but the roads are going to be iced over."

"We're on our way." Emily began to throw on whatever clothes she could find.

April panicked. "You can't bring anyone. Just you."

Emily put her hand over the receiver. "She wants me to come alone."

"Her family knows me." Emily hesitated but Noah wasn't about to let her walk into this alone. "If I'm not needed once we get there, I'll make myself scarce."

She nodded but didn't look happy. "Noah will keep out of our way. He's going to drive because of the ice. We are on our way now."

April screamed. "What are you? Get out of my house! Get away from him! Michael!" The line went dead. Emily tried to reconnect the call, but the phone went directly to voice mail. Noah grabbed her hand.

"We've got to go now."

Noah called Dark Wolf first and then the police. In the car, he drove along dark forest roads at a speed that made the tree line blend into one blurry dark mass that all at once felt threatening. Emily tried, again and again, to reconnect the call with no success. They pulled up in front of a small white ranch-style house and slid to a stop. The house was dark, and the street was quiet, but April's front door was hanging off the hinges as if it had been kicked down. Emily heard Noah bark at her to wait for him, but she'd already jumped out of the car.

The door lay half-hinged in a mass of twisted metal and wood. She heard Michael crying from somewhere in the house and pushed what was left of the door open to step inside. Without warning Noah's arms came around her like a vice. He held her still growling in her ear, "Be quiet. If you can't follow my orders, then I will lock you in the car. Do you understand?" When she didn't respond he gave her a little shake. "Do you understand?"

Emily answered through clenched teeth. "Yes."

Immediately he let go of her and moved cautiously into the living room. One of Emily's candle's flickered in the background casting long shadows over the friendly pale-yellow walls of the house. The warmth from the heating system poured out the front door.

"Call for her."

"April? It's Emily. Can you hear me?" The crying immediately stopped leaving behind a profound silence.

Noah whispered, "The house has a circular build around the kitchen. We can't let anyone get behind us. Go left, I'll go right. If you see anyone, yell for me and then get the hell out of there." He didn't wait for her to agree but moved off to the right. Emily's heart was pounding as she moved down the quiet hall. She switched the lights on in the first room she came to. It was a child's nursery painted green and filled with tubs of organized toys. The beautiful crib in the corner held a sniffling monster.

It looked up at her with a familiar expression of sadness. Its body was flesh-colored, but its face and limbs were dark grey, almost as if they had been scorched on the ends. Its fingers and toes were garishly long and moved bonelessly like tentacles. Its pointed ragged ears set strangely on the sides of its fuzzy head. It waved its pudgy little arms at Emily and then reached toward the floor. "Mamamama." It began crying but it wasn't a monster's voice, it was Michael's. Emily shook her head to clear the image but all she could see was the monster reaching toward the floor. She followed the motion and spotted April lying face down and motionless beside the crib.

"Noah! I found them. I think April's hurt."

Michael burst into renewed wails. Emily knelt beside April rolling her over gently onto her back. Her eyes were open, and she appeared to be breathing. Noah came instantly looking first at Michael and then April.

"Damn it," he muttered and moved her aside checking that April was breathing and then checking her pulse. He then rolled her to her side in a recovery position gently tilting her head back.

"She's breathing normally. We just need to keep an eye on her until the medical team gets here."

Emily nodded grateful he'd insisted on coming. He stood and walked over to the cradle picking up the monster, checking its limbs, and then settling it against his hip. Emily opened her mouth to warn him, but it was clear he wasn't seeing what she was. She blinked again hoping to clear her vision as she had before, but this Michael was still a monster. Noah pulled out his phone and dialed still looking around the room as if he expected an attack.

"I need a medical recovery unit at 17 Easton Street now. Tell them I need Cicero here to investigate a related break-in."

He looked at Emily shaking his head. "I'm not alone. I'll explain when they get here." He rocked the monster gently bouncing it softly in his arms. "It's okay, little guy. Mommy's okay. We're going to make her all better."

The monster continued to whimper pitifully. Noah

checked over his shoulder to make sure they were alone before kneeling beside them.

"Take Michael and close the door behind me. I'm going to double-check the house and make sure whoever did this isn't still here." He handed her the truck keys. "If I'm not back in 2 minutes, get Michael out of here." He held the baby out to her, but Emily couldn't make herself take him. "Emily, you need to take Michael so I can check the house."

She shook her head. "That's not Michael."

He looked at her sharply. "What do you mean?"

Emily opened her mouth but didn't know what to say. She was going crazy, and she couldn't afford to tell anyone right now. She nodded holding out her arms. He passed the monster to her and started to leave the room. She held it away from her and it began to cry louder.

Noah looked back at her frowning. "I need you to calm him down so that he doesn't upset April."

She looked at the baby again seeing the terror and confusion in his little face. She brought it close to her body cradling it gently and trying not to wince as she felt the tentacle-like finger wrap around her hands and clutch a piece of her hair. She repeated in her head that it was just Michael, the same baby she'd seen on the street, the same one she held and rocked in the store.

Closing her eyes, she listened to his distressed little sounds and made herself calm down and comfort him. When she opened her eyes again, Michael's perfect little face looked up at her but there was something different in his wise little gaze. A shadow that she felt was reflected in her own face. They no longer trusted one another. What was worse, Emily didn't trust herself. There was no other plausible explanation for Noah not seeing Michael as a monster except that she was losing her grip on sanity. When this was over, she would call her mother and go get some help. She just had to keep herself together until then.

It seemed like an eternity before Noah came back.

"There's no one here now. I'll have Cicero check the house perimeter later". He knelt and put the back of his hand to April's head. "Come on April. Don't shut down. You're safe now. You can do this. Come back to us."

She didn't move. Just lay sightless on her side like a doll. Noah came to Emily scooping Michael out of her arms with a concerned look. "When we're out of this, we are going to talk about what happened and what you saw tonight. I want the truth."

The ambulance arrived not even three minutes later. They placed April on a stretcher talking to Noah in low voices. A slight man in a dark-colored uniform with a silver wolf's head that Emily recognized as Dark Wolf's followed closely. There was no question in anyone's mind that Noah was in charge. The man took Michael from Noah cradling the baby against his shoulder. "I'll take him to Nick, Sir. I'll let him know what happened."

Emily watched Michael begin to cry again and scramble away, his features moving like a slow camera shutter between monster and baby. He reached toward Emily crying, "*Me-me-me-me.*"

She took an involuntary step back from him, shook her head, and then walked forward to collect him. The man in the uniform watched her for a moment bouncing

Michael softly and giving Emily a look that could only be described as disgust. "Let's go, little man. You don't need her." He took Michael without a backward glance.

🦪

Noah went back to the living room to begin his investigation. Although the door was torn open, nothing else in the house appeared to be out of place. One of Emily's candles flickered on the television stand sending strange shadows around the unlit room. The scent of wild magic was all over the house, but Noah needed time to separate the scents of Nick and Michael from the ones of the intruder. Someone had broken into April's home to force her through the Veil. He would not allow this kind of attack to go unpunished.

Emily stood physically beside him, but he could feel her putting distance between them. Although she accepted him as her lover, she didn't view them as a team. Had he not been with her tonight, she would have come into this house alone. The thought that she might have put herself in danger made him angry and edgy. That she'd seen Michael as he really was, Noah had no doubt. The expression he'd seen on her face when he'd tried to hand her the baby was one of unguarded revulsion. He wanted to believe that she was one of the Unguided, but her reactions weren't consistent with the other cases.

They drove home in silence. When Noah started to pass Emily's house and take her back to his, she stopped him. "Let me out here. I have some things I need to take care of. I'm going to call the hospital to see what I can do for April."

Noah parked the truck in her drive. He needed to get back to April's house before the trail went cold. "There's no need. Nick will take care of it. We've already contacted him. April's going directly into treatment so you can check on her tomorrow. I'll go back now and make sure the police have everything."

Emily glared at him. "I wasn't asking your permission I was telling you what I'm going to do. We should have waited at the house for the police."

"You're tired, and it's not safe. I've got some investigation to do, and I need you safe so I can concentrate."

"Investigation? You aren't the police, and you don't know any more than I do."

Noah gripped his steering wheel. "April is a Dark Wolf client."

Emily opened the door and got out of the truck. "Bullshit. April could barely afford milk, much less a personal security system. What is going on here, Noah? I saw your face when you saw April. You weren't surprised. You knew exactly what was happening to her."

"You tell me what was going on back there! You've seen Michael a dozen times a day since April started working for you, and suddenly you won't hold him so that I can care for her? Why?"

She flinched. "I panicked."

"Now, who is bullshitting?" Noah snarled, leaning across the seat. "I saw your expression. I know you-"

Emily held up her hand, cutting him off. "You don't know anything about me."

Noah flinched as if she'd struck him. "Maybe you're right. But that isn't because I'm not trying. I need to get back to the house. When you're ready to start talking to me, give me a call."

Emily's eyes narrowed. "Ditto." She slammed the door and walked away.

When Noah returned to April's house, he noted two cars that hadn't been there before. He mounted the porch scenting blood and violence. When he came through the open door into April's living room, he saw Cicero holding Nick Wilde away from James. Goblins, even Hobgoblins like Nick, were dangerous and unpredictable when they were angry. James was leaning against the far wall with his arms crossed over his chest where deep furrows leaked blood.

"What's going on here?"

Nick hissed a high-pitched hollow sound that made the hair on Noah's neck stand up. "He broke in and forced my April through the Veil. As Wild Fey, I claim the right of retribution."

"To the Unenlightened, I am very attractive," James replied to Noah rather than answering Nick. "She invited me in."

"Is that how you got close to Shawna?" Cicero asked softly.

James stiffened. "I don't know anyone called Shawna. I came here to talk to April. She smiled, opened the door, and invited me to sit and speak to her. She brought one of the candles she sells out from the kitchen and lit it while we talked of her work. Then she turned around and just started screaming for help."

Noah's gaze landed on the large green candle in the corner.

Nick snarled. "You say nothing happened and yet she came through the Veil with only you present."

"It was the candle-"

"Liar! Your words are worthless." Noah winced at the force of Nick's insult. "She lights those candles every day at work and has never had a problem. You broke the door down-"

"I didn't touch her. I came to question her on a different matter. She started screaming for help. I broke the door to get away from her. I pulled the lock through the door frame, but I was leaving, not breaking in."

It was Cicero's turn to look unconvinced. "Where did you go? You weren't here when I arrived."

Nick snarled again, his eyes turning red. "Because he is a liar."

James sighed. "I was here but I didn't make myself known. Noah told me plainly to stay away from his life-mate. When I saw she was with him, I got out of the way."

Noah turned to Cicero for confirmation.

Cicero shook his head. "I didn't sense him when I was here the first time, but I also wasn't looking for him. When I came back, he and Nick were already fighting."

"I have permission to be in this territory. The Goblin attacked me before I had any opportunity to explain. If your warlock hadn't arrived-"

"I'm a necromancer. Not a warlock, not a sorcerer, not a magician. A necromancer."

"I couldn't care less what you choose to call yourself, magic thief," James said waving a hand at Cicero to silence him. "The real Enlightened are talking to one another."

Prejudice against witches and necromancers was common in the older Enlightened. Witches didn't fully fall into either the Enlightened or the Unenlightened category which meant that they were an uncomfortable fit in both worlds. Necromancers usually started out as witches, depending on their power, their awakenings were typically self-inflicted. There were also witches with dark hearts who trapped and drained demons to gain more power. Cicero had sought sanctuary here after he'd discovered the coven he worked with was draining power from other Enlightened but not before he'd had a drink of the power. As paths went, Cicero was still fighting the temptation.

The narrowing of his eyes was all the warning Noah got before Cicero simply released Nick Wilde. Had Noah been able to move at light speed, he could not have prevented Nick's attack. Rather than physically striking again, Nick tapped his enormously elongated fingers on the ground in a complex pattern. Werewolves were unaffected by curses, but Cicero put his hands over his ears so that he couldn't absorb the sound. A small shock wave vibrated up from the ground engulfing James in sharp golden light. James looked at the light with such an expression of unrestrained desire and longing that Noah felt like an intruder for watching. James put his hand out to touch what only he could see.

"January?"

The whisper was a lover's call. Then the light disappeared, and James folded in on himself like a broken toy. He crouched there without moving, almost without breathing.

Nick's eyes narrowed and then he began to giggle. "Already cursed, huh, Word Breaker? Did you think nothing could be worse than a broken heart?"

Noah touched Nick gently on the shoulder. "Cursing is forbidden in the Sanctuary. The penalty is banishment. You suggested that law yourself."

Nick rubbed his hands together with glee. "I didn't curse him. I gave him a glimpse of having his one true desire and then I took it away. May he get the same help achieving his dreams that he gave my daughter!" Nick huffed in anger and then scuffed both his feet against the floor and marched out the door.

Noah was stunned. He had wondered what January would have been able to promise to James to get a guarantee to protect Phoebe, but he'd been thinking too literally. If James had promised to keep January's life-mate safe, believing the whole time that it was himself he would be protecting, then the exchange made sense.

Because of his promise James had sworn to January to protect the one woman who stood in the way of his own happiness. Failing to protect her or killing her himself would mean failing in his word to January. If James could keep her human or prove that she was responsible for the unsanctioned awakenings, he could wait for time or justice to take its course and January would eventually seek another companion. James quivered on the floor his face covered in blood-red tears, his eyes fixed on a vision only he could see.

Cicero met Noah's eyes over the demon's body with a shrug. "I'm sorry."

Noah bared his teeth. "I gave James permission to be here and with that permission, my protection."

Cicero blinked surprised. "I didn't know—"

"And you did it anyway," Noah interrupted. "Your pride was worth more than your promise to me to protect. You will support James until he makes his recovery. After that, you will inform him that his welcome in this territory has been rescinded and escort him to his Recovery Center for questioning about Shawna's death. Inform him that I do not welcome liars."

Cicero nodded but didn't respond. Instead, he knelt to put his hands on James to teleport out.

"Cicero?"

He paused but didn't meet Noah's eyes this time.

"The next time you choose retribution over loyalty in my territory, it will be the last time you are welcome here. Do we understand each other?"

"I understand."

Noah's phone rang as Cicero disappeared. "It's not a good time, Selene."

"Noah? I'm at the Augusta Recovery Center. Joseph just brought Katrin in."

20

The shadow-self exists within every witch. It is a dark place where we store our taboo thoughts, desires, dark feelings, and personality traits we don't want others to see. In order to be balanced, that shadow-self must be acknowledged not rejected. She is a working part of you that keeps your feet on the good path. honor her work but do not indulge her. --Valerie Black, *Everyday Solutions to Magic Problems*

Even when Noah saw Joseph and Katrin in the Recovery Center, he couldn't believe it. The couple were sitting across from each other at a small table playing cards. Although Joseph was wearing his black security uniform, he'd traded his combat boots for tennis shoes. Noah also noted that Katrin had a small travel bag sitting beside her bed. She looked highly amused; Joseph looked like he was on the verge of killing someone.

"You're cheating," Joseph said laying a card down.

Katrin tilted her head and pursed her lips in an expression of pure mocking. "Does your werewolf superpowers tell you that?"

He sighed. "They're not superpowers."

She picked two cards up. "Yeah? Well, when my bones shift around in my body, they don't pop back into place. Also, how am I supposed to believe you? I have no idea what you can and can't do."

Joseph flinched as if she'd kicked him. "I'm sorry."

"You should be."

Noah cleared his throat. Joseph laid down his cards, snatched Katrin's, and jumped to his feet landing in front of her in a blink of an eye. For the first time in their relationship, he let her see the speed he was capable of.

She stared for a moment with her mouth open. "You can move that fast and it took you three days to clean up the garage?"

Joseph didn't answer; instead, he addressed Noah. "I contacted Angela as soon as it happened. She said to come here. It's my fault."

Katrin came around the table to take her husband's hand. Where she'd been playful with Joseph, she regarded Noah with frank wariness. "This," she waved her hand around to encompass the whole room. "Whatever this is. It's my fault. I was trying to surprise him. Lingerie kind of surprise, not catch him doing…whatever it is he does when he goes all bendy and weird."

Noah gave Joseph a hard look. "Did you shift too close to your house?"

Katrin stepped in front of her husband in a blatant

show of protection. "Don't you blame him, Noah Hernandez. You knew too and you didn't think to say anything to me? We've been friends since high school."

"Katrin," Joseph pulled her back catching Noah's eye over her shoulder and giving him a shrug.

"What happened?"

Joseph started, "We were having a date night. Candles, roses, wine. Katrin was-"

Katrin elbowed him in the ribs. "You don't have to tell him that."

"She wasn't supposed to be home. I forgot the wine in the truck. It was stupid. I turned and made a jump from our back porch to the truck bed."

Katrin's face lit with excitement. "Yeah, his legs got all bendy and he leaps like thirty feet back to the truck. No running start. I thought he was being abducted by aliens."

Joseph lovingly stroked Katrin's purple hair. "There's no such thing as aliens."

She glared at him over her shoulder. "Yeah, well this morning there was no such thing as werewolves either."

Joseph continued. "She screamed and everything I knew about guided and unguided left my brain. I had to get to her. I shifted-"

"And I passed out. Some help I'm going to be in a zombie apocalypse."

"There is no such thing-"

Katrin held up her hand. "Sorry, sunshine, nothing you say from now on can be taken at face value."

"Noah, help me explain," Joseph pleaded.

"She came through completely? No shutting down?"

Katrin snapped her fingers in Noah's face. "She is standing right here and would like to be addressed in first person."

"I'm sorry, Katrin. Joseph's penalty for bringing you through the Veil, even accidentally, is very serious."

Joseph nodded. "I would deserve death if I'd done what you say but didn't you hear her? She didn't scream because she saw me phase and jump, she screamed because she thought I was being abducted. Noah, she watched me phase. She was already through the Veil when she saw me."

"She fainted because she saw you shift."

Katrin poked them both in the chest to get their attention. "Again, very rude to talk like I am not standing right here. Yes, I feinted but not for the reason you two doofuses think. I fangirled and I'm not proud. I mean, how long have I been writing werewolf fanfiction? Like, my whole life. Now I am not only married to the sexiest man alive, but he's also a werewolf. It's like finding a unicorn in your bathroom." She pointed at Joseph, "Don't tell me there's no such thing as unicorns."

He smiled at her. "There are unicorns."

"Shut up!" She threw her arms around him and squealed, "Let's go find one right now. When are they letting me out of here, anyway?"

It was Noah's turn to shrug. "It takes most Unguided about a month to come around, if they come around at all. Most of the time, they shut down and don't make it. That's why it's a serious offense."

Katrin hugged Joseph closer to her. "No one's hurt."

"It doesn't matter. I need you both to be completely

honest, have you been in contact with any other Enlightened in the area?"

Katrin looked up at Joseph. "What's an Enlightened? Wait, is your word for muggle Unenlightened? That's harsh."

Noah opened his mouth to respond when he saw a glint of red out of the corner of his eye. The woman that James had been looking for, and that Alex said disappeared, was walking toward the reception desk holding the hand of a vampire. January wore his name well. He looked like a black-and-white photo save for the barest hint of blue in his eyes. It was like watching fire and ice walk down the hall. "Phoebe Pearce?"

The redhead turned to look at him just before her partner swept her behind his back. Power radiated off the man, a threat so primal that Joseph stepped to Noah's side in defense. The vampire bared his teeth and Katrin gasped in delight.

"Get out of my way and stop being ridiculous," Phoebe said coming out from around the vampire like he was an obnoxious puppy. She walked up to Noah without so much as a glance over her shoulder. "I'm sorry, have we met?"

Katrin pushed her way between Joseph and Noah. "Holy shit, that's a vampire. Unicorns, vampires, and werewolves. Today just keeps getting better and better."

Katrin's voice caught the attention of one of the nursing attendants. "Mr. Landis, please take your wife back to her room. Mr. Hernandez, take your conversation outside, you're disturbing my ward."

January didn't greet Noah or the nurse at the station. He simply pulled Phoebe into his arms and vanished.

21

Tea leaf reading, like any form of divination, should be treated as a Rorschach "inkblot" test. Although these divinations might reveal futures, they do so through a series of simple images with complex personal meanings. A butterfly in one cup means transformation but in the cup of a person suffering from Lepidopterophobia it means facing fears. Your job is to clarify, not predict. – Mildred Macclesfield, *The Art of Fortune Telling for Financial Gain*

Noah checked on Emily himself after work. Sleeping away from her for the last two nights had been torture and he wasn't looking forward to a third, but she'd still not indicated she was ready to talk and he wasn't going to force her. He'd assigned a security team to the woods around her house to keep himself from going insane, but hadn't approached himself until now because he knew that he would knock on the door and they both needed space.

He'd spent most of yesterday and today at the Augusta Recovery Center helping Joseph and Katrin put together a defense for Katrin's awakening. His mother would want proof that Katrin's safety had not been compromised by Joseph's indiscretion, but Noah doubted that she would find Joseph guilty, particularly since Katrin herself was determined to defend him.

The difference in their relationship was palpable. Katrin asked questions which Joseph answered without reservation for the first time in their long relationship. They were rediscovering one another and the richness of their love. Their frequent touches, gentle teasing, and not-so-subtle innuendos, heightened Noah's longing to make peace with Emily. He realized by listening to Katrin's resistance to Joseph's guidance that his expectations of his own bonded relationship were unrealistic and unfair.

He didn't know what Emily saw in April's house, but it had frightened her and he had reacted to that fear with force rather than comfort. He had demanded that she follow him like a fellow pack member, but she wasn't a wolf. Only now could he admit to himself that he was hurt rather than angry that she wouldn't confide in him.

He loved her and she desired him, but he hadn't been with her long enough by human standards to have a real place in her life. He only hoped that by apologizing, he could begin to really earn the trust and position in her world that he wanted.

Kiss-Me-Knot was standing outside of Emily's kitchen window when he arrived. "What are you doing here?"

She looked up with a start and took a deep breath.

"Probably the same as you. I'm soaking in the loose magic."

Noah spotted Emily in the back of her kitchen dressed in a long slinky black night shirt with the sleeves pushed up over her elbows. She was making candles. Her concentration was so absolute, and her music so loud, that she didn't even glance toward the windows at the sounds of their voices. She brushed her fingers over the green candles, just over the surfaces, her mouth moving as she worked.

The song in the background sounded as if it were in another language, a lyrical chanting piece that was twisted with longing. To another person, it might have appeared that Emily was casting a spell on the candles, but Noah recognized that she was singing along with the music half a second or so behind the song lyrics. "Cicero assured me she was Unenlightened. Emily's singing not casting."

Kiss-Me-Knot moved a little closer to Noah so that she would not be spotted through the window. "I thought so too but something is going on here. Cicero and I tested her, and both went home believing she was just another dumb human but then I remembered something my grand-mère told me. Don't believe everything you see. I know magic when I feel it and the woods around this cabin are wet with it. I'm not the only one that's noticed." Kiss-Me-Knot looked at Noah seriously. "If I wanted the Enlightened to believe I was just a harmless Unenlightened human, what would I do?"

Noah looked back at Emily bopping around the kitchen to the music adorably clueless about the world around her. "You would ignore anything supernatural."

"Exactly. Cicero and I have a bet going. He says she's an unguided witch bringing herself through the Veil, I say she's some sort of angel. I asked Garland but he says the Recovery Units have all angels listed or recruited. I don't remember angels casting spells, but I remember that they were good at hiding their blessings. I've been keeping a close eye on this one." Kiss-Me-Knot pointed at the candles around Emily. "That looks like an exceptional way of hiding blessings from me."

Noah shook his head. "Impossible. The Recovery Unit trains angels as agents almost from birth. There are so few of them. There's no way she would be able to hide this long."

"Maybe she isn't working alone, or she doesn't know what she's doing, or maybe her blessings aren't meant to make lives better. People like to forget that not all angels are good. That's why the Recovery Unit keeps track of them. Have you tried to look her up on the database yet?"

"Joseph ran her name through the system when she first moved into town. She's not registered on the network. Did Garland know why you were asking?"

"No. Whatever she is, she obviously doesn't want to be found. I didn't tell Garland I was asking about a real woman because I remember a time in the not too distant past when a question like that could get a woman burned at the stake." Kiss-Me-Knot showed Noah her hands twisted with scars of burning that she chose not to heal with her magic. Only her hands were visibly scarred meaning that she'd reached into the fire rather than being burned herself. The burning days were what every Enlightened person feared, but none so much as those who'd already lived through it. Noah shivered. The Enlightened were already uneasy about the Unguided, he didn't need rumors of Emily being a rogue angel on top of it. "Can you keep this information between us?"

Kiss-Me-Knot tucked her arms behind her long white hair and smiled revealing her sharp pointed teeth. "For a price."

"What do you want?"

She pretended to think about it. "I want Cicero's true name."

A necromancer's name, like that of a fairy, would mean that Kiss-Me-Knot would have the power to summon and bind him. Noah didn't know it, and even if he did, he wouldn't give it to her. She was angling for something controversial. "It's not mine to give."

"Fine," she shrugged. "Then I want permission to lead someone where I want them, even if that means their death."

"Don't be ridiculous. I won't give you another's life any more than I would give you Cicero's true name. It isn't mine to give. What do you really want?"

Kiss-Me-Knot looked into the kitchen. "To give you a secret, not keep one for you."

Noah nodded. "Can we trade? A secret for a secret?" Kiss-Me-Knot's eyes turned green with glee. All Fey loved to bargain.

"I name the terms," she said licking her lips. "You keep my secret until you're dead. I keep your secret for the same amount of time." She looked at Emily for a thoughtful moment. "No exceptions."

"Three exceptions," Noah countered.

She scoffed, "That's not keeping a secret at all."

"I can't lie to my life-mate. If she guesses, then I've broken my word."

Kiss-Me-Knot nodded. "Very well, one exception. A confirmation but only if the secret is guessed."

"What's the penalty if I break my word?" Like demons, a Fey bargain needed to be spelled out in minute detail.

Kiss-Me-Knot shook her head. "If you share it then you will promise to make sure that I am dead when I disappear. Don't let me just vanish so that I can spend eternity in some dungeon wrapped in iron. You swear to retrieve either myself or my body, wherever it is."

"You have my word. Your penalty, if you break your word, is that you will protect Emily from any repercussions resulting from that information."

Kiss-Me-Knot pursed her lips. "For how long?"

"Twenty years and a day."

She nodded. "Done." She breathed a soft sigh of relief. "I saw something on the shore the other night. I heard a young girl scream." She showed her hands to Noah again turning them over so that the scars caught the light from Emily's window. "I couldn't save my daughter from burning and I couldn't save the young mortal from being drowned."

Noah's body stilled. "Who killed her? Why was she killed?"

Kiss-Me-Knot gritted her teeth. "I can't say his name. He has forbidden it. But he's looking for a witch. She can only hear the truth. He can't allow her to live."

"He's Unseelie. That's why you can't say his name to me."

"Yes. But that isn't my secret. I'm telling you that because of who you are." She moved closer, her eyes scanning the woods, her voice so low that Noah could barely discern her words even with his wolf hearing. "The Veil isn't a natural barrier between the Enlightened and the Unenlightened. It's a curse and someone has begun to undo it. Water, Air, Earth...," she looked at Emily, "and Fire. That's why there are people coming through. The curse is coming apart. When all the elements surround the Truth Speaker, the curse will be undone. The Veil will fall completely."

"Do you know who they are? How can we find them?"

She shook her head. "I don't have that information to exchange. The Unseelie will do anything to keep The Veil intact. The Witch who hears only the truth is Unguided. The Unseelie are killing the newly awakened witches in order to find her and stop her before she breaks the curse."

"Why?"

Kiss-Me-Knot shrugged. "It's easier to deceive when everyone has only half the information."

Almost as if sensing his distress, Emily came to the kitchen window. Noah grabbed Kiss-Me-Knot pulling her more fully into the shadows. "James. James killed the girl. He's not a demon, he's Unseelie. He's not just interested in Phoebe; he's hunting the newly awakened witches in this territory."

Kiss-Me-Knot's eyes lit with excitement. "Yes, but Phoebe is not the Truth Speaker."

"But it doesn't matter. Her awakening as a witch means that James can kill her only while she's still a witch, but not if she's a vampire. The Unseelie will regard it as a sacrifice. His word for their purpose."

"I've said all that I can tell you." She looked around the forest warily. "A secret for a secret. You take it to your grave."

"That secret involves hundreds of innocent lives. It involves all the Enlightened."

Kiss-Me-Knot nodded her eyes pleading with him to understand something that she couldn't say. "I know. You promised. If you share my secret, you will find me or my body no matter where it is. Keep your word. Do not leave me to the Unseelie."

"I can't fight the entire Unseelie court. I am only one wolf."

"Angelo? Are you out there?" Emily's voice sounded from the porch.

"One exception. Remember. Only if they guess." Kiss-Me-Knot spoke slowly so that he couldn't mistake her double meaning then she disappeared into the forest. Noah waited for Emily to go back inside and then headed toward his mother's house.

Four batches of candles cooling, one ready for blessing, plus a full day of work at the shop, and a bottle of wine had done very little to dull the ache in Emily's heart. She needed to bless these new candles, but she couldn't do it with a mind full of questions. Picking up her phone, she dialed the one person who might be able to tell her what to do.

Her mother picked up the phone almost before the first ring finished. "There's my baby. I was starting to think that being a big business owner might mean you were too busy to chat with your Momma."

"Hey Mom, how's riverboat cooking?"

"Riverboat cooking? Oh, yes. Well, I didn't end up taking that job. I'm in Orange Beach, Alabama."

"What are you doing down there?"

"Trying to decide if I need to drive to Maine and kick someone's backside for upsetting my daughter. What's the matter, honey?"

Emily took a glass of water to her couch and sat down trying to figure out how to ask her question. "You remember when Grandma told me she talked to trees and trees talked back? And I said she was crazy, and you said she just had a different way of looking at the world?"

Deja laughed. "And you told me she could treat that "different" with some good medications. Yeah, I remember. What's she done now?"

"It's not her, Mom. It's me. I think I might need that medication myself."

Silence. "Are trees talking to you, honey?"

The question should have sounded ridiculous, but her mother's tone was serious.

"No. Yes? I don't know. I'm seeing things, Mom. Things that are impossible. And I'm seeing this guy and I think he sees the things I see too, but I can't ask because I like him and I don't want him to think I'm crazy. We had a fight…" Emily felt tears trickling down her face. "And now I can't bless my candles because I can't tell what's real and what isn't, and I can't decide if I want to pack all this up and just go home."

"Ahh, sweetheart. Don't quit. You've come so far and worked so hard for this. If you are seeing funny things, just chalk it up to too much of your grandma's blood, and don't worry about it until I get there. We'll figure out what's going on and if we don't, I'll help you find that medication, or pack your stuff and find you somewhere else to go."

Emily felt better already. "You don't have to come. I know it's a long way."

"Too late now, chick-a-dee. You cried on the phone to your Momma, and you never cry. I got some work to sort out here, but I'll be there in a couple of days. Hang tight. Do one of those crazy meditations my mom is always harping on about and bless your candles with a clear heart. If one of those things comes knocking on your door, just ask what it wants. I love you, baby girl. I'm on my way."

Emily sniffed feeling both loved and silly. "I love you too."

She hung up the phone and went to the guest room where her cooled Enlightenment candles sat all in a row. She pulled a large quilt from over the door and spread it on the floor in the center of the room and brought in the box that held her spell kit. In the middle of the quilt, a large hand-stitched red pentacle reflected the light.

Like she'd done for every batch of candles since she'd started making them, she laid Earth from the soil outside, Air in the form of lit incense, fire in the form of a white candle, and water fetched from the beach earlier in the day at the North, East, South, and West corners around her pentacle. Producing a singing bowl from the box, she slowly coaxed a cleansing note from the bowl allowing it to grow louder and louder until everything in her home appeared to be vibrating at the same frequency. Setting down the bowl, she picked up the incense stick and drew a circle three times clockwise around herself.

"I am safe within myself. I am safe within the circle," she whispered and then began to chant, Earth, Air, Fire, Water until the sound of her voice filled her mind and quieted it. "I bless these candles with Enlightenment. May those who seek their Enlightened life pass unharmed to the next level of consciousness. May they be greeted by love."

As the words left her mouth, she picked up the singing bowl striking four times in honor of each element. A hum of energy and peace went through her as it always had. Magic.

"This spell is done with harm to none. As I will it, so shall it be."

The candle flickered brightly four times and then returned to burning normally letting Emily know that the blessing was complete. She opened the circle putting away her ritual items and allowing her candle to burn out fully. When the naked glowing woman she's seen around her woods came into the room rubbing her hands, Emily stood and smiled at her.

"I'm listening now. What do you need?"

Conversations had been tense and frustrating, but Noah had managed to relay the information that he could to his mother and to Selene without breaking his word to Kiss-Me-Knot. Selene had formally requested information about the number of missing or dead Unguided from The National Recovery Units as part of her research. The results were heartbreaking.

When Frank Carlos realized the number of dead witches was unusually high, he initiated an investigation and additional security for the already vulnerable group. It was all Noah could do for now. With that done, he walked down the main street of Larkshead determined to catch Emily as she left the store and apologize.

January was leaning against a wall in the early evening sun a few stores down from The Ace of Cups. That he could be out in the sunlight at all indicated both his age and his power. Arms folded across his chest; he was watching Emily stock shelves. For a moment they both watched daylight tangle through her disheveled hair. She hulked a box onto her hip stumbling back under the weight and he heard her laugh at something Kayleigh said. Fear slid through every nerve in his body.

"Do you know what it's like to lose a wife?" January's voice was casual as if he'd asked Noah to recommend a coffee place. "I was born in a time where my word was God's and yet nothing I could promise, nothing I could do, could save my first wife." He looked Noah straight in the eye and then looked back at Emily.

"If you touch her-"

"Spare me your threats. If I lose Phoebe, then I will seek the death you promise in the quickest way I can find it. That woman," he indicated to Emily with a flick of his chin, "will never see her death coming. When I have drained the life out of your mate and you hold her for the last time against your body knowing there is no way to get her back, then you may tell me how to proceed with mine. Until then, wolf, stay away from Phoebe."

He pushed away from the wall, but Noah grabbed his shoulder. "Phoebe has a right to know the truth about the choice she's making."

January shrugged Noah's hand off and straightened his sweater. "And have you given your own life-mate that choice? Did you lay all her options out in front of her or only the ones that led back to you?"

"Emily is Unenlightened."

"If you believe that, then she is a more talented liar than I gave her credit for."

Noah clenched his fists. Fighting wasn't the solution. "What are you talking about?"

"Every time an Enlightened person stands in front of her, she freezes for a split second. If you are looking for the first Unguided in your area, she's been right in front of you the whole time. But she doesn't come from this area, does she? She moves around, sells candles world-wide tainted with a single magical suggestion."

"Emily isn't that kind of witch. She would never put another person in danger."

"Wouldn't she? Can you prove it to the National Recovery Unit? To Carl Wedgewood? Phoebe says she read a spell from a book in her Boston shop and popped through the Veil all on her own, but if you checked your life-mate's sales lists, one of the shops listed would be The Craft Shop. The shop that Phoebe works in."

The explanation felt both plausible and ridiculous. "Then how do you know it's not Phoebe who taints and sells the candles?"

"Because it isn't all of the candles that are tainted. Just one type. I bet you already suspect what it's called."

Noah shook his head looking back at Emily. "You're wrong."

"Am I? Then allow James to ask her about her candle sales. For that matter, let him ask her about the weather. If she doesn't react, I'm wrong and she is innocent. If I'm right, your life-mate has method and opportunity. It won't take a Recovery unit long to discover her motives."

"James is no longer welcome in this territory. He's dangerous, especially for Phoebe. You can't trust him."

January's eyes narrowed in interest. "What did you hear about James?"

"That he's Unseelie and that he's in love with you. But you knew that already, didn't you? Did you know that when you asked him to swear to protect Phoebe?"

"I knew he loved me once but was no longer in love with me. That was why he offered to protect Phoebe-"

"He will kill her if he finds her. He is killing unguided witches."

January pushed himself away from the wall and walked away. Noah jogged after him. "I don't want to hurt Phoebe or take her from you. Please. I just want her to talk to my sister, Selene."

January spun around so fast that Noah almost ran straight into him. "Why?"

"Because Selene oversees tracking of the outbreaks in this area. She might be able to prove that neither Phoebe nor Emily is the source."

Noah looked back at Emily hoping he was right.

"But she might also prove that they are the source." January smiled, his fangs gleaming in the dying sunlight. "No one ever believes that they're a villain in the story."

Noah flinched. If he really believed that Emily was innocent, why hadn't he gone to Selene when Kiss-Me-Knot made the same suggestion that James had? Because he was afraid too. If Emily was responsible, even accidentally, the repercussions would be immeasurable.

"Now you see my problem," January said speaking to Noah as if he'd never made a threat. "Phoebe was through the Veil before she read her incantation. Whether or not she's responsible for the Boston outbreak, I won't allow her to be punished for it. While my life-mate lives an uneventful life, you and Emily have nothing to fear from me. I expect the same courtesy. In the meantime, if I were you, I'd have a very serious talk with Emily Rollins." With a courtly bow, January walked away.

Noah waited until he was sure January was gone to cross the street and enter the shop. Kayleigh bounded up to him with a smile.

"Uncle Noah!"

She stopped just short of giving him a hug. She was coming to the age where she was painfully aware of pack rank and her lack thereof. Noah pulled her in for a quick hug. "What are you still doing here?"

"April's sick. Emily said I should go home but I didn't want to leave her alone in the store." Kayleigh's eyes flickered from Noah's to across the street and back again. She'd stayed to protect Emily from the vampire.

He pulled a strand of her blue-green hair. "Thank you for your help. I owe you a debt."

Emily came out of the stock room with her handbag and keys. She stopped when she saw Noah.

"Thank you for your help tonight, Kayleigh. Why don't you head home, and Noah and I will finish locking up? I'll see you tomorrow after school and we'll see if we have enough time for me to teach you to track the online orders."

Noah watched Kayleigh blush with pleasure. "You're not worried that I'll screw it up."

It was a statement, but Emily responded as if it were a question. "You have an amazing eye for detail. I'm hoping you'll be better at it than I am, so I don't have to do it anymore."

Kayleigh laughed and glanced between the two of them. "Umm, you guys have fun." She waved and left the store. He half wished that the ringing of the bell as the door shut would be all that was required to clear the air between them. Emily came across the store holding her coat and handbag to her chest. "How's April?"

"Nick says she's speaking but still not very coherent. The doctors are doing what they can. Nick's keeping Michael until she's better. I called the police and they have been through the house. Nothing was taken. They have put out a couple more patrols in the area just in case." Noah moved toward her, but she took a step back placing the counter between them.

"No one will tell me where she is because I'm not family."

"She's in Augusta, at the hospital Selene works in. We can go visit when Nick says she's feeling up to it." They stared at one another. Noah moved slowly and deliberately toward her. "I'm sorry, Emily. I was scared that you might be in danger, and I didn't handle it well. I ordered you around like you were an employee rather than discussing it with you as my partner. I should have explained myself better."

Emily rubbed her forehead. "I'm sorry too. I can't explain what happened. It's not because I don't want to, it's because I don't know how. When I saw April laying on the floor...I thought she was dead. I guess the kind of work you and Cicero do prepares you for dealing with things like that, but I wasn't thinking straight."

Noah took Emily's coat and bag and set them on the counter. He wrapped her in his arms tucking her gently into the cradle of his body. He felt her breath on his throat and then the soft brush of her lips.

"You've got nothing to be sorry for. Finding her like that was a shock, for both of us. Her family and mine have been friends for a long time."

He held her tightly while he stroked his hands up and down her back. The relief he felt being next to her made his knees weak. The sound of her tears brought tears to his own eyes, but he didn't attempt to quiet her. She brushed her lips against his skin again. His lips found hers of their own accord. He was tired of being alone and of fighting alone.

He kissed the tears from her cheeks his hands moving over her to confirm for himself that she was real and safe, but the movements tore at his confidence. She didn't need him like he needed her. She was becoming everything that made life worth living to him and no matter the possible gain; he would never risk losing her. "Let me come home with you. Please. I need you," he whispered the words against her skin letting his feelings fill his plea with emotions that were too hard to express.

She sniffed shaking back her hair and dashing away her tears. "I need you too. But we should probably go to your place."

"Why?"

Emily's brows came together in a worried frown although her tone was completely casual. "Because my house is a mess and I think it might be haunted."

22

Yule is the winter solstice and the longest night of the year in the Western Hemisphere. It is a night to honor and make peace with the ghosts of your past. You cannot move out of the darkness and into the light of the coming spring if you are carrying too many shadows. —Olivia Goldstein, *Mastering Magic*

Emily was holding mulled wine in one hand and Noah's hand in the other. He was walking patiently beside her while she attempted to taste, touch, and experience everything in the Christmas Market all at once. Up and down the streets, the Christmas vendors were now set up selling everything from hand carved wooden trains to a state-of-the-art Santa tracker. They had eaten mysterious meat on skewers, sausages filled with everything from cheese and red onion to Branston Pickle, some strange Tahini wrap that the vendor swore was from a long-cherished family recipe, and she hadn't even started on the desserts yet.

Her body still wasn't up to the New England winter,

but she was having so much fun, she didn't mind the cold. She'd pulled Noah into a prime spot to watch the Christmas Tree Lighting when Sebastian darted up to them, Kayleigh in tow.

"Emily!" he shouted completely ignoring his brother. He and Kayleigh scuffled while Sebastian took a brightly wrapped package out of her hand and held it out.

Noah took it from Sebastian with a grunt and handed it back to Kayleigh. "It's hers to give, not yours."

Emily cleared her throat and all at once Sebastian's boisterousness turned to bashfulness. "Kayleigh made you an ornament for your tree but she's too self-conscious to give it to you."

Kayleigh looked at Emily with a panicked expression. "You don't have to hang it if you don't like it. You just said at the shop you didn't have any ornaments…." she trailed off and then punched Sebastian in the arm.

He winced but looked unrepentant. "She won't give them to you because she doesn't think they're good enough. This is her eighth attempt."

Kayleigh avoided Emily's gaze and timidly held out her package. Emily handed Noah her mulled wine and opened the present carefully. Inside were three flat round sections of a thick tree branch with bark on the outside that created frames for the little paintings in the middle. One painting was a candle where the detail of the light was so realistic that Emily half expected it to glow. The next was a Robin looking straight ahead on a turquoise background and the last was a blue-grey wolf with bright golden eyes. They were exquisite, better than anything Emily had seen in the market so far.

"They're beautiful, Kayleigh. Thank you. They are perfect," Emily said trying to talk around the emotions in her throat. "Did you sign them?"

Kayleigh blushed but she stopped avoiding Emily's gaze. "I didn't want to ruin the pictures with my signature."

"Sign the back, genius," Sebastian said trying to peek over Kayleigh's shoulder and not get elbowed in the chest.

"I don't have a pen," she mumbled.

Emily wrapped her in a hug. "I'll invite you over for dinner when I put my tree up. You can sign them there."

Sebastian's eyes lit up. "Can I come to?"

"Not unless Kayleigh invites you," Noah said putting his hands on Emily's shoulders. He gave his niece a savvy nod.

Sebastian turned to her with a scowl. "What's it going to cost me?"

It was Kayleigh's turn to look superior. "A lot."

While Sebastian began bargaining, the Larkshead Choir had just finished an upbeat version of "Rocking Around the Christmas Tree." Nick Wilde, dressed as Santa Clause, stood on a raised dais beside a big red button and an even bigger Christmas tree smiling at the whole crowd as if they were all long-lost friends. The tree theme this year was Enchanted Forest which meant that some of last year's Christmas mermaids now had fairy wings and well-placed skirts. Combined with wildlife-themed ornaments and a mixture of elaborate stars, the tree wasn't unlike Noah's wrapping paper.

If it was possible to be perfectly happy, Emily felt it was now. She blew softly on a cup of mulled wine trying to take everything in. "How does the town afford to change themes every year?"

Noah looked at the tree with pride. "The ornaments are auctioned off at the end of the season. Ornaments that don't go are re-purposed, some of the proceeds go into a fund for next year, and the rest go to a charity that the town votes on around Valentine's Day. That was one of Nick's better ideas."

Nick Wilde watched the choir finish 'O'Holy Night.' The dark clouds chose that moment to pause their persistent distribution of icy cotton-like puffs.

"Ladies and gentlemen. Thanksgiving is just now past. Tonight, we are thankful for our strong community, for our wonderful choir, but most of all for the 32nd opening of the Larkshead Christmas Market!"

Applause came from all around and then broke into chants of, "Light the tree!"

"Without further ado," Nick rubbed his hands together and smacked his hand down on a ridiculously big red button labelled ON. All at once the tree lit up with hundreds of white twinkling lights. The ornaments that had looked modest in the daylight seemed to amplify both in size and color dazzling Emily with their vibrancy.

Everything looked just like a Christmas card including the ecstatic goblin-like Santa on the stage. She turned toward Noah who was looking at her rather than the tree. He leaned forward and brushed snow out of her hair. Her heart pounded because she knew without a doubt that at that moment, she loved him. Reaching up to catch his hand and hold it to her chest, she tried to tell him.

There was a greenish flash of light so bright that Emily

was momentarily blind. When her vision cleared, the people around her were gasping and instead of a jolly ol' Saint Nick, Nick Wilde appeared to be a twisted Santa-like goblin. From his sharp pointed teeth to his long clawed-tipped fingers, Nick looked like something straight out of nightmares. She looked quickly around noting that where the crowd had been filled with human onlookers, it was now filled with people who had become supernatural with wings, horns, claws, and multiple eyes.

Kayleigh and Sebastian pressed close enough to jostle Noah and spill their mulled wine over the top of his hands.

He grumbled at them, "Hey you guys, watch out."

But neither of them was listening. Unlike the other times when Emily was alone in her visions, everyone around them seemed to be gawking at someone. She looked at Kayleigh and noticed that not only was her hair blue but her skin and eyes also had a frosted turquoise tint. She met Emily's gaze with both fear and hope.

There was a high-pitched shriek and then another bright green flash and just like that, all the faces were human again. A thick heavy silence settled between the people gathered around the tree staring at one another. Emily noted there were distinct differences in the stares. The people who had been monsters only moments before were looking around in confusion; the people who had remained people were looking at the people who had been monsters with fear. Emily turned to look at Noah watching him scan the crowd with confusion.

"What just happened here?" Noah pulled her, Sebastian, and Kayleigh closer.

"You didn't see them?" Emily felt ice slide down her spine that had nothing to do with the snow. He was one of the monsters. "No. You've always seen them."

Noah's dark brown eyes flashed gold. "Seen who? What happened here?"

Emily started to say something but there was another shriek and then another. Around them, men and women crumpled to the ground like broken dolls. Noah pushed Emily toward Sebastian and Kayleigh. "You guys get out of here. Go back to the shop!"

Noah headed toward Angela and Malachi on the other side of the market. Sebastian nodded and Kayleigh grabbed her hand. They began stepping over and around people pulling her toward The Ace of Cups. All around her, there were people laying on the ground in the snow, their eyes wide open and their faces expressionless, just like April.

"Stop!" Emily shouted standing still. Kayleigh turned to look at her. Emily shrugged off her purse, dug out her keys, and handed them both to Kayleigh. "I want you to take Sebastian into the shop. Lock the doors behind you and then call 9-1-1. Wait for either myself or Noah to come get you."

Sebastian looked at Kayleigh. "Noah said all of us had to go."

"I don't care what he said. I'm saying we need to help these people quickly. Now go!" She turned back into the crowd without giving them an opportunity to argue. In less than two steps she ran into someone. It was like hitting a stone wall. Strong hands grabbed her arms to keep her from falling.

"Easy there," said a smooth rumbling voice. Emily looked up into the face of a demon. Her apology died in her throat. He didn't have horns, but both his wings and his body were made of dark red leathery skin that was in sharp contrast to his long black hair. Emily might have thought of him as beautiful if it weren't for the cold flatness of his black eyes. Her gaze wandered down to where his hands held her arms and the loose strands of her nightmares popped together to form a coherent picture of this man holding her under the water. She looked around her for confirmation that she wasn't dreaming again but the sounds and smells of the market were too vivid for this to be another vision. She swallowed hard.

"I'm sorry," she whispered trying to take a step back. "I didn't see you." The demon held on tightly bringing her close to look into her eyes. Emily's heart hammered in her chest, but she schooled her features into an apologetic smile.

"I think you see me just fine."

"Let go of her."

The demon and Emily both turned to look at Kayleigh who was standing with her fists bunched at her sides and a don't-mess-with-me expression on her face.

"I'm looking for Noah Hernandez," the demon said to Kayleigh baring his teeth at her.

She widened her stance and for a horrible moment, Emily thought she might attack the demon.

"Well, you have hold of Emily. Let go of her."

He brought Emily closer looking surprised and pleased with a smile that was colder than the emptiness in his flat eyes. "Emily. Emily Rollins, is it? Owner of The

Ace of Cups? I wouldn't mind having a chat with you later after I've located Mr. Hernandez."

Kayleigh growled a low angry sound her eyes turning gold. "Uncle Noah is on the other side of the Christmas tree."

He let go of Emily giving her a little push to put some distance between them. "I'll catch up with you later, Emily." He turned and disappeared into the crowd.

The words sounded innocent enough, but a knowing had joined the coldness of his eyes. Emily had no doubt that he was aware that she'd seen him, really seen him.

Kayleigh wrapped her arms around herself. "Whatever that man wants, you need to be as far away as possible."

Emily laughed but the sound came out strained. "You won't have to tell me twice." She hugged Kayleigh close and stepped back. "I thought I told you to go back to the shop?"

"I felt like you needed me."

Emily shivered. "I did. Thank you. Did you call 9-1-1?

"Sebastian is on the phone with them now."

Emily wrapped the girl in a big hug. "Good. I'm going to the town hall to help with the sick. Can you find Selene and head to 'Lost and Found' to make a place for any children who have been separated from their parents? Whatever happened here seems to have affected only the adults."

Kayleigh nodded. "I can do that."

The last of the ambulances pulled away while Emily stood folding blankets in the town Hall. She was so tired she could barely stand up and her stomach was churning with fear of bumping back into the demon she'd seen earlier. Dark Wolf Security had shown up and immediately reported to Noah. Unlike the playful go-lucky man she was used to, this side of Noah was efficient to the point of being ruthless.

Like the commander he likely was, he sent teams out to help move the injured, to direct traffic, and to help the vendors get their wares locked up for the night. He'd even given instructions on clean-up which was how Emily had ended up with Nick and Rowan Martin in the Town Hall. That she hadn't suspected this side of him existed reminded her of how new this relationship and this man was in her life. She was falling in love, and falling fast, but what she really knew about Noah Hernandez was precious little. *He hadn't seen the monsters.*

The confusion on his face hadn't been the same as everyone else's. Now that Emily had seen him with the security unit, she recognized that part of that expression had been calculating, like he had been expecting the event the whole time. She shook her head realizing that her tired thoughts were looking for some ways to explain the unexplainable. He'd given her a brief kiss about an hour ago and instructed her not to stay too long, and then he was gone.

Rowan Martin had not been what Emily was expecting. For one thing, she was shorter than Nick Wilde, which was saying something. She made up for her lack of height with a wealth of attitude. Nick was still wearing his Santa Suit, sweeping floors, and putting away occasional chairs. He attempted to talk to a couple of the locals, but it was obvious that some people were avoiding him.

Nick's shoulders drooped with disappointment, but he kept working as if he could win back the town's trust by the simple act of work. Nick and Rowan had worked stiffly with one another at first until Rowan had stopped what she was doing and put her arms around Nick to comfort him. They didn't say anything and didn't have to. Whatever their family differences were, Rowan was willing to put them aside rather than see Nick suffer.

The growl of Rowan's stomach was answered by Emily's, and they stared at each other from across the empty hall. All at once, Emily started to laugh.

"Come on guys, we've done enough tonight. Let's go get something to eat." She stacked the blankets on a nearby table and put her hands on her hips. "I'm tired and I didn't get to eat nearly the amount of junk food I wanted tonight."

"The city has rolled up the sidewalks. I'm not sure there is anywhere to get anything good to eat at this time of night," Rowan sighed gathering her things.

Nick's white eyebrows seemed to meet in the middle over his eyes. There was hope underneath his casual smile. "I happen to know there are powdered doughnuts and some very bad coffee in the kitchen here."

"I bought some very good herbal tea at the market," Rowan said holding up her handbag triumphantly.

"Sounds like heaven," Emily said rolling her stiff shoulders. "Coffee this late at night gives me nightmares."

Nick led them to the back of the building without switching on the lights. The rows and rows of largish rooms surrounded by blocks of windows reminded Emily of her old high school.

"It was an elementary school before it was a town hall. Larkshead moved the school out of the center of town because the parking was hectic," Rowan replied as if Emily had made the observation out loud. Emily stopped stunned. Rowan was looking down at her phone and still managing to follow Nick even though Emily was struggling to make out her feet in the darkened hall. She shook her head wondering if she was tired enough not to realize that she was talking out loud.

Nick flipped the light on in a large kitchen that still bore the marks of school-room-sized refrigerators. He opened a cupboard and pulled out three packs of bite-sized doughnuts. "If you turn on the pot in the corner and put the tea in the carafe, it should be fully brewed by the time these doughnuts make it critical to have a drink."

"I'll do it," Rowan said shaking back her wealth of coffee-colored ringlets. Emily watched her find a spoon and scoop loose tea leaves into the pot. Before she put the last one into the carafe, she brought it up to her mouth and whispered something over the tea leaves.

Nick nodded appreciatively. "Good idea. Freshen us up and give us a little glimpse at what's happening here."

When they noticed Emily staring Nick added, "Rowan's going to read our tea leaves. She's very good at it."

Rowan looked at him pleased. "Not as good as Jessie Wilde."

Nick chuckled. "The Norns themselves aren't as good as Jessie. Too bad she's dead-set on not telling anyone what she sees."

Rowan and Nick looked at each other for a second and then both started howling with laughter. It was infectious, passing to Emily and breaking down the last of her resistance to this strange little community. Emily got up and poured their tea. They sat in silence eating doughnuts and staring down into the fragrant brew. Although Emily tried not to bring dark thoughts into the happiness of the place, the tea in her hands bore a red tint. Without warning, one of her visions struck her.

The Demon from the market standing over her in the sea, his hands fisted in the front of her shirt. Then water washed over her that was so cold it burned. She felt a gentle hand on her arm. In the vision, Rowan appeared but was standing on top of the water. She reached down and pulled Emily out of her struggling body in the vision and to the side so that she could see the whole scene. The demon pushed the vision of herself under the water and held her there.

She stepped forward to help herself, but Rowan reached for her hands and threaded her fingers through Emily's. "Watch, don't interfere, and don't get involved. Separate yourself from the future so you can decide if this is an event you can avoid."

The water and the scene disappeared, and Emily was now holding her cup in both hands. Rowan was facing her with her hands cupped around Emily's. Rather than feeling terrified, Emily felt clear-headed and in control. "How did you do that?"

Rowan smiled letting go of her. "Practice. Getting the hang of second sight is a pain in the ass."

"Amen," Nick said taking a deep drink of his tea. "I don't have the gift, but I've seen it tear Jessie out of this reality so fast you'd think she was dead."

There was no judgement, no rejection. Not only did they not think Emily was crazy, they understood what was happening. She took a slow, cleansing deep breath trying not to cry. "I thought I was going crazy."

Rowan sat back taking a deep breath and then a slow sip of her own tea. "Visions have often been confused for insanity. Everyone who has the gift uses it differently. I can only see choices, but not the results. If I'm not mistaken your visions are a warning system."

"Did you see the demon?"

Rowan looked at Nick for a minute and Emily got the sense that they were trying to decide what to tell her. Emily tried again, "I saw him today in real life in the market, but I've also been seeing him in my visions for weeks. Ever since I moved here."

Nick's eyes narrowed. "The demon was here today? What did he want?"

Relief flowed hot and heavy through Emily. Neither Nick nor Rowan were looking at her as if she'd lost her mind. If they could see him too, then there was a chance they could help her avoid him. "He was looking for Noah."

"Damn," Nick said slinging back his tea and setting it on the table. He pulled a key from an enormous key ring and threw it at Rowan. "Lock this place up when you're finished. Go straight home, the both of you. I'll head over to Dark Wolf and talk to Noah."

Emily stood up. "I'll text him."

Nick was already heading toward the door. "Good. Let him know I'm coming."

Emily picked up her phone and sent a quick text to Noah. Rowan picked up Nick's teacup, turned it over in the saucer, and then flipped it back around.

"Let's see what he got."

She gazed into the cup for a couple of seconds and then frowned. She drained her own glass in a single gulp and then repeated the actions. Taking the last drink from her cup, she flipped it over without being told and then sat it back in the saucer and pushed it over to Rowan.

Rowan scooped it up frantically and sat it down with the others. Her eyes darted between the three and her face lost all color.

"What do they say?" Emily stood to investigate the cups.

"Look for yourself."

What she expected was a scatter of shapes that she would need to make sense of but instead, the leaves formed a perfect closed circle, like a dark moon on the bottom of her cup, with not even a scattering of leaves up the side. Looking into Rowan's cup and then into Nick's, her stomach sank. They all had the exact same shape.

"I don't understand."

Rowan wrapped her arms around herself. "The New Moon, new beginnings, and the Dark Goddess. Big change and a complete circle, but there are no other symbols in the cups."

"What does that mean?"

"Whatever this change is, it dominates all other life movements, eclipses them."

"Ends them?" Emily asked wanting to make sure.

Rowan looked at her and shrugged. "All new beginnings are an ending of some sort. That's the most frustrating thing about divination; you only ever learn enough to worry."

She picked up all three cups and took them to the sink washing them out and putting them on the draining board while Emily put the doughnut packages into the garbage. When they were finished, they looked over the quiet kitchen together. The silence was punctuated by the crackle of the settling building and the tick of the heater.

Emily went to the door while Rowan turned off the lights in the kitchen. Walking back through the dark hallways Emily felt a sense of alarm beating in the back of her mind. She felt Rowan's arm brush hers and noticed the other woman was also casting cautious glances around. She grabbed Emily's hand and pulled her quickly toward the door.

"Let's get out of here quick. This place gives me the creeps after dark."

Neither of them noticed the dark figure standing behind them at the end of the hall.

23

Opening yourself up to receive the powers of the universe is a charming thought but a conceited idea. It's a little like pouring an ocean into a shot glass. Messy and no matter how fast you pour, you can only hold so much at a time. A better exercise is to submerge yourself in the powers of the universe. Then you have the power to choose what you will hold. -- Valerie Black, *Everyday Solutions to Magic Problems*

Noah pulled into Emily's drive in the early morning hours. The house was dark and still. Larkshead was wrapped in deep sleep, counting down to the last days that the world would be divided into Enlightened and Unenlightened. He put his head on the steering wheel of his truck knowing that he should just go home. He'd always assumed, stupidly, that it wouldn't make a difference to Emily that he was a werewolf, but he hadn't thought about what it would look like from her side. He was a wolf with the power to rip her in half with his bare hands. He could run for miles without being tired, withstand temperatures that would cripple humans, hell, he could scent her and hear her breathing anywhere in her home. *How could she possibly take in that information without fear? How could anyone?*

Disturbing her because he was disturbed was selfish but more than sleep, his whole body cried out to touch hers while her arms were still open to him. Nick's warning that Emily had been approached by James released dark and ugly emotions in him.

James told Emily he was looking for Noah, but throughout the long night, he'd never made contact. Cicero said he escorted James out of Larkshead a week ago which meant that the demon had purposely invaded Noah's territory. Nothing that Noah knew about the situation could explain why except that the demon suspected Emily was an unguided witch. If James were caught in this territory, Noah was within his rights to destroy him. The Unseelie highly valued their lives, more so than most Enlightened, so why James would risk his didn't make sense.

Noah looked back toward Emily's door. Even if she wasn't now afraid of him, it was likely that she was still angry about several of his thoughtless actions, not the least of which was abandoning her to clean up the mess made by last night's events while he went to Dark Wolf. He shook his head determined to leave her in peace when she stuck her head out of the door with her quilt wrapped around her shoulders.

"What are you doing out there?"

He opened the door and slid out of the truck. "I don't want to sleep without you."

She blinked tilting her head in question. "I meant, why are you still outside in the truck? Come inside, we're letting all my heat out."

He came in allowing her to help him shrug out of his coat and to take off his boots. They were both too aware that adding their voices to the weight of the questions between them would be enough to break the fragile beauty of this moment. She led them to her bedroom stopping at the end of her bed to throw her make-shift robe back over the bed.

Noah winced internally remembering that he'd still not found a way to either destroy or bring back Emily's robe. He undressed and climbed into the blankets that she held open for him. His head hit the pillows and she hovered over him gently tracing his frowning features. She kissed his lips softly and then lay her head on his chest bringing the blankets around them with the bedside light still on.

He wrapped his arms tightly around her closing his eyes and breathing the comfort she offered him deep into his soul. With her hand over his heart, he felt like she was opening him up to let out the darkness and the fear that seemed to be taking over his body. Her body felt tense beside him, and he wanted more than anything to comfort her as much as she did him. All at once he realized that he hadn't disturbed her sleep. She had been waiting for him. He kissed the top of her head and hugged her tightly.

"Are you okay?"

She hesitated taking a deep breath. "Not really. I need to tell you something, but I want you to promise to hear me out before you jump to conclusions."

"I can promise that."

"I can sometimes see my future in dreams. It's a gift. My mom and grandma can do it too. Before I came to Larkshead, I just saw stupid things like what someone would be wearing or what song would be on the radio next."

Noah brushed his finger down the length of her hair and kissed the top of her head again. "Did you ever see us?"

She shook her head. "I knew I needed to be here. I just didn't know why. My visions are jumbled together. Like a warning about something that I can't escape."

Noah felt enormous relief. If all she was hiding was second sight, then everything would be okay. "Tell me what you saw, and we'll think of a way around it."

"I wish it were that easy. I've tried a hundred times to dodge my visions, but as soon as I see them, every decision I make, no matter how random, seems to lead me right to them."

Noah hugged her tight. "Go on."

"In my visions, there are red hands and a man with wings pushing me under the water somewhere on the coast. The water is freezing. I wasn't afraid of this vision because I thought this one was impossible. I thought there is no such thing as a red man with wings. But tonight, I ran into him right in the middle of town."

Noah frowned down at her. "You were with me during the flash, I didn't see a red man."

She looked up at him with a hopeful expression. "You believe me, too. Just like Rowan and Nick did. They didn't even look at me funny. He's not a red man, he looks like some sort of demon."

"Nick and Rowan practice witchcraft. They're used to the unusual. Larkshead has more than its fair share of weirdness."

She dropped her head to his chest for a moment in relief. "Like what happened tonight with the faces during the flash. You saw them, didn't you? The monsters in the crowd were confused and the people were afraid...but you..."

Noah closed his eyes unwilling to lie to her but afraid that the information would overload her. He would not carry her sightless body to a Recovery Center. "I don't know what I saw, not yet, not enough to explain it to you."

She nodded snuggling back into his arms. "I don't know what I saw either. We can talk about it in the morning. Thank you."

"For what?"

"For believing me. I wanted to tell you before, but I was afraid you'd think I was nuts."

"You can always trust me, Emily. Even if I thought you were crazy, I'd still be on your side."

She propped her chin on his chest with her hands and smiled sleepily. "You can trust me too, you know. I can see something is worrying you."

"Besides the fact someone wants to drown my one true love?"

She sat up smiling. "Your one true love? You know that after four weeks?"

Noah pulled her back onto his chest. "I think I knew I loved you in the grocery store. I keep telling you that you're the one who's a little slow on the feelings here."

Her mouth dropped open. "Hey-"

He covered her mouth with his hand. "Nope, you've killed the romance. When you're ready to tell me you love me, I want it to be romantic."

She bit him. Noah scooped her up rolling her under him placing little kisses everywhere he could reach while she giggled wildly. They were interrupted by a buzzing noise coming from Emily's phone. She lay under him with her hands pinned above her head still smiling.

He looked down at her with mock ferociousness. "If I let you up, are you going to behave?"

She thought about it a moment then leaned up and kissed him. "I'm too sleepy for revenge." He let go and she reached for the phone. Noah watched her read the message her mouth moving into a radiant smile.

"Is everything okay?"

Emily tilted the phone toward him so that he could read the message: *Any good Peking Duck in Larkshead?*

He shook his head. "I don't know what that means."

Emily laughed. "It means my mom will be here tomorrow."

Noah woke up alone. He vaguely remembered Emily kissing him before she left for work. The late morning sunshine fell across the empty bed reminding him of the likely consequences of what he was about to do. He got dressed slowly trying to decide what the best course of action would be and if that course could be taken without betraying the trust Emily had given him last night. Walking into the kitchen he saw a note leaning against the coffee maker that read: *Push start. Half-strength coffee to get you through your day. —Heart, Emily*

He turned on the coffee pot and looked out the kitchen window. Kiss-Me-Knot's warning, January's accusation, Katrin and April's Enlightenment, and the threat of James meant that he needed to know some answers before he took any action. He reasoned that he could not protect Emily if he didn't know what to protect her from, but the reason rang hollow in the empty house.

He finished the coffee, washed the dishes in the sink, and then carried the note to the couch knowing that he couldn't put off the inevitable any longer. Feeling like a traitor, he dialed the phone number for The Craft Shop and waited to talk to the owner. He thought about what Kiss-Me-Knot said. A candle blessed with a single suggestion, the blessing of Enlightenment. Was it possible that Emily had done it but didn't know her power?

He felt like he was standing on the brink of a chasm of understanding that would change the course of his life and some part of himself screamed at him to let it go. To just love Emily and try to build a life with her. But he'd asked Selene for that map of the Unguided outbreaks after the meeting at Dark Wolf last night. It sat in his truck, but he didn't need it to recall the image of the ring of awakenings around The Craft Shop in Boston or the matching ones in Larkshead, Maine, and Paducah, Kentucky.

He told himself it didn't mean anything even as he headed toward Emily's laptop on the coffee table. He opened the laptop hoping that he was wrong or that Emily had a passcode on her computer so that he could give up and tell himself that he'd tried but the home screen lit up. It didn't take him long to find the records he was looking for. Emily was a brilliant businesswoman and a meticulous record keeper. Not only did she track her sales, but she also charted the prices and places where she ordered her supplies. She knew which candles were gifts and which had been sent out as samples. Noah copied the information and sent it to himself and to Selene. He closed the screen and shut the laptop feeling like the thief he was. If this information proved that she was guilty of the unsanctioned awakenings, he knew he would destroy it rather than see her destroyed. He dialed Selene's number before he lost his nerve.

"Hey big brother, what's with the email full of Emily's sales information?"

"I need you to take the map you made for me and Frank Carlos and see if you can match the outbreaks to these sales."

"Did she give you this information?"

Noah swallowed hard trying to stop himself from just telling her to delete the email. "No."

"Then forget it," Selene said with anger. "She's my friend. You can't ask me to do this."

Her refusal confirmed what he suspected. Somehow Emily was involved. "She's my life-mate. I am asking you. Only you. We can't protect her if I don't know what we're fighting."

"Fine," Selene bit out. "But if she asks where this information came from, I'm not lying about it."

"I wouldn't ask you to." He heard his sister slamming things in her office.

"And if it shows correlation, that doesn't prove causation."

"I know," Noah said softly.

"Good."

Selene hung up the phone.

Noah closed out the screens and shut the laptop without clearing the history.

24

There are not as many Gods and Goddesses in the universe as one might think. Some of what the unenlightened think of as gods are just very old Enlightened who once gave some sound advice to humans and are now forever confused and irritated about how their simple guidance became so garbled over time.
—Phoebe Pearce, *Witchcraft for the Newly Enlightened.*

The world was falling around him. Both the Enlightened and the Unenlightened were panicking. News of the green flash and the resulting collapses were coming in from across the world. Explanations for what happened ranged from mass hallucinations and Alien contact to chemical weapons and government conspiracy, but none of these explanations could help the number of people lying on hospital beds physically healthy but unresponsive. There had been suggestions of invoking martial law and of shutting borders until the contagion could be isolated but so far, nothing more than government pleas for calm had happened.

Angela issued commands for Noah and Joseph to call all Dark Wolf's employees to secure their families and report to the security centers for instructions. The demand for targeted communications meant that they needed Katrin's gift for moving and concealing information. In addition, Angela called a gathering of Guides and Enlightened medical staff familiar with awakening procedures and instructed them to report all occurrences to Selene. The number of Larkshead residents who'd been affected was minor compared to places like Chicago, but the results were the same. Fear.

In the midst of this Emily sent Noah a text about midday asking him to meet her and her mother at The Jade Village just outside of Larkshead, at 7 pm. She was going a little earlier so that she could catch up and prepare her mother for meeting him.

"Wear something nice," Cicero said reading the text message over Noah's shoulder.

"I've got a lot to do here. I don't really have time to go to dinner tonight."

Cicero shook his head. "Make time, boy. If you're still entertaining thoughts of sharing a white picket fence with Miss Emily Rollins, you better dress up nice, pay for dinner, smile, and say 'Yes Ma'am.' Better to be on the wrong side of the Devil than the wrong side of a Southern Mama."

. . .

When Noah pulled up to the restaurant at 7:05, Emily stood outside shivering with her arms wrapped around her chest.

"Damn," she muttered under her breath. Noah got out of his truck and waved at her. She met him halfway and gave him a big hug and kiss. "You beat her here. I swear she's going to be late to her own funeral."

Noah kissed her a second time more slowly rubbing his hands up and down her arms to warm her. "You are freezing. Did you check for her inside?"

"Twice, and just to be sure, I checked the bathrooms too."

"Does she hide in bathrooms often?" Noah asked tucking her under his arm and heading toward the door.

Emily scanned the parking lot anxiously. "The last couple of times we've met, she's said she was on time but in the bathroom."

"Cicero likes to use that one too. Let's wait for her inside and hope this weather passes us by."

"We might as well get a seat." She put her icy hand in his. "If we're lucky, she'll arrive right about the same time the appetizers do."

"And if we're not lucky?"

Emily checked her watch. "We'll have to come back tomorrow."

They turned to go inside when a high-pitched Southern twang rang out from the parking lot. "Wait for me, chick-a-dee."

Noah turned to see a tall woman with wild maroon hair dropping down out of the cab of an Eighteen-wheeler at the end of the parking lot. She waved the truck driver off and then skipped merrily toward them over snow and ice on high-heeled boots that would have made Dolly Parton proud.

Deja was a born-again hippy, meaning that she was too young to have lived through the flower power age, but she was determined to keep the style alive. Wearing flared jeans with daisies embroidered down the leg, a white poet's blouse, her only protection against the snowy weather was a knee length cardigan that was every color of the rainbow. She threw herself into Emily's open arms almost knocking them both over.

"Hello baby." Deja pushed herself back cupping Emily's face and looking her over. "Sorry I'm late. You look great. All this freezing cold salt air must be good for you."

"I missed you too." Emily stepped back holding her mom's hand. "Where are your things? What happened to your car?"

"Broke down somewhere in Alabama. The woman who is fixing it said she'd bring it up to me tomorrow evening. We're going to go take a tour of Canada over Christmas. Do you want to come with me, baby?"

Noah was aghast but Emily just shook her head with a laugh like this sort of thing happened all the time. "No thanks. I've got a store to run." She pulled Noah forward. "Mom, this is Noah Hernandez. Noah, this is my mom, Deja Rollins."

Deja turned to Noah with a delighted smile that faltered on her lips a brief second as she offered her hand.

"Pleased to meet you, Noah. Emily's told me a lot about you."

Deja squeezed his hand hard enough to make him

wince letting him know in no uncertain terms that she was Enlightened. She met his eyes unflinchingly, her smile so sweet that for a moment, he doubted what had happened.

"Good stuff, I hope," Noah said smiling at her. An Enlightened mother with an Unenlightened daughter was sure to be overprotective.

"Very good," Deja said. "Almost too good."

"Mother," Emily groused pulling Deja toward the restaurant. "He doesn't have to know that I think he's perfect."

A woman in a black apron greeted them at the door turning the sign over from open to closed. "I'm sorry. We're closing early. State of Maine has issued a winter storm warning and after all the hubbub on the news today, what with the green flash, the boss wants us to get home safe."

Emily nodded but her disappointment was obvious. Deja touched the waitress's arm with a smile so beautiful it hurt Noah's heart. "We understand honey. Any chance you could pack us a dinner to go? We don't mind leftovers."

The waitress blinked a moment and then smiled back at Deja as if they were long lost friends. In fact, Noah himself was tempted to go behind the counter and find Deja whatever she wanted. He shook his head wondering what the hell was happening here. Werewolves, as a rule, were immune to charms.

"I'd be happy to," the waitress said picking up her order pad and pen. "Anything in particular you want?"

"You don't make any effort for us, sweetheart. You're

already doing us a favor. Just get what you have, and we'll be mighty pleased to have it."

Noah watched stunned while the waitress brought three bags full of different kinds of Chinese food including Peking duck. She'd tried to give Deja the food for free, but Deja wouldn't have it. She paid for the meal before Noah could pull out his wallet.

Emily took the bags with a wink at Noah. "Told you, she makes friends fast. Let's take this back to my house."

"Go ahead, honey. I'm sure Noah won't mind if I ride with him. We can start getting to know one another."

Noah wasn't fooled and neither was Emily. He smiled. "I'd be happy to have you ride with me."

Emily looked suspiciously at them both but then sighed. "Have it your way." She gave Noah and her mom a hug and a kiss. "I'm going to stop at the grocery store quickly and get soy sauce and something for breakfast." She wagged her finger at her mom. "Play nice."

Deja gave Emily another big hug and then slid her arm through Noah's. "I'm always nice."

They watched her walk toward her car and then turned to get into Noah's truck. After his second failed attempt to start a conversation with Deja, Noah gave up. All pretenses of her liking him had left with Emily. He'd never been in this situation before. They pulled up to Emily's house and Noah turned off the truck. The click of seatbelts had barely faded away when she grabbed hold of his jaw with unimaginable strength.

"Do you want to explain to me why my daughter, whose longest relationship lasted about two months, is talking about Christmas plans with you? Unless I'm doing the math wrong, she's only known you a few weeks."

Deja let go of him and shrugged out of her seatbelt. She got out of the car coming around to his side before he could finish opening the door.

"What do you want with my daughter? Who sent you?"

Noah slid out of the car cautiously trying to determine what type of Enlightened she was. "No one sent me."

"You can drop your innocent act. I know what you are. Emily said that a dog showed up the first day she was here and that he's been hanging around the house. I knew that Larkshead is a werewolf sanctuary, but where I come from there are rules about shapeshifting."

"I haven't broken any rules." He felt himself blush. "I just wanted to make sure she was safe."

She crowded him against the truck. "Is that how you justify it to yourself?"

Noah squared his shoulders. "She's Unenlightened."

Deja hit the door frame of the truck with the palm of her hand hard enough to rock it. "Damn straight, and if you know what's good for you, she better stay that way." She strode away from him up the path to Emily's front door.

Noah followed her at a distance. "You're Enlightened."

She turned narrowing her eyes. "I'm much more than that."

She took off her long sweater and extended her large wings. Rather than being white, her wings were like those on the breast of a falcon, ivory tipped with shades of brown. She flexed them and then leaped into the air maintaining the height of her leap with powerful thrusts of her wings.

"I knew the fate of everyone born before the first of you crawled from the sea. You really think you're Enlightened?"

Her dark maroon hair, so much like Emily's, floated around her creating the impression of a fiery halo that was so much a part of the legends connected to her kind. He met her gaze feeling a sensation that he'd forgotten he had ever known. A warm protection from the womb, a connection to everything that was living, a feeling as if he were loved no matter what. As suddenly as the feeling started it was gone. Noah gasped falling to his knees. She landed close to him but did not offer him her hand.

"Angels are easy to love because we are made of love. If I had a quarter for every Enlightened person who was sure I was their life-mate, I would be rich. Don't mistake your loneliness for her love."

Noah pushed himself solemnly to his feet. "Whatever else she is, Emily is my life-mate." Memories of Emily's description of her childhood flooded his mind. "You're part of a Recovery Unit team, aren't you? That's why you're always moving."

Deja dropped to the ground as gently as a feather, tucking her wings behind her. She picked up her sweater and smoothed her hair closing her eyes and breathing deep. "Since I can remember, I've been part of a Recovery Unit team. All angels are. We are registered and then they start coming to talk to us. We hunt down the darkness and we bring it to justice. That's what the job description says." She turned back toward the cabin and walked up the steps to the porch inspecting the house. "They turn us into hunters, healers, and trackers, without ever giving us a chance to be anything else. Is that what you want for Emily?"

"No. Of course not. Emily's not an angel."

Noah watched as Deja leaned forward and whispered something to the cabin. A golden light shimmered over the place. A ward. Where the cabin and woods had been soaked with loose magic, now he could feel nothing.

"She was born Unenlightened and without wings. Her gift is different than mine, more like my mother's, but she is my child. I thought she had a chance at a real life until she came here."

"I love her. I would never put her in danger."

Deja slammed her hand onto the porch rail shaking dust from the rafters. "You're already putting her in danger. The exposure to you and to this place is bringing her through the Veil."

"I think Emily was already through. That she's been unguided for a while. She needs help."

Deja sat down on the porch step like a gargoyle guarding the door. "That's why I'm here. If she needs a Guide, I will guide her."

Headlights flashed and Emily pulled up into the drive. Noah watched the light flee across Deja's face chasing away any evidence of her anger. Emily got out of her car balancing the take-out and her shopping bags.

Smiling ear to ear she practically bounced up the path with their dinner. "Why are you guys standing out in the yard?"

Deja came forward to take most of the bags. "Noah's

just apologizing for not being able to come in with us." She gave him a steady look. "He's got things to do."

Emily slid her free arm around him pulling his head down to hers for a kiss. He closed his eyes savoring the taste of her lips. She stood on tip-toe and whispered playfully in his ear. "Coward. I had to hang out with your parents."

He felt his heart hammer. "I think your mom wants a little alone time with you. I'll try again tomorrow." He kissed her cheek softly. "I owe you."

Stepping back, he saw an apology in her eyes. Unenlightened or not, she knew his conversation with her mom hadn't gone well. "Don't you forget it." She kissed him again and then turned to walk her mother inside.

He watched them until the door shut behind them.

25

Although the Fey are known for working toward their own agenda, when a witch's agenda matches up with theirs, they will eagerly add their power to a spell...whether that power is actually desired or not is of little concern to them. — Ichabod Rimmington, *Surviving Fairies*

Over margaritas and Peking duck Emily told her mother about her visions and seeing monsters.

"Monsters?" Deja used her chopsticks to dip her duck into soy sauce. "Being different doesn't make you a monster, honey. You know better than that."

Emily tipped her rice out into a bowl and covered it with enough soy sauce to make her mom grimace. "I know that but I don't know how else to explain it. Horns, feathers, scales, you name it and I've seen someone with it."

"Well, the first thing to do is just talk to them like normal people. You could be seeing past lives, fairies, what they think of themselves. Until you know what you're looking at it's probably best just to ignore it."

"You think it has something to do with second sight?"

Deja licked the salt off the rim of her glass and then took a big swallow of margarita. She gave Emily a saucy smile and a playful shiver. "Yes ma'am, I do. Your grandma wasn't born talking to trees. As you get older, your powers develop and change. It's just a matter of getting used to it."

"What about the demon visions?" Emily got up to make herself another margarita. Her mom could drink a sailor under the table, so she didn't bother to try and keep up.

"Yeah, I don't like it any more than you do. And you're sure you saw him?"

"Absolutely sure. I recognized him from the vision but he didn't know me." Emily began to salt the glass and her mom perked up.

"Let me put an extra blessing on that pentacle I gave you. Keep it on until I get back. I got an idea or two that might help but I need to check with your grandma first."

Emily brought the pentacle in. A blessing from her mom couldn't hurt.

"What's the blessing do?"

Deja blew on the pentacle and murmured softly in her own special language which made Emily immediately feel safe and protected.

"Two things. It hides you. You'd have to drive to him in order for him to find you."

"And the other?"

Her mom put the pentacle around her neck. "It's a

blessing, sweetheart. That you will live a long and happy life."

Emily picked up her drink and handed her mother hers. "Cheers! To a long and happy life." They clinked their glasses together and both took a drink.

Deja turned a wicked grin on her daughter. "So, what are you wearing to your grandma's wedding in April?"

Just like that, everything was okay again. Mostly. Noah came back to Emily's the next morning to bring them breakfast, but Deja had already asked Emily to drive her back to the restaurant to be picked up by a friend. Her mother hadn't said two words all night about meeting Noah. To say that their meeting hadn't been the warmest was putting it mildly. That she hadn't waited to say goodbye to him made her stance on the matter clear. Considering how warmly Noah's family had welcomed Emily she was both surprised and disappointed with her mother's reaction.

She and Noah worked side by side setting the table and putting the breakfast burritos, donuts, and fruit on the table. Her mother's rejection had hurt him and she threaded her fingers through his leading him to the table hoping to ease the worry in his eyes.

"Well, that's meeting my mom out of the way. Are you going to tell me what happened between you two in the truck or are you going to be closed lipped and mysterious like she was?"

"I'm going to take option two in the interest of peace. I

think she's just worried about how fast we're moving. She gave me a stiff warning to back off." He gave Emily a rueful smile. "I decided not to tell her that we are still working out a bed schedule."

Emily popped a strawberry in her mouth with a chuckle. "No one had to tell her. I had real fun explaining to her why my hairbrush and toothbrush were at your house."

She'd also had to skirt around why she had no groceries to speak of and why her candles were still stacked around all her available living space. For a woman looking to establish a home for herself, she was doing a poor job of it. The thought should have worried her because admitting that she didn't like sleeping without Noah sounded weak and clingy, but it was also the truth, and she was grown up enough to admit that to herself.

"Speaking of, let's walk to your house and go get my hairbrush after breakfast to clear my head. She's given me a lot to think about and thanks to the snow, I've got till 11 am to sort myself out."

Noah still looked unhappy. She leaned forward, picked up his breakfast burrito and took a bite looking him straight in the eyes. "Speaking of bed schedules, are we going to start flipping a coin or just rotate when the sheets need washing?"

He laughed picking up her burrito and taking a bite. "Yours has more cheese in it."

"Give it back then." As they exchanged burritos Emily caught Noah's chin. "She's just trying to see if she can scare you off. Don't let her win."

"I'm not going anywhere."

They finished breakfast and bundled up. She grabbed his hand and pulled him toward the forest path. He didn't resist, instead, he shrugged off his coat and put it over hers. His warmth and scent wrapped around her easing a tension in her body that she hadn't been aware of. "It's winter, you know. You're going to get cold."

"Not as cold as you are. I was born here. You can warm me up later."

The winter forest air was so crisp and clean that she almost felt guilty about leaving footprints. Beside her, Noah weaved gracefully through and around obstructions in the snow showing no signs of feeling the cold. He stopped her from turning toward the ocean at the first fork in the path. "There's a shorter path."

Emily laughed following him into the dense woods. "You took me the long way around the first time?"

"It's more scenic and I wanted to ensure a second date."

The forest folded around them bouncing around the crunchy sounds of their footprints in the downy snow. Noah's movements lost some of their earlier hesitations the deeper they went into the forest. The snow shined like glitter and fell from the trees around them in soft little thuds as if the branches were alive and waving their arms to shake off the weight. It was because her focus was on the trees and not on her feet that she stumbled over the body in the snow.

She would have hit the ground hard except that Noah caught her by the arm. She shrugged him off kneeling next to the snow-covered woman. Lying on her side with her eyes closed and her head cradled in the crook of her arm, the woman looked as if she were merely napping on the frozen ground. Her hair was completely white blending in with the surrounding snow and her skin had turned a frosty color blue. She was dusted with snow that perched on her naked skin unaltered by body heat.

"Call an ambulance," Emily said brushing the woman's damp cold hair away from her face and checking her pulse. Even without medical experience, she could see the woman was dead.

Noah knelt beside her but didn't touch the body. "I can't. There's no phone signal here."

Emily continued to brush the snow from the woman's skin. Although the snow wasn't melting, the woman herself still felt warm. "Then you need to go get help. I'll stay here. You're faster in the woods."

Noah looked carefully around their location for danger. Not to Kiss-Me-Knot, she was too far away for anyone to harm her again, but to them. It took a powerful Enlightened being to kill a Wil-o-the-Wisp, especially one as old as Kiss-Me-Knot. The location and positioning of her body meant that someone had dumped her here to send a message. He opened his senses fully taking in every detail he could. What struck him most was the complete absence of scents. Neither the body, the trees, nor the wet earth could be scented around her. Someone had erased the evidence knowing he would track them.

"Noah!" Emily's voice broke his concentration "We need to call an ambulance."

"We need to go. We can't help her. Whoever did this might still be here."

Emily compressed her lips laying her hand unconsciously on Kiss-Me-Knot. "You're probably right, but we need to try anyway." She shrugged off his coat and her own and wrapped them around the girl. Before he could stop her, she rolled Kiss-Me-Knot on her back and began to administer CPR. She breathed once, twice, three times into the woman on the ground and then returned to doing chest compressions.

"Come on honey," Emily whispered invitingly, "It can't be that bad. It's almost Christmas. You don't want to die on such a beautiful day."

She did more chest compressions breathing warm breath into Kiss-Me-Knot's mouth. All at once he felt warmth. Against Kiss-Me-Knot's lips, he heard Emily whisper, "By earth, by air, by fire, by water. Bless the life of your magical daughter." She breathed into the Wisp's lungs.

"Come back now."

Noah reached down to pull Emily away just as he heard Kiss-Me-Knot start to cough. Emily quickly turned her on her side as she vomited salt water.

"Holy shit! She's alive! Noah, she's alive!"

Noah heard the unmistakable clacking of wings and with it, the scent of the undead. The Unseelie was here. Noah scrambled forward pushing Emily out of the way.

"I can carry her. We need to leave now."

She nodded as he scooped up the coughing Wil-o-the-

Wisp. Kiss-Me-Knot's head lulled, and her eyes frantically scanned the forest. Emily reached over to grasp her hand.

"You're okay. We've got you."

He had always considered the forest welcoming to his kind, but that was before he'd run through it with Emily and Kiss-Me-Knot. Ice disappeared underneath his feet, branches and trees seemed to move out of his way and the ground under his feet stabilized allowing him and Emily to find purchase on every surface. The path itself was so clear that a child could have followed it.

The air around the three of them began heating up enough to cause Noah to sweat beneath his thick sweater but neither woman noticed. They were focused on one another like their eye contact alone was the only thing keeping either of them alive. Noah had only limited experience with wild fey magic, but he knew that this was something more.

While he carried her, Kiss-Me-Knot's body began to warm and return to a more natural color. While she looked at Emily, her expression was one of complete devotion but when her eyes scanned the forest her expression turned to rage. The Unseelie would not get the drop on Kiss-Me-Knot again. By the time they reached his porch, he had no doubt that she was fully recovered. She allowed herself to be carried by Noah for Emily's benefit.

Emily opened the door and Noah brought Kiss-Me-Knot inside and sat her down on the couch. He pulled his phone from his pocket. "I'll call the ambulance. There's an extra blanket in the bottom of my closet we can use to keep her warm instead of the coats."

Emily started to leave the room, but Kiss-Me-Knot wouldn't let go of her hand. Emily knelt beside her brushing her hands through the other woman's hair. "It's alright. You're safe with us."

"You returned my life to me. How can I repay you?"

Emily smiled. "Live a long and happy life. That's all the payment I require." She left the room and returned several minutes later.

He called an ambulance, but after doing so he texted Cicero instructing him to see to Kiss-Me-Knot's needs. Kiss-Me-Knot was bound to the forest and couldn't leave it without considerable pain. Emily came back into the room with the blanket and her own pink house robe.

Noah's heart stopped when he saw it. Emily wouldn't look at him, but her movements were stiff and angry. She removed the coats and reverently wrapped Kiss-Me-Knot in both the robe and the blanket. Cicero and an Enlightened ambulance team arrived at the same time. He didn't look at Noah or Emily, he simply scooped Kiss-Me-Knot into his arms whispering endearments against her brow. Noah gave instructions to the medical team assuring them he and Emily would follow up on the event with a police report. Cicero climbed into the ambulance still holding the Wisp close to him as they drove off. Noah turned back to the house and found Emily in his bedroom quietly collecting all her things.

"I can explain," Noah tried calmly.

"Can you?" she said softly, "because I sure as hell can't."

He opened his mouth trying to think of a reasonable answer, but nothing came to mind. She headed toward the door. "Emily, wait."

"My mother was right. You are too good to be true." She rounded on him. "Were you stalking me? Did you break into my house the first day I was here? Is that why you told me I should lock my doors?"

She moved around the house collecting everything that was hers, brush, toothbrush, coffee mugs, even the shells she'd laid in the window on their first date.

"I am such an idiot. You always just happen to appear right outside my door, and my shop, and I never thought about what reason you had to be there-"

He was losing her. She would walk out and he deserved it. "I swear it's not like that."

"Isn't it? What did you do to Angelo?"

Noah stood frozen in his own living room. "What?"

She bundled her things into her arms, tears streaming down her face. "You start coming around all the time and all of a sudden he disappears."

His brain scrambled for something to say, the truth hovering on the back of his tongue. She marched to the couch and grabbed her coat. She left the gloves and hat he'd bought her behind. He stepped into her path. "Emily, look at me."

"Get out of my way or I'll call the police."

"Please. Just listen to me for a second. I'm outside your place all the time because you live close to my house, we're dating, and I want to be close to you. That's all. Nothing creepy. Most of the time I've been invited."

"And my robe?" she demanded holding her things tighter to her chest.

Noah exhaled. "I can't tell you why I have your robe. It's not just my secret to tell."

She shoved past him going out onto the front porch. "Then whose secret, is it? Is it April's, Katrin's, or Cicero's? Because it's my bathrobe hidden in the closet under the blankets, not theirs. Mine!"

Noah flinched knowing she was right. "I would never hurt you or anything that you loved."

Her eyes narrowed. "Then tell me why my robe is here."

"I will. I promise. But not yet."

"Then stay away from me until you can."

Without another word, she walked down the steps out of his life.

26

In a witch's household a good number of everyday objects from broomsticks to coffee pots might be blessed, enchanted or be-spelled. Some older witches believe that spells should be limited to natural objects; others write runes across their laptops in order to prevent electronic mishaps. It is up to the individual witch how they limit their beliefs about what their powers can do. It is also up to them to remove those limits when they no longer serve a purpose. –Olivia Goldstein, *Mastering Magic*

Christmas was a week away and the shoppers were becoming manic, but December 15th brought with it a bitter wind which meant that the foot traffic in town was minor. She'd seen about four people since she opened this morning. April was back at work with a vague explana-tion of medications causing her attack. Although she said the doctors had released her with a clean bill of health, Emily noticed that she was quieter and more contempla-tive than before. She was writing Christmas cards at the counter humming along while the Larkshead Choir sang 'Silent Night.'

Emily moved to the back of her shop trying to stop the trickle of tears that kept springing to her eyes. In April's time in the hospital Nick had found a day care that suited Michael and April now had whole days where her only responsibility was to take care of herself.

"A little alone time is the best kind of magic," April said running her tongue along the envelope to seal it shut.

Emily wasn't sure she agreed. While she worked, she could make-believe that she was okay. She stayed late to avoid going home and the time without Noah had allowed her to make the candles she would need for the rest of the season. She'd put up pictures in her cabin, baked cookies, and bought a Christmas tree, but these things had done nothing to make her house a home.

Although she hadn't spoken to Noah, he made sure her driveway and car were cleared before she got up. Despite herself, she'd attempted to catch a glimpse of him, but he seemed to have a sixth sense for when she got up. Angelo was also still missing, the water in his bowl frozen and the food on the porch untouched.

The Hernandez family were giving her a wide berth. Whether this was just because the holidays were really in full swing or because they knew that she and Noah weren't speaking, she wasn't sure, but their absence was palpable.

In a turn of events that had surprised Emily, her mother had taken Noah's side in the argument.

"Maybe he's got a good reason."

"Like what?" Emily carried the phone to the window looking out into the dark forest.

"You don't know- he might have some sort of kleptomania running in his family."

Emily rolled her eyes even though her mother couldn't see her. "You don't really believe that do you?"

Her mother laughed. "No, but I also don't believe he's the kind of psycho you're making him out to be."

"My bathrobe was at his house," Emily said tracing tree shapes with her fingers on the window glass.

"So was your hairbrush and toothbrush, but you didn't seem so bothered about that."

"You're deliberately missing the point. It's been missing since my first day here. Unless it likes to wander around by itself, the only explanation is that he took it."

"Listen chick-a-dee, I hear what you're asking but I can't tell you what happened because I don't know. He's not the only man in the world. You have options. If Noah told you that he had a good reason to take the robe, then you either trust him or you don't. It's that simple. If you don't want to wait for his explanation, cut him loose and stop punishing yourself."

Those words had been running through her mind all morning. Could she really cut him loose?

A little after noon, April came into the back room where Emily was packing the online orders for the shipping pick-up at 3 pm and handed her a tissue. Emily hadn't even noticed the tears making their way down her face. April took the order list from her hand and gave her a hug.

"Go home, Emily. You are exhausted. Start a fire, pour yourself a hot chocolate, read a book, watch a movie, whatever you need to do to feel better. Kayleigh is on her way and there is too much snow for there to be any big rush."

Emily dashed away her tears with an embarrassed sniff. "Thank you. I'll check back in later."

She gathered her things and headed to her car trying not to think too hard. While clearing the snow from her car her ice scraper caught the edge of a yellow note tucked under her windshield wiper. She felt her heart catch in her throat as she smoothed the edges.

Emily,

We need to talk. Please meet me at Red Warf Bay. I'll be waiting.

Noah

Elation hit her hard. He wanted to talk. She wasn't entirely sure where Red Warf Bay was, but he'd made the first move and she wasn't going to complicate things by being awkward. She finished clearing her car, checked her watch, and then pulled her Sat Nav out of her glove box. It easily found the public parking area closest to the Bay, not far from The Last Stop where she'd returned her trailer.

She sent a text to Noah to let him know that she was

leaving now and that she would see him in about half an hour.

❦

Sebastian was flipping through Dark Wolf's mail when Noah walked through the door. Normally Joseph sorted out what was junk and what was important, but he was taking time off to guide Katrin through the many rules of the Enlightened. Sebastian gave him a strange look. "What are you doing here?"

Noah tossed his gloves on his desk. "I still work here last time I checked."

Sebastian tossed some of the mail he was looking through toward the trash. "Ok, but you're going to be later than Emily for your date."

Noah felt his heart thud in his chest. "Did she call for me?"

"Yeah. She said to tell you she got your note and she's going to be a couple of minutes late because she needs to pop by her house to get her big coat." Sebastian laughed. "She's got a fifteen-minute head start. I'd consider skipping the car, wolfing out, and risking showing up naked if I were you."

"I didn't leave her a note." Noah felt sick inside. "Think, Sebastian. Did she say where she was going?"

Sebastian stood up anxiously. "No. She acted like you made the arrangements. She just said that she'd got your note and that she was on her way."

Noah came around the desk patting his jacket to find his phone. He'd turned it off to keep himself from continuously checking for a message from her. When it rebooted, the text message that he'd been waiting for since their argument sat in his inbox. All it said was that she was leaving now, and would be there in thirty minutes.

"Damn it." He dialed Emily but the call went straight to voice mail. Wherever she was, she wasn't getting any reception. Noah was already stripping down preparing to shift. "I'm going to try to catch her at home. Call Mom. Tell her I need the pack to search the woods in a thirty-minute radius from Larkshead town center. Emily's in trouble."

Noah burst through Carl Wedgwood's door twenty minutes later to find the man sitting at his kitchen table with Janet, each had a cup of coffee.

Carl stood instantly. "What's wrong?"

Noah's breath heaved from his run. He didn't bother with clothing or formality. "Mr. Wedgewood, I need a favor."

Carl reached over to stroke his wife's hand. "You've done a lot for us, ask it."

"I need you to search the coastline as fast as you can. My life-mate, Emily, someone lured her out under the guise of meeting me. I need to find her fast. My family is searching the roads and the woods, but we're slower searching the coastline than you would be." Noah closed his eyes. "She had a premonition of being drowned."

Carl began to strip down and head for the beach. "What am I looking for?"

"Her name is Emily Rollins. She's about five and a half feet tall, with long blonde hair. Her winter coat is turquoise so she's going to be difficult to spot from a distance."

Carl ushered Noah out the door. "Which direction is your family coming from?"

"Most of them are coming from town."

"I'll move north then. Check the places that are difficult to get to. What do I do when I find her?"

"Please, keep her safe. Whatever the cost-"

"I understand." Carl moved swiftly into the water, one minute he was a man, when he surfaced again, he was a selkie. Noah didn't watch long, he shifted into a werewolf again and followed Carl up the coast.

Emily stored her purse in the trunk of her car and zipped her coat closer but without her scarf, hat, and gloves, she was still shivering. If they ever got over this fight, she was going to have to remind Noah that her version of romance included fireplaces and hot chocolate rather than icy beaches.

The place he'd chosen was a little more off the beaten path than she was used to, and it took her several minutes to find the trail down to the rocky beach. He wasn't normally so mysterious but maybe he needed the solitude to talk about what happened. Hadn't Selene said that the forest was home to him? It didn't matter. They would clear the air and work on the rest from there.

Frost yet to catch the rays of the weak winter sun

clung to the dark sides of the volcanic slabs that jutted out of the salt water. She slid down the steep side of the rocky beach looking for signs of Noah. If she was on the wrong beach, she'd just go back to his house and wait for him there. The water was beautiful in a forbidding way. It rattled rocks and sent a fine sheet of sparkling salt spray into the air. The sun was already starting to make its way toward the water.

Emily took a deep breath and reached up for her pentacle. The longest night, the Winter Solstice was coming up on them fast. Turning away from the sea, the first thing she noticed was that there was no way onto or off the beach other than the way she came down. The second thing she noticed was the demon from the Christmas Market was now standing at the top of the steep path. His body was muscled in places that Emily was sure shouldn't have muscles, and his wings were fully extended casting a long sinister shadow into the forest until he folded them behind him with a clicking sound.

She stepped back toward the water wrapping her arms around herself. He jumped into the air with a powerful thrust of his wings and then glided into the space just in front of Emily. She swallowed hard and forced herself to smile.

"That was an impressive jump." He didn't return her smile.

"You see me, don't you?"

She tried to make her laugh casual. "It's broad daylight, of course I can see you."

He reached toward her face, but she backed up

another couple of steps looking for a way to get around him.

"I have never seen an angel in real life, but you are the image I have always held in my heart. I saw you in the woods. I killed that girl to keep a secret and you breathed life right back into her. Are you an angel, Emily?"

His voice was so beautiful, but his words made Emily's blood ran cold. He was telling her he'd attempted to murder that woman in the woods.

"I think you have me confused with someone else. I don't know what you're talking about."

The demon laughed a hollow dry sound. "Did you know the ocean is around 37 degrees here? It takes about fifteen minutes, maybe less, before the cold starts to affect a human. Shall we see how long it takes to affect an angel? I have all day to get what I need from you."

He moved closer and she lunged toward him hitting him square in the chest with both fists trying to give herself a chance to run around him. Instead, he grabbed both of her arms locking them behind her back. He trapped her against his chest and began to move toward the ocean.

Can you see me, Emily?

She made herself stay calm as waves washed over the tops of her shoes, so cold it felt like fire when it touched her skin.

"What are you talking about? Of course, I see you. You're not invisible."

"What do you see?"

Emily's mind scrambled for something to say. "I see someone who is very confused-"

"Wrong answer."

He took a flying leap forward dragging her with him, landing in water that was waist-deep for Emily. She gasped, the frigid water stealing her ability to scream. His strength was incredible, like being held in stone. She looked down at his red hands as the water hit her again. This wasn't a vision. The exhilaration was in his eyes. The demon was enjoying her pain.

"Tell me the truth. Are you working with Phoebe Pearce to bring down the Veil?"

Emily tried to appeal to him. "Please. I don't know what you're talking about but whatever this is, we can discuss it on the beach. If I freeze, you will too."

"No little angel, I won't."

He moved deeper into the water and then pushed her head under holding her there for a few seconds before he brought her out again.

"You see what I really am, don't you? Maybe you always have. Now, what color is my hair?"

Emily gripped his wrists shivering so hard it felt like she was being wrung like a cloth. "B-black."

"Good girl. I knew you could tell the truth. What color is my skin?"

Emily gritted her teeth. He pushed her underwater again and then brought her up.

"What am I?"

"An a-asshole," she growled suddenly understanding that it didn't matter what answer she gave. He was going to kill her.

He laughed then pushed her under the water holding her for a few moments and then bringing her up. "You're a fighter just like your wolf mate. I couldn't wait for him, though. He doesn't know you're here."

The moment she'd seen the demon she'd known Noah hadn't left the note. He wouldn't know that she'd been here or that she'd come to work things out. The demon brought her close to his body and she felt him heat up, like he was burning inside. His eyes turned red, but she clung to his warmth because she wanted to live. He brought his face down close to hers. "How long have you been seeing monsters?"

The information hit her like a punch to the chest. They were real. It wasn't second sight. Everything she had seen was real. "S-since I came to Larkshead."

"How long have you been bringing people through the Veil? Did you really think I would let you and that little witch outsmart me?"

Emily relaxed in his grip hoping to give him a sense that she was succumbing to the cold. "What witch?"

He gnashed his pointed teeth. "Phoebe." He pushed her under again for a little longer before bringing her choking and gasping to the surface. When he pulled her up this time, her coat came unzipped and her pentacle contacted his skin. He shrieked in rage and let go of her. She swam away as fast as she could but he reached out and caught her jacket. She shrugged out of it managing to break away and began moving toward the shore. She screamed for help, but the demon used his wings to leap out of the water and land between her and the shore.

His hands tangled in her hair dragging her toward deeper water. She saw something large and dark move swiftly out of the corner of her eye. Suddenly, a large dark body pushed between her and the demon. Blood filled the water, and she was released again. She scrambled through the churning sea trying to get her confused limbs to swim toward shore. Hands grabbed her and she screamed.

"Hold your breath."

The dark thing became a man who was pulling her out further into the sea even as the injured demon moved toward them.

"He won't come out into the deep water."

She struggled, but the man hugged her to his chest placing his hand over her mouth and nose to prevent her from breathing and dived deep under the water. Moving fast, he made his way up the coast oblivious to the cold. Her brain reminded her that she needed air, and so did the burning in her lungs, but the spaces between her thoughts were becoming hard to navigate. Just as she thought she might pass out; they broke the surface again. She breathed in a greedy lungful of air only half aware that the man was now using his body to keep her out of the water.

"It's okay, Emily. Noah sent me to get you. Keep breathing. I'll get you home."

"There was a monster...h-he can fly."

"He can glide, but he can't swim. If he comes at us again, we'll go back underwater."

The coastline slipped by her and the cold sliced through her. A sharp yipping sound followed by long howls made her look toward the beach. Two wolves ran along the shore, one black and the other she recognized.

"Angelo?"

Her voice felt rough and far away. In an instant, the

wolves became two naked men. One was Joseph, the other was Noah. She felt hot tears burning her eyes and she opened her mouth to call out to him. He stepped forward to come get her.

The man beneath her headed for the shore shouting, "Stay out of the water. She's going to need your body heat. Tell your friend to go find your car. We need to get her inside now."

She was lying fully on top of a man with huge black eyes and fins. Then she was in his arms as he carried her toward land. He set her on her feet on the shore, but Emily discovered that her knees refused to hold her.

"We have to get her clothes off and cover her with something warm."

Noah's forestry training kicked in. He stripped Emily as fast as he could throwing aside layers and layers of soaked clothing. For once in her life, she was properly dressed for Maine. Carl helped to get her jeans off and then transferred her into Noah's lap. Emily looked at him with a strange smile on her face. "Angelo?"

He held her close rubbing his hands back and forth over her limbs to try to stimulate circulation. "Yep, you're right. Noah Angelo Hernandez. That's me."

"I'm freezing. I came to talk to you." She couldn't think straight. *Did he say his name was Angelo?* She frowned at him. "Are you my dog?"

He smoothed her hair away from her face but didn't answer.

She looked back at the sea. "Noah, the hands. I saw...a man with fins...I saw..." Tears slid down her cheeks and she began to push him away frantically looking around.

He trapped her arms between them and continued to try and calm her. "Emily, stay here. Stay with me. I know what you saw."

Her body went limp against his, her head lulling back, her eyes wide open like a doll's.

"Emily!"

Carl touched him on the shoulder. "Car's here. We need to go."

The heat was on maximum. Noah held Emily in his arms while Selene checked her heart rate, blood pressure, hands, feet, and ears for signs of hypothermia. Emily didn't respond, not to Selene's questions, not to the pinpricks on her fingertips. She just sat wide-eyed and let both Noah and Selene move her around.

Selene wrapped the stethoscope around her throat. "I am not a qualified medical doctor. She needs to be in the Recovery Center. They're trained to deal with this."

Noah held Emily closer. "Carl's mate struggled with the separation."

Selene looked at him anxiously. "Are you fully bonded?"

"We haven't exchanged the words, but I am fully bonded."

She pursed her lips. "Then go with her. You'll have to stay close and wait for her to process what happened."

"Will she come through the Veil safely like the others?"

Selene shrugged. "I don't know. You said she talked to you when she woke up. That's usually a good sign, but it depends on what she saw and whether she's willing to deal with it." Selene tucked a blanket around them both. "If anyone can help her to come through safely, it's you."

"What do I tell her, Selene? Where do I even start?"

"Tell her the truth. Ask her how you can help her. Listen to her answers. Let her take the lead in her recovery." Selene leaned down and closed Emily's sightless eyes not bothering to hide her own tears. "Tell her we screwed up but we love her. We'll make sure she's safe. We will never let anyone hurt her again."

Noah caught his sister's eye. "I'll tell her. Call Cicero. Tell him I need him."

Cicero came around the end of the couch. "I'm here, boss. Tell me what you need and it's yours.

Noah held his life-mate close. "Take us to the Recovery Center."

Cicero put his hand on Noah and Emily. "No problem, boss. I'm ready to go when you are."

She was in a strange bed, boiling hot, and with a screaming headache. Noah was facing her with the blankets wrapped around them in such a complicated knot that she couldn't decide how to untangle herself. The moment she put her hand on his arm, his eyes snapped open.

"Emily?"

She looked up at him with a half-smile. "Hey, caveman. Where are we? I just had the weirdest dream."

He put his forehead against hers and burst into tears. "I'm so sorry, baby. I wasn't there. I couldn't tell you."

She didn't want to think about what happened yet. She was safe, warm, and in Noah's arms, the exact place she'd wanted to be since their fight.

"Hey. Don't cry. It's okay." She smoothed his hair away from his face. "I dreamed you were Angelo."

He smiled sadly but didn't deny it. "Do you remember why you were in the water?"

Emily stopped not sure of what to say. Choices opened in front of her like a fork in the road. She could tell the truth, or she could hide again. If she hid, then whoever that psycho was that had pushed her into the sea, and tried to murder the woman in the woods, would find another victim. She should call the police. He needed to be caught, but the police would want a description and what could she tell them? She wouldn't lie to Noah again.

Drawing in a shaky breath, she closed her eyes and told the truth. "I found a note from you on my car to say that you wanted to meet me at Red Warf Bay. It said we needed to talk. I was going to tell you…" Emily shook her head and tried again. "I was waiting for you and the demon from my visions found me and tried to drown me in the sea."

"He's Unseelie, dark Fey, not a demon, though, from my experience, they are hard to tell apart. Did he say why he was trying to hurt you? Can you describe him?"

Emily couldn't believe she was having this conversation. "He was huge. Muscular. Deep red skin like he'd been burned."

"Did he have any scars or brands?"

Emily let his acceptance wash over her. Noah could see the monsters. "No, but he had wings. Large leathery wings. He was clicking them-"

"That double-damned bastard. I'm so sorry. Did he ask you about Phoebe Pearce?"

"Yes." She shook her head, "He kept asking about a Veil." Information about the event rushed through her mind. She sat up shrugging the blankets off and scrubbed her hands over her face and looked at him. "Noah, are you my dog?"

He sat up with her brushing the hair from around her face. "I'm the man that loves you more than anything in the world. I am your life-mate and someday, I hope to be your husband." He leaned forward and kissed her.

"That's a very romantic way to avoid my question."

"Sometimes I am Noah your lover, sometimes I am Angelo the wolf at the foot of your bed. The-ah-one that for some reason woke up naked in your bed and had to take your bathrobe to get home."

Emily flinched hardly believing that she was still here listening. It couldn't be true. "Show me."

Noah shook his head scooting closer to her. "You've had a lot of shocks today. I don't want to push you."

She pushed against his chest with both hands. "Either we are both crazy, or neither of us is. I have to know."

Noah got out of bed and came around to stand in front of her. She took a moment to admire his beauty her mind trying to sort out what he just said. He rolled his shoulders and for a moment his body wavered, then it lost all shape as if it were made of liquid, then it reformed. Noah was gone and Angelo sat on the floor.

She scrambled back putting the length of the bed between them still not believing what she had seen. He reversed the transformation and stood in front of her again as a man. He stood perfectly still looking at her intently, silently, pleading for understanding.

"What are you?" Her question was a whisper to her own ears.

"I'm a werewolf."

Emily held her hand up as if doing so would stop the information from seeping into her bones. "You came into my house my first night here. You slept with me. I bought you a dog bowl."

Noah came forward to sit on the end of the bed but didn't reach for her. "I don't remember the first time I came to your house. I only remember waking up there. I couldn't explain to myself what I was doing there, much less explain it to you. I blame Nick and hobgoblin wine. I knew from the first time I saw you going into The Ace of Cups that I wanted you. I told myself that I was giving you choices, but I only gave you the options that led back to me."

Emily rubbed her hands over her face. "Be careful what you wish for."

Noah cocked his head. "What does that mean?"

"That night. The night you came. I was also a little drunk and I made a wish."

"You wished for me?"

"Never mind." Emily waved her hand trying to maintain the high ground. "And after that? Why did you pretend to be my dog?"

"I don't have a defense for that. It was wrong. It's why

your mother was so angry with me. You seemed uncomfortable with my human self around all the time, and I was uncomfortable without you. I thought that coming as Angelo might help us both-"

Emily crawled to the end of the bed furious. "My mother knows you're a werewolf but I don't? Why does she get to know? Don't answer that. I'm going to call her." She began rubbing her forehead. "You know, you were the only normal thing I have ever had in my life."

He tilted his head just like Angelo would have. "We're in trouble if I'm your measurement of normal." He came slowly forward until they were sitting in the middle of the bed with their knees touching.

Emily reached out to touch his leg. "I can't do this. It's too much."

He reached out to catch her hand and hold it. "You're already doing it. Tell me about the candles."

Emily frowned looking up at him. "I don't understand the question. They're just candles. I sell them, Phoebe sells them. That's all."

"Do you wish for something when you're creating them?"

Her mouth dropped open. "How did you know that?" She shrugged suddenly embarrassed. "No. Not all of them. They're blessings to help people. Love, comfort, prosperity, normal stuff like that."

"What about Enlightenment?"

"They were the first kind of candle that I made, and I figured that the people who bought a candle called enlightenment needed help finding their way in the world as badly as I did when I first started out."

Noah laughed but the sound was hollow and there were tears in his eyes.

"I've done something wrong, haven't I?"

He hesitated.

"No more lies."

"I don't know for sure. I'm just guessing. But your blessings are working. I think the Enlightenment candles are bringing people through the Veil."

"What is the Veil?"

"Humans and what you call the supernatural have always lived side by side. When Christianity really started to take hold, those who were different, who represented a different way of worship, they were persecuted. No one knows for sure what happened, but werewolf legend says that a witch called Cecil was captured during the werewolf trials in France sometime in the early 15th century.

She pleaded for her life, but the judges had no mercy. She cursed the hunters to be blind to all things supernatural. She did it to protect her family, but the result was a kind of Veil between two worlds…almost like overlapping realities. On one side are the Enlightened, the ones who are different and can see the real world, on the other are the Unenlightened, the ones who see only what they expect to see."

"How do you keep the worlds separate? There are photographs and videos. It seems impossible."

"It would be except that the Unenlightened won't see the Enlightened, even when it is right in front of their face. If we had been standing on the roadside and someone had seen me shift, they would find a way to logically explain it. Sun in their eyes, overly tired, too many horror movies…anything but the truth. Even if they suspected what they saw was true, who would believe them?"

Emily leaned back stunned. "But some humans come through, right? They come through on their own."

"When someone comes through the Veil intact, they are assigned a guide to help them understand what to acknowledge and what to stay quiet about. The Enlightened have very strict rules of behavior because if a human sees something they absolutely can't explain, then their mind just shuts down. They can't process the information. They almost never come back."

"They die?"

"In a way. It's more like a permanent coma. That's why there are such strict rules about behavior. There are Recovery Centers around the world dedicated to keeping both the Enlightened and Unenlightened safe, but that safety is compromised when a person comes through the Veil unguided. To violate those rules sometimes means death for the Enlightened because the fear of persecution for some outweighs the value of life for another."

Emily swallowed against the lump forming in her throat. "Was the demon sent here to kill me because of my blessing?"

Noah leaned forward to kiss her. "Of course not. No. You're safe. Larkshead is a werewolf sanctuary."

"But I'm not a werewolf."

Noah kissed her again. "The protection of the sanctuary extends to you through me. I am your life-mate. Whatever your fate is, you won't face it alone."

Emily pushed away from him gently. "How can you be so sure that I'm your life-mate?"

He smiled rubbing a bit of her salt-crusted hair between his fingers. "How do you know what your favorite color is? Why do you love one kind of food but not another? There are a thousand little ways I know you are perfect for me. None of them make sense by themselves but when I add them up together, they mean I love you."

"I love you too."

Noah got up from the bed, scooped Emily out, and swung her around hugging her so hard to his chest that her feet dangled. Shrieking and laughing, she wrapped her arms around his neck.

"You're crushing me, caveman!"

"Say it again."

"Say wha-" He squeezed her again until she was almost crying with laughter. "Alright. I love you, Noah Angelo Hernandez."

He sat down with her on the bed settling her in his lap. "Allow me to always remain by your side. I am your life-mate. Never above you. Never below you. Always beside you. Repeat my words and declare yourself as mine."

She shook her head. "I am not declaring anything until I know how this is going to turn out. I take responsibility for my own actions. If I screwed up, I'll pay for it myself."

He growled but did not release her. "The words are a formality. You are mine. I will stand with you."

She brushed her lips across his. "If they don't matter then don't worry about it."

27

Sometimes the best thing to fix a situation isn't magic; it's just saying you are sorry. Other times, no amount of apologizing will make a difference, so a witch has no choice but to roll up her sleeves, put on her pointed hat, and remind them who they are dealing with. —Valerie Black, *Everyday Solutions to Magic Problems*

When they arrived back at Emily's house, there were three cars and a van already in the driveway. Her front door was open, and Joseph and Cicero were loading her candle making equipment into the van. Kiss-Me-Knot moved out of the forest still wearing Emily's bathrobe. Noah barely had time to stop the car before Emily jumped out. Kiss-Me-Knot was instantly at her side.

"Just what the hell is going on here?" She demanded stepping directly in front of the van.

Joseph and Cicero stopped, each of them holding a box of Emily's candles. A woman in a dark suit came out from around the van holding a clip board followed by the Unseelie, James. Kiss-Me-Knot hissed in fury. Noah watched Emily's face lose color.

"Emily Rollins? My name is Jessica Boyce. I've been ordered by the National Recovery unit to confiscate your equipment and place you in custody. You have been accused of 103 counts of unsanctioned awakenings."

James adopted a fighting stance, but Noah whipped through his defenses as if he were standing still. The impact of the attack knocked James off his feet, but Noah dragged him up from the ground by his hair. Before anyone could think to intervene, Noah broke James's arm, nose, and one of his wings. "You almost killed her," he snarled.

"Me next! He owes me too." Kiss-Me-Knot chimed with obvious excitement.

Agent Boyce shouted at Joseph. "Stop him!"

Joseph shrugged and looked at Cicero. "Feel free to intervene."

Cicero spat off the side of the porch. "Forget it. I'm not getting my ass kicked for a demon."

Emily stomped her foot. "Stop, everyone just stop!"

Kiss-Me-Knot looked at Emily questioningly then nodded and snapped her fingers twice. Like pushing pause on a film, everyone froze in place. Without missing a beat, Emily pointed at Cicero and Joseph. "Get my stuff out of that van and put it back where it belongs." She pointed to Noah and Agent Boyce. "Get inside and sit down at the table. When I've had two cups of coffee, we can talk about what's going on here." She pointed at James. "You. Get lost and never come back here again."

Kiss-Me-Knot nodded again. Her malevolent delight was unmistakable. She snapped her fingers twice again. Power, like lightning, flashed through the air and James disappeared out of Noah's grasp as if he'd never been there. Emily turned to Kiss-Me-Knot and smiled. "Thank you."

"Definitely my pleasure," the Wisp responded.

Agent Boyce stammered, "Ms. Rollins you are in no position..."

Emily turned on her heel to walk into her home. "If you don't want to end up lost with him, then shut up. I'm tired of people telling me what to do."

Cicero put down the box he was holding and whistled. Just as he passed Noah heading for the van he smiled politely.

"I really like her, so just so we're clear, you'd better be careful in there because I'm not getting my ass kicked for you either."

Joseph snickered.

The Recovery Center questioning room reminded Emily more of a television FBI headquarters than a hospital. Everyone moved with authority and precision and not one of them was completely human. Emily's trial would start and end today. She and Noah made love recklessly last night and this morning, but Noah was unable to convince Emily to declare him as her life-mate. Angela, as Alpha at the Sanctuary, was appointed judge for the trial.

Because Emily would not declare herself as Noah's

mate, she would not be allowed to claim sanctuary through Noah if the case was not ruled in her favor. Angela had informed her that Emily had exchanged food with the pack, and had brought down a sanctuary enemy, so she could apply for sanctuary in her own right.

As their Enforcer, it would normally be Noah's job to carry out her sentence, but Angela flatly refused to consider that Emily was responsible. Her bias as a judge was something that the National Recovery Unit was aware of, and they had assigned his mother as judge anyway. It gave Noah hope.

Officially Emily was Unguided. He walked beside her holding her hand and naming the different kinds of Enlightened they passed while listing their primary problems when it came to fitting into the mundane world. Kiss-Me-Knot followed so close that occasionally she stepped on Noah's heels.

In no uncertain terms, she had explained to Noah and Emily that she would stay with Emily to fulfill her life price, which Emily had set as a long and happy life. Kiss-Me-Knot's Fey reasoning was that nothing, but Emily's happiness made her happy right now. An abundance of Fey affection was almost a curse itself, but Emily greeted Kiss-Me-Knot's coddling with praise and gratitude which further encouraged the Wil-o-the-Wisp. Much to her delight, Emily had given Kiss-Me-Knot a pentacle necklace which she wore now in exchange for the bathrobe.

Emily just nodded, the information not always making sense to her. "Is this where April was?"

"Yes. Once Cicero brought Michael back to her, she was already coming through. Her Guide feels that she already knew something was different about Michael which made her adjustment easier. Nick is the same as Michael. He's been with her every day. Without Nick, she wouldn't have been able to return home till after Christmas."

"Why?"

Noah rubbed the back of his neck. "The Recovery Centers don't have enough trained Guides to make sure she's safe. There is a lot to learn on the Enlightened side of the Veil."

They passed a series of black doors without name tags or designations on them. Noah paused at the last one. "It's not enough just to show people around, when an Enlightened person volunteers to be a Guide, it's a long-term commitment. There aren't a whole lot of Enlightened in the world, and we try to encourage a non-discriminatory society, but there are some groups that thrive on division, ignorance, and cultism. It's up to the Guides to make sure that the newly awakened are making an informed choice."

He held the door open for her. It wasn't a courtroom like Emily had imagined it would be, it was just a conference table with chairs. Noah led her to the extreme end of the table opposite Angela. On the left side sat Agent Boyce and a harassed-looking older gentleman, and on the right was Selene. Before Emily could be seated Selene approached her and wrapped her arms around her.

"I'm so sorry. This is our fault."

Emily returned the hug gratefully. "Hardly. I've never seen you bless a candle."

The older gentleman stood up and offered his hand to Emily. "I wish we were meeting under better circumstances, Ms. Rollins. I'm Frank Carlos, I'm bringing the charge against you on behalf of the National Recovery Unit and your original accuser, James, as I understand it, is lost." Frank gave Emily a wry smile.

Agent Boyce frowned. "You have Ms. Rollins to thank for that."

Frank glanced over his shoulder. "As I understand it, Ms. Rollins, James as a Recovery Agent seriously violated the code of conduct when he questioned you. He also brought you completely through the Veil regardless of the effect that it would have on yourself or this case. He will be delt with."

Angela stood up and placed both hands on the table. Emily had never seen her look as fierce as she did at that moment. "He has also violated Larkshead Sanctuary laws by crossing onto our territory without permission and after his permission was revoked, attacking two members of my community, killing one underage Unenlightened girl, and authorizing spirit possession."

Agent Boyce blinked and put her hand across her heart. "The Last Stop girl?"

Angela nodded.

Agent Boyce bowed her head. "I didn't know. It is unforgivable."

Frank sat down. "If he's found, he will be held responsible for all charges."

Emily rubbed her forehead. "He won't stay lost. I said to get lost and never come back, not stay lost. I checked with Kiss-Me-Knot, and she said he could be physically lost, mentally lost, or emotionally lost. Probably all three.

I'm afraid I wasn't very specific on how he should get lost, and the wording is apparently important."

Frank indicated for Emily to take a seat and sat. "You aren't the one who sent him away." He looked skeptically at Kiss-Me-Knot. "The rules of fairness according to the Wild Fey are difficult to navigate but I think under the circumstances, you both let him off easy. Now let's talk about your case."

Agent Boyce leaned forward and placed a large green candle from Emily's store on the table. "Ms. Rollins, are you the primary maker of these candles?"

Emily picked it up turning it over sadly. "As far as I know, I'm the only maker."

"Your mother never helps you?"

"No." Emily shook her head. "She's never participated."

"And for the record, can you tell me what the name and purpose of this candle is."

"It's a scented candle made with a blend of beeswax, Star Anise, Eyebright, Bilberry, Mugwort, Lavender, Juniper, and Blue Lotus. The name of the candle is called Enlightenment and I made it to help people find the enlightenment they were looking for."

Frank threaded his fingers together. "So, you meant it to bring people through the Veil?"

She shook her head. "No. Until two days ago, I didn't even know there was such a thing as the Veil."

Agent Boyce crossed her arms over her chest. "Our reports say that you were aware of the Enlightened."

"In a way, but-"

"A recent report filed by Dr. Hernandez also shows a

correlation between the sales of your candles and outbreaks of unsanctioned awakenings."

"Dr. Hernandez?" Noah said his eyes swinging to Selene.

Selene's chin went up. "There isn't 100% correlation, and even if there was, correlation doesn't necessarily mean causation. I haven't finished my investigation for that report, and that report wasn't filed, it was stolen."

Frank looked at Agent Boyce for a long moment. "How was this report obtained, Agent Boyce?"

"I can't say. James used it when he went to defend a vampire called January in Boston. I took it from those proceedings."

Selene pulled some papers from a folder on the table. "Then you won't have seen this data. Although the candles are present in 103 documented cases of unsanctioned awakenings, when you compare those findings with the total number of unsanctioned awakenings across the world, there isn't a statistically significant correlation."

Angela looked at Emily. "Unfortunately, our law states that even one case of an Enlightened person awakening an Unenlightened person is punishable."

Agent Boyce nodded. "Then I would like to point out that one case could be April Wilde."

Noah frowned. "But not Janet Wedgewood?"

"That doesn't matter," Agent Boyce said.

"Doesn't it? When Agent Garland and I investigated Janet Wedgewood's house, there were no candles. In fact, Carl Wedgewood said his wife didn't believe in anything supernatural. I believe it's safe to suggest she wouldn't purchase a candle called Enlightenment."

Selene scanned the paperwork in front of her. "I also don't see Carl or Janet Wedgewood on the sales sheets."

Emily's mouth dropped open. "Where did you get my sales records?"

Selene looked accusingly at Noah for a second. "Noah sent them to me. We wanted to prove you weren't involved."

"Ms. Rollins, how long have you been Enlightened? There seems to be some confusion on the fact. James states in his report that you have been Enlightened your whole life and that you have pretended to be Unenlightened in order to mask your crimes."

Selene shook her head. "That's not possible. I examined Emily after your agent almost drowned her and she was in complete shutdown. This reaction is typically caused by a forced awakening."

Agent Boyce interrupted. "Are you a medical doctor?"

"I'm an epidemiologist who specializes in awakenings. That qualifies me to determine whether someone is exhibiting signs of forced awakening."

Selene and Agent Boyce glared at one another.

Angela smiled. "Forgive me Mr. Carlos, but I'm afraid you don't have a case here. If Emily was awakened a couple of days ago, she can't be held responsible for any of these other awakenings because the law applies only to the Enlightened."

Agent Boyce slammed her fist on the table. "Emily Rollins saw James, knew James was Unseelie before he began to question her. Whether she was aware she was Enlightened or not, she has put people in danger. Alexa Saunders, Maya Cheng, Lakshmi Davies, Flinn Jones…

each of these people had a candle and were brought injured into a Recovery Center completely shut down."

Emily felt sick. "Are they okay?"

"No, Ms. Rollins, they aren't okay. We're not okay. Unsanctioned awakening endangers all of us. Every time someone points a finger at one of us, we risk setting off a witch hunt. One hundred and three people have had their lives irrevocably destroyed because of you."

Selene held up her hand. "Changed, not destroyed. For the record, Agent Boyce, tell Ms. Rollins how many of these cases have resulted in an unrecoverable shutdown."

Agent Boyce raised her chin defiantly. "That's beside the point. The Unguided are dangerous to us. She is dangerous. Ignorance about what she is capable of is not a defense."

Angela growled. "How many, Agent Boyce?"

Frank took the report from Selene's hands and scanned the page. He whistled setting back hard in his chair. "Is this information correct?"

Emily felt her heart sink. "How many?"

"None. Not even one." Frank's smile seemed to split his face in two. "Ms. Rollins, what you've accomplished with your candles is a miracle. The National and International Recovery Units have been unable to sanction many awakenings because they aren't safe. If you've discovered a way to manufacture a safe awakening, I wonder if I could talk to you on behalf of all the Recovery Centers worldwide about exclusively purchasing these candles."

"These people cannot be abandoned. Unguided or not,

she must take responsibility for her actions," Agent Boyce said but with less vehemence.

Noah put his arm around Emily. "What if Emily and I take responsibility for the newly awakened? If they haven't been hurt by their awakening, then Emily's responsibility should only be to either guide them or find a guide for them."

Emily looked at him incredulously. "How could I guide 103 people? I have no idea what the rules of this world are myself?"

Angela gave Frank a serious look. "Dark Wolf Security has offices in other states. I will ask for volunteers to locate and provide guidance for those that the candles have affected starting with Emily. She needs to be assigned a guide."

Noah looked between Frank and Emily concerned. "I have put an application in to be her Guide. So has Selene, Kayleigh Hernandez, and Rowan Martin." He looked at Emily seriously. "The choice of Guides is yours. If you don't want any of these people, we can find someone else. No one here, including myself, has the right to tell you what to do."

Frank cleared his throat. "She will also need to track down the Enlightenment candles already sold and retrieve them."

"Emily has a new business to run," Noah objected, "She can't do that successfully and track candles around the world."

Angela crossed her arms over her chest. "You can't ask her to endanger her livelihood without compensation."

"For compensation, I will hunt down the candles,"

Selene said trying not to meet her mother's eyes. "I already have the sales mapped out. It would be helpful to my research and to the Recovery Unit." She looked at Emily with a hopeful smile. "I've always wanted to travel. It's a hobby that doesn't have to include bug spray. Please. Let me do this for you. My research is being used against you. Let me fix this."

Emily could barely talk around the lump in her throat. "Are you sure? It sounds like a lifetime of work."

Selene straightened. "I've never been more sure of anything in my life."

Frank nodded. "Dr. Hernandez, since Agent Boyce is so interested in seeing justice done, she can join you and help with your recovery efforts."

Frank turned to Emily and Kiss-Me-Knot. "I offer an apology for the attack done by an agent in my command."

He looked at Agent Boyce a long moment before returning his gaze to Emily and Noah. "I won't allow anyone to abuse their position with the Recovery Unit for personal reasons. When James is found, he will be stripped of all privileges and permissions granted to him by my office and held responsible for the lives he destroyed."

He looked at Kiss-Me-Knot again. "As a personal favor, I'd appreciate it if he didn't meet with any more accidents if he's found."

Emily frowned looking at Kiss-Me-Knot who was ignoring the conversation happily twirling the pentacle on her necklace. The Wil-o-the-Wisp had been censored for her use of magic several times but like most of the Fey born before the 11th century, she took very little notice.

They began to leave but Kiss-Me-Knot grabbed Noah's arm.

"Is this a good time to guess your secret?"

Noah blinked suddenly understanding why Kiss-Me-Knot had demanded to be here. "Yes. Go ahead and guess. What's my secret?"

She looked at Frank Carlos seriously. "Noah's secret. I guess he isn't telling you that the Veil is a curse, and it is being broken. I also guess that he isn't telling you that the Unseelie do not want it to fall. Deceit is easier for them when the world is split in two. They are killing unguided witches to keep Earth, Air, Fire and Water, from surrounding the Truth Speaker. The Unseelie will fail. The Veil will fall. I guess the Enlightened don't have long to prepare."

"What can we do?" Frank asked her softly.

"Get ready for the world to change." Kiss-Me-Knot reached over to grab Emily's hand. "And direct your energies for a peaceful outcome."

"I wish this would have a peaceful outcome and everyone I cared for would be safe," Emily said suddenly.

Kiss-Me-Knot chuckled and snapped her fingers twice. "Maybe you are an angel and a witch."

Emily frowned. "You're the second Enlightened to call me an angel this week. Why?"

Kiss-Me-Knot shrugged with a mischievous snicker. "That's not my secret."

---

28

*There will always be ways to split people up into groups;
Enlightened or Unenlightened, Witch or Werewolf, Seelie or
Unseelie, poor or rich. With those groupings comes an oversim-
plification of a complex group of individuals. The newly Awakened witch should remember that each person they encounter is
an individual with hopes, fears, and dreams whether or not they
also have fins, feathers, or fur. That one piece of knowledge is
the key to becoming fully Enlightened.* —Phoebe Pearce,
Witchcraft for the Newly Awakened

Emily and Noah moved around the Christmas Market
putting the ghost-like memories of the Christmas Tree
lighting to bed by eating, drinking, and enjoying the
company of family and friends. There were candles,
torches, suns, moons, and pentacles everywhere.

Jessie Wilde stood holding the hand of Rowan Martin
as they opened the Yule celebrations with a Goddess
chant backed up by the Larkshead Christmas Choir.

Music, dancing, and small bonfires were lit around the square and although there were still some Unenlightened in their midst, the Enlighten showed off their skills, scales, and smiles wherever they could. Noah had strictly forbidden anyone from jumping over the Yule fires for health and safety reasons but that didn't stop any of the witches, including Emily, from indulging in the tradition while his back was turned.

Emily wasn't surprised to find that April had sold all the Sugar Plum Fairies 3 times over according to the stock list. Or that the other fairies showing up at the shop were real fairies that had struck a deal with Nick Wilde to find new homes. Or that one particularly tough-looking Sugar Plum Fairy called Gilly was officially taking up residence at The Ace of Cups and wanted to be paid in Irish whiskey for her services.

Emily had bargained with the fairy to include preventing shoplifting as one of her duties along with her original offer not to break, spill, or interfere with the cash register speaking with the debit card machine. Gilly had agreed to the extra duties and restrictions so long as her whiskey was a single malt. Noah assured her that she'd made a good deal.

Kiss-Me-Knot's affection had turned to friendship. Granting Emily's last desire had cost her most of her magic and would probably still only soothe the coming transition, but every little bit helped. She did not join the Yule celebrations because she said some ghosts could only be faced alone.

When the public celebrations ended, Emily invited Noah back to her home. They made it up the steps before

Emily turned to him and handed him a small box wrapped in white paper with red squirrels wearing Santa hats.

"Happy Solstice."

He grinned gently opening the package to reveal a box containing a small, misshaped block of fudge and a house key. His eyes met hers with surprise. "What's this?"

"A key to my house and the only piece of fudge that came out edible when your mom tried to show me how to make it." She gave him a soft kiss. "Noah Angelo Hernandez, I am your life-mate. Never above you. Never below you. Always beside you." Emily took the fudge out of the box with trembling hands, split it in half, and put it in her mouth. She winced offering him the other half. "Maybe edible is a generous term here."

Noah ate the fudge from her hand and then scooped her up into his arms and held her close. "Emily Rollins, I am your life-mate. Never above you. Never below you. Always beside you." They held each other for a long moment before Noah leaned back with a frown. "What is your middle name anyway?"

Emily grinned in a very Kiss-Me-Knot way. "It's a secret."

They opened the front door together and went inside hand in hand.

-END-

ACKNOWLEDGMENTS

A special thanks to Michelle De La Garza and DLG Publishing Partners for giving me a chance to share my story. Hannah Bell, Emma Ransom-Jones, and the Moon Kittens for cheering me on no matter what, and Steena who was my first official fan.

ABOUT THE AUTHOR

Dr. DeAnn Bell is a Kentucky-born, New Mexico-raised writer who lives permanently in Wales with her husband and cats. She is widely published in places such as Open Pen, Women's Archive Wales, Witches and Pagans, and Sage Woman. She has a Ph.D. in Creative and Critical Writing and is a professional member of the National Association of Writers in Education, The Society of Authors, and organizes the North Wales Pagan Moot Group. She loves coffee, cats, and genre-bending fiction with complex conflicts and real-world issues, especially if they have happy endings.

The Athenian Option

radical reform for the House of Lords

Anthony Barnett
and
Peter Carty

imprint-academic.com/sortition

First edition published in 1998 by Demos

2008 edition published in the UK by Imprint Academic
PO Box 200, Exeter EX5 5YX, UK
2008 edition published in the USA by Imprint Academic
Philosophy Documentation Center
PO Box 7147, Charlottesville, VA 22906-7147, USA

ISBN 978-1845401399 (paper)
ISBN 978-1845401405 (cloth)

A CIP catalogue record for this book is available from the
British Library and US Library of Congress

Front cover illustration:
Hellenistic *kleroterion* (lottery machine), c. 200 BCE
Athens, Epigraphical Museum

Contents

For Ian Christie,
our first publisher

I am arguing for a new constitutional settlement,
a new deal between the people and the state that
puts the citizen centre stage. A deal that gives people
new powers and a stronger voice in the affairs
of the nation. And a deal that restores a sense of
cohesion and vitality to our national life.

I want to see a fundamental shift in the balance of
power between the citizen and the state—a shift away
from an over-powering state to a citizens' democracy
where people have rights and powers and where
they are served by accountable and responsive
government.

Rt. Hon. John Smith MP
1 March 1993

Preface to the New Edition

More than a decade has passed since we wrote the pamphlet which comprises the bulk of this slim volume. This is a good moment for taking stock, for looking back at its reception and for examining the prospects for its central idea. When it was published the response we received was on a scale and of an intensity not normally associated with think-tank papers, which are usually of interest only to small groups of commentators and experts. Our core arguments (set out in the summary on page 15) aroused widespread and very strong reactions. By any reckoning this feedback was not always positive, including as it did brutal dismissiveness, accusations of irrelevance and straightforward ridicule.

Professional politicians, perhaps inevitably, could not welcome proposals which questioned their stranglehold over so much of our democracy. We experienced this cold-shouldering at first hand, when we gave evidence to the Royal Commission on the Reform of the House of Lords in May 1999. Contempt and hostility were almost palpable behind a veneer of strained civility. This was not surprising, because the Commission's panel of mostly superannuated politicians and associated camp followers was part of the very group-

ing whose domination of the Lords we had come along
to challenge.

Their chairman, Lord Wakeham, was widely
acknowledged to be a fixer extraordinaire. He had
been Tory leader of the Lords and remained head of
the Press Complaints Commission while he undertook
the role of steering the Royal Commission. Its conclusions were that the status quo could hardly be
improved upon, and that the UK's appointed upper
house should continue largely unaltered with perhaps
a smattering of elected peers to give it a facade of popular approval. The feeling was that the Prime Minister
wanted it this way, at least while he was in office.

We were surprised, but not astonished, to learn that
Wakeham was also extending his professional expertise to Texas in a role on the board of Enron, at least
until its complete collapse in scandal and fraud—for
which he was in no way responsible. People remember
Enron as a salutatory lesson, but who recalls the collapse into irrelevance of the Wakeham Commission?
On the other hand, perhaps this kind of forgetting is
one of the time-honoured routines by which the British way of government preserves itself.

Be that as it may, some members of the Commission
were afflicted with a kind of bemused puzzlement
about our proposed 'Athenian Option'. There was
something here, they felt, that could not quite be
stamped upon, that was slipping and sliding away
from their best efforts to humanely put it down. A
Conservative peer deigned to address one of us in the
lift on the way up to the proceedings. 'You know', said
this grey-faced timeserver, with an air of bafflement,
'wherever we go in the country, people keep coming
up to us with this idea.' It had clearly never crossed his
mind for a moment that if people were spontaneously
suggesting the principles of the jury system could be

applied to hold government to account, then there might therefore be something to the idea.

Reaction from media commentators was, with honourable exceptions, severe. This was to be expected and we are not going to pretend that there is any mystery behind it. The society in which we live is predicated upon a self-perpetuating hierarchy and the fourth estate is an integral part of an excluding establishment. A couple of dozen private schools and a couple of universities supply the ballast both of our executive and of our senior editors and commentators. Accordingly, when it comes to politics the media concerns itself with day-to-day factional disputes, scandals and administrative malpractices. It has little stomach for tackling fundamental and pressing issues of democracy and government. It followed that where the media was not overtly dismissive it ran stories concerned with the perceived newness of the idea, rather than subjecting it to serious and dispassionate analysis. Novelty sells newspapers, after all.

At the same time there has been a definite change in the underlying mood, which itself may have contributed to the momentum behind the publication of a splendid spread of studies of the experience and potential of 'sortition' (as we are learning to call it), of which this second edition of *The Athenian Option* is now a part.

As the idea is simple enough, the reaction to it becomes an important part of the argument. We have therefore added two appendices. The first consists of the submission we sent the Wakeham Commission (whose members' names are listed) followed by the proceedings in which we gave oral evidence to them in public. As you can see, most of them felt that silence was the kindest form of asphyxiation, but to some degree our idea was tested, even challenged. There is a striking exchange at the start when Wakeham objects to our proposal on the grounds that the Lords could not continue to play the same role as a legislative chamber, initiating a large part of the work of parliament in the way it does at present. This was revealing for two reasons:

- The formal terms of reference for the Commission were sweeping, specifically permitting a complete reconsideration of the Lords' legislative role and function, provided the Commons retained its primacy. In fact the Commission's chairman assumed from the outset that the status quo would not be fundamentally changed.
- Members of the public think of the Lords as a second chamber that scrutinises bills passed by the first, and most are surely unaware that it plays a significant role in initiating legislation, even though it has no democratic legitimacy.

If readers are interested in the Commission's conclusions, the tenor of its approach is captured by brief extracts from the following clauses:

- (13) No radical change is needed in the balance of power between the two Houses of Parliament....
- (14) ... the new second chamber should have the same powers as the present House of Lords ...
- (16) There should be no significant changes in the second chamber's law-making functions...
- (17) The second chamber's role in protecting the constitution should be maintained.

Perhaps we can claim to have helped make a small dent in the ancient armory of the British constitution: it was officially admitted that our approach existed. In the executive summary of its findings the Commission's Report states:

After making a detailed analysis of potential methods of composition we do not recommend:

- a wholly or largely directly elected second chamber;
- indirect election from the devolved institutions (or local government electoral colleges) or from among United Kingdom MEPs;
- random selection
- co-option.

It did not share its 'detailed analysis' with the public. But it did publish some of the results of a survey. It offered the thousand people who attended the public sessions of the Commission a questionnaire which about 600 filled in, as did 340 people from the Commission's website. Of this sample 13 per cent supported 'random selection' as their preferred method of appointing an upper house. This was the lowest scoring system. Direct election got the highest score, but with only 45 per cent support; while 34 per cent supported 'a mixture of two or more methods'. But note that 'random selection' is the most misleading description possible. If members of the public had been asked to choose 'like a jury drawn from a cross-sample of citizens' the number would have been higher.

Our second appendix reproduces some of the press response, in particular that in the Times, which made the story its own, with an Editorial and an op-ed article by Anthony. It then published two sets of lively letters from its readers. The Guardian by contrast ignored the publication but carried a column by Hugo Young which showed that he had not deigned to read the pamphlet before blasting it with his scorn. This is a warning. However carefully advocates of experiments with sortition may be, they should not expect their care and precision to be respected. Our joint letter in response was not published but we have included it here. We have not reproduced some of the other generous coverage such as the report in the Daily Mail.

There are two changes of context which make reading *The Athenian Option* a different experience from a
decade ago, one global and the other national.

We have mentioned the way the idea was apparently being spontaneously suggested by regular
people when they thought about how to recruit a second chamber. Indeed we ourselves came to the idea
separately and, learning of each other's proposals,
decided to collaborate. We were unaware that in the
United States Ernest Callenbach and Michael Phillips
had proposed *A Citizen Legislature* (also republished in
this series). The parallels are remarkable: for example
both make the suggestion that one aim and outcome of
sortition would be clear, comprehensible laws. They
point out that one sentence of the US Inland Revenue
Code is 506 words long and that once, in 1983, the
House of Representatives passed 200 bills in an afternoon without discussion. (As an experiment, if you
have the good fortune to meet an MP, ask him or her
how much of the legislation they have voted on they
have read, and what would happen if we made it a
rule that MPs read at least half of the words they turn
into law.) Today there is a genuine literature on
sortition and Oliver Dowlen's new study[1] reveals a
long, rich history, which shows that the Athenian epi-
sode, although outstanding, was not unique.

Meanwhile there has been a flowering of experiments with deliberative democracy. James Fishkin has
developed the technique of 'deliberative polling' at his
Stanford Centre for Deliberative Democracy and is
building an international body of experience. In Canada, in British Columbia and Ontario, full scale experiments in deliberative assemblies have taken place. In

---

[1] Oliver Dowlen, *The Political Potential of Sortition: A study of the
random selection of citizens for public office* (Exeter: Imprint
Academic, 2008).

the EU, under Commissioner Margot Wallstrom, 'Plan-D' has poured resources into deliberative processes in an attempt to close the gap between the peoples of Europe and Brussels.

Unfortunately in addition to multiplication of initiatives, since publication there have also been a lot of experiments that often only nominally fall into the domain of direct democracy. In particular, the number of experiments with citizens' juries at local and national level has been growing. This does not provide much cause for optimism since, in lieu of any decision-making powers, they have been no more than focus groups by another name. Professional politicians are past masters of dissimulation and equivocation, and — above all in this context — procrastination.

Which brings us to the Lords itself, a decade on. Will the legislature remain mired in tortuous attempts to reform itself? Recently the House of Commons has voted in favour of a largely elected second chamber and the government is now attempting to secure all-party agreement for this in the Lords itself. Once — when the Lords was a hereditary house of utterly conservative views and the stench of ermine — this would indeed have promised a radical democratization. Today, however, being filled with often independent-minded nominated peers, it can be if anything to the left of the House of Commons, more principled and democratic in its temperament. This may not be saying much, but it has been enough to bring the parties together in a determined effort to abolish this impediment to their dictatorship. Almost certainly their new proposals will create a second chamber of party-political nominees elected under a system that makes it almost impossible for independents to win many, or indeed any, seats.

But this also means that a national debate on the nature and the role of the second chamber could take place with some practical effect. An elected chamber cannot be called a house of 'Lords'. Replacing its name will symbolize that half the country's parliament is to be altered. Disenchantment with political parties could open the way for those who want to see more direct forms of political self-determination where sortition can play a part. The age of deference has gone forever and it becomes ever more obvious that professional politicians are of no more or less ability than the rest of us. This recognition must inform and give impetus to efforts to reform our government.

We therefore decided to tax the patience of our new publishers, and hold completion until the promised White Paper on how Britain will proceed to a new second chamber was released. Our response to it follows the original pamphlet (see below, p.60).

Our proposals look forward to and celebrate the rise of a society and community which is not based upon social exclusion and the conservation of a ruling elite. We think a populace which enjoys much greater equality of access to superior education and fulfilling employment will expect and demand its concerns to be represented much more directly in the processes by which we are ruled. Given the swift pace of change in our social fabric, changes often facilitated and inaugurated by new technology, we may not have long to wait.

Anthony Barnett and Peter Carty
London, August 2008

The Athenian Option

Summary

- This paper proposes an 'Athenian' solution to the reform of the House of Lords. This could take the form of an experimental programme over several years to apply the most advanced methods of deliberative polling and direct democracy to the work of the second chamber. This approach would bring the reform of the Lords into the rapidly developing debate on radical experimentation with new democratic bodies and procedures at local and regional level, in the interest of revitalising our democracy. The last state in the world to cling to the hereditary principle in its parliament would become the first to introduce modern principles of citizen scrutiny at the highest level.

- The authors propose that the House of Lords should be changed into a second chamber with broadly similar powers to those exercised by the present one: a chamber of scrutiny unable to challenge the legislative will of the Commons. Except that it should have three enhanced powers of scrutiny: it should be able to insist that new legislation is drafted in clear English; that new laws should not lead to outcomes that are at odds with the Government's declared intentions; and that new laws do not endanger basic constitutional values.

- To exercise such a role, the reformed second chamber needs an impartial, nonparty political character. This can be obtained by selecting a proportion — ideally, ultimately the majority — of its members by lot from among registered voters, on the lines of a jury. This should not be entirely random. Different regions should be represented in proportion to their population, each with an equal number of men and women.

- Those selected could be called PPs (Peers in Parliament). They could serve full-time for a fixed period or they could be selected to scrutinise a particular piece of legislation. The paper seeks to establish only the viability of the principle; it offers different options for implementation. It also argues that there would be a need for nominated PPs, similar to present life peers, to serve alongside those selected by lot.

- Around the world, second chambers often reflect national traditions. An Athenian solution to the problem of reforming the Lords would continue the random and non-party-political aspect of hereditary entitlement while abolishing the hereditary principle. It would also preserve the existing relationship of the two houses of parliament, and it would do both in a creative and democratic fashion. *Instead of trying to 'catch up' with other countries, Britain should use the opportunity offered by constitutional reform to move ahead and experiment with new forms of democracy.*

Introduction

A national debate is under way on the reform of the House of Lords. Broadly, three options are available for modernising our second chamber of parliament. We can create a new elected house. We can set up a new version of an appointed chamber. Or we can introduce a radical reform to create a wholly new form of assembly that will complement the work and make-up of the Commons and add a new dimension to democracy in the UK. This essay proposes that *a reformed upper chamber should consist largely, but not entirely, of representative groups of citizens chosen by lot from among the electorate on the lines of a jury.* We argue that this reform, which could be introduced gradually on an experimental basis, could help revitalise the work of parliament as a whole, avoid the problems associated with the other options for reinventing the Lords and contribute to the wider process of reinvigorating British democracy at national, regional and local level.

The background to the argument

The Government has established a seven-person Cabinet sub-committee to oversee its policy on the reform of the House of Lords.[1] Its brief is to advise on how to remove hereditary peers by statute from their role as voting members of the British houses of parliament. This step is often referred to as 'the first stage' and it

---

[1] It is known as CRP(HL). Its members are Lord Irvine of Lairg (Lord Chancellor), Lord Richard QC (Leader of the Lords), Ann Taylor MP (Leader of the House), Nick Brown MP (Chief Whip), Lord Carter (Chief Whip, Lords), Jack Straw MP (Home Secretary), Peter Mandelson MP (Minister Without Portfolio). See *Central Lobby* No 2, February-March 1998, published by Charter 88, a useful guide to the current state of constitutional legislation, and *Reforming the Lords: a step by step guide*, The Constitution Unit, January 1998.

is one of Labour's clear manifesto commitments. The manifesto also recognises that more will be needed. Abolishing the right of hereditary peers to sit and vote 'will be the first stage in a process of reform to make the House of Lords more democratic and representative'.

The sub-committee will therefore consider:

- whether the government should be committed to a 'second stage' at the same time as it carries out the first stage
- what kind of reform or replacement of the Lords this should entail
- how to bring about such reform or replacement.

Britain is now entering a period of comprehensive constitutional change. Reforms are already underway, from the Scottish Parliament, the Welsh Assembly and a London Mayor, to the human rights legislation. These reforms will have a dynamic and novel impact on the relationships between government and the governed, a change amplified by the European dimension. In these circumstances, why should our mental framework see no further than the grooves of the American or German models of a constitution—or a fudge of our present, unwritten one?

The overall reform of the Lords provides an opportunity to take advantage of what has been termed the 'democratisation of democracy'.[2] New methods of debate and accountability, from citizens' juries and focus groups to deliberative assemblies and tele-polling, are being developed. The Government and many other bodies are considering ways in which the often moribund state of local democracy in the UK could be revitalised through the introduction of

[2] See *Lean Democracy, Demos Quarterly,* issue 3; Coote A. and Lenaghan. J, 1997, *Citizens' Juries: theories into practice,* IPPR, London.

new forms of direct participation — such as local citizens' juries, mayoral elections, deliberative opinion polls, standing citizens' panels, referendums and forums.[3] There is a growing willingness to entertain the idea of *radical experimentation* in the cause of modernising and reinvigorating our democracy at the local and regional level. We see no reason why ideas for radical pilot schemes at the United Kingdom level for bodies such as the second chamber should be viewed as exotic or impractical, while plans for such initiatives are rightly applauded at the level of local and regional governance. Our proposal should be seen as a contribution to this new wave of debate and willingness to experiment.

In terms of the bigger picture, it is now clear that over the next few years Britain will move towards a new constitutional settlement. At such a moment it would be fatal to see this as an exercise that is limited to 'catching up' — as if the problem were simply one of overcoming the backwardness of the relatively archaic British state. For a start, there is no ideal democratic regime elsewhere with which we should aim to catch up: democracy everywhere stands in need of improvement and revitalisation. At the same time, other governments are advancing. The commitment to the Euro, for example, is a far more radical step than would be the creation of a written constitution for the UK. Although the reform we are advocating is a modest one, its spirit is adventurous and ambitious. *We need a new approach to democracy.* One that closes the gap between rulers and ruled; one that increases, in a practical and efficient manner, the capacity of citizens to participate in the process of democratic government.

---

[3] Department of the Environment, Transport and the Regions, 1998, *Modernising Local Government*, DETR, London, esp ch. 4.

Our argument is that a reformed upper chamber should consist largely, but not entirely, of representative groups of citizens chosen by lot from among the electorate along the lines of a jury. The members of this reformed upper house would be partly selected by a form of lot that would produce a representative sample of citizens. Through such an initiative, introduced gradually through experimentation over several years, we could see the world's first full-scale application at a national level of contemporary methods of citizen scrutiny and 'deliberative' democracy. The last state to cling to the hereditary principle might become the first to apply modern, direct democratic processes within its parliament.[4]

It is said that there are three stages in the life of every important idea. First it is ignored. Next it is ridiculed. Then it becomes accepted wisdom. A 'citizens' second chamber' is not a new idea, but until now the proposal has been largely ignored. Things, however, seem to be hotting up, and the ridicule stage has been reached. The *Independent* used the idea for its 1998 April Fool story with the headline: 'People's Lords to replace hereditary peers'. The witty part of the spoof was to suggest that Labour would select voters by lot to replace hereditary peers as they die — thus preserving the Lords in its existing role. But by focusing on this particular target, the paper seemed to treat the very idea that 'ordinary citizens' could participate in the legislature as ridiculous. A good supply of April Fool headlines lies in store. One might be 'New law to give readers the power to replace editors' (now come to think of it...)

---

[4]   Discussed along with an overview of 1997, the nature of the British constitution and a theory of change, in Barnett A., 1997, *This Time: Our constitutional revolution*, London.

In a way, the spoof version of the proposal has already had an informal airing in the Lords itself. In a two-day debate on the future of the Lords in July 1996 the Conservative leader in the Chamber, Robert Cranborne, attempted to defend the *status quo*. At one point, he argued that the biological and hence non-party-political nature of hereditary peers meant that they are in many ways just like 'ordinary people'. In this respect, he suggested, they could be compared to the ancient legislators of Athens where, for 150 years, a jury selected at random from free, male citizens ruled that famous city state. Cranborne seemed a mite embarrassed as he made the comparison. After all, most hereditary peers went to privileged, private schools — 47 per cent of Tory peers went to Eton.[5] Even if one of them is now 'an ordinary doctor or dentist', they are all too un-random a selection of the British people, and he knew it.[6]

At any rate, the idea that genuinely random selection might be a useful way of constituting our upper chamber is not new.[7] This paper, however, is a first attempt to look seriously at what powers such a chamber might have and exercise, and why; how its participants might actually be chosen; and what other appointments along the lines of current life peers may be needed for it to work. The aim is a replace-

[5] MacAskill E, *Guardian*, 8 January 1998.
[6] The phrase with its unwittingly revealing glimpse of what ordinariness means to aristocrats comes from the Earl of Camarvon and others, *Second Chamber, Some remarks on reforming the House of Lords, 1995*, p. 27. In an aside, it too compares the random nature of hereditary selection with classical Athens.
[7] *A House of Peers: The Athenian Solution*, draft paper for Charter 88 Council by Anthony Barnett, 6 July 1996, see Polly Toynbee in the *Independent* 29 January 1997. The present, joint paper came about after Peter Carty developed the core idea independently and learnt of Barnett's draft.

ment of the Lords that would nonetheless fit within the existing, if rapidly changing, British constitution.

As for specific proposals about how 'jury selection' could be implemented, a range of alternatives has resulted from our collaboration, and we hope that other ideas will be stimulated by this paper. For there are different ways in which randomly selected voters might be incorporated into the legislative process to create deliberative assemblies of representative citizens: from a virtually permanent body on which members serve for a number of years to juries selected on a 'case by case' basis to scrutinise and oversee the passage of specific legislation.

We will show that a second chamber that draws on Athenian principles of selection and deliberation can have a genuinely representative character; that it could have sufficient legitimacy to be stronger than the present House of Lords when necessary without becoming a competitor with the Commons in a way that might gridlock the political system; that it could add a new interest among the public in policy making; and that it meets the six criteria set out (whether cynically or sincerely is beside the point) by the Conservative Party for an acceptable upper house.

Our proposal for citizens to take part in an 'Athenian' style chamber of scrutiny is *not* an attack on party politics. Rather it suggests a way in which members of the public can play a *complementary* and not a competitive role alongside elected politicians whose democratic mandate will give them the exclusive right to propose new legislation. For British politics already has a strong elective component, powerful party traditions and a historic chamber, the House of Commons, which has established its legislative priority based upon its elected character. A reformed second chamber needs to reinforce, not undermine, the Commons. If anything, its influence should be designed to encourage and enhance the ability of MPs, of whom there are already 650, to hold the executive to account. A second house selected largely, though not solely, by lot would be just such a constructive addition. Party politics urgently needs to be reconnected to modern life and our suggestion is one way that the new connection might be made.

We are *not* saying that selection by a form of lot is better than elections. On the contrary, in a society the size of ours representative democracy is essential and central. What we are saying is that we already have enough nationally elected politicians. We may need more elected representatives at the regional level, or as mayors in the towns and cities, or to represent the parish. But we already send plenty of them to Westminster. The question is how they are to be *helped to rule:* how can scrutiny improve the legislation they already produce and check the excesses they are capable of committing?

By contrast, an elected second chamber is likely to create a potentially destructive alternative to the House of Commons. However much it may be constrained by rules, when critical votes have to be made politicians (and those who are elected *are* politicians) will mostly vote on the basis of their loyalty to the party that selected and then helped elect them. They will either seize the chance to try and bring down the government in the Commons if they are in opposition to it, or they will dutifully support it when it has staked all on a policy that dispassionate argument has exposed as fundamentally flawed, such as the Poll Tax.

The arguments in favour of an Athenian solution are therefore twofold. There is the intrinsic, positive argument in its favour and there is the negative argument that alternatives are worse.

Of course, a new upper house should not be designed around a preferred manner of selecting its members. Rather, the method of selection should be decided so as to best fit the role that a second chamber should play. This is the order the argument will follow.

The Significance of the Issue

First, however, it may be valuable to emphasise the importance of the issue. There have been many proposals for a new upper chamber, and indeed the 1911 Act that reformed the Lords has encouraged people to reinvent the body. This Act included in its preamble a famous example of words becoming a surrogate for action:

> it is intended to substitute for the House of Lords as presently constituted a second chamber constituted on a popular instead of a hereditary basis.

This game seems to be over. Labour's commitment means hereditary peers are doomed. An unelected house of appointed life peers cannot long replace them. It will not have the legitimacy to be supportable. And it will not be supported, as both the Conservative and Liberal Democrat parties have made clear. In so far as anything is certain in British politics, therefore, there is going to be a new upper house in the coming period.

This is going to have a profound effect on the way constitutional change is perceived, especially in England. In Scotland and Wales, Labour's legislation is creating new institutions that already provide a popular image and focus for change and open up a new space for democratic politics. In England there has been no such effect. Rather there is a feeling that politics is more tightly controlled, manipulated and is less democratic since May 1997. Voters do not believe that they have acquired their human rights, or that the relationship between them and government is being improved — in the way that the prime minister states is the case in his preface to the Freedom of Information White Paper.

There are a number reasons for this. One is the poor and self-contradictory presentation of genuine reforms by ministers. The problem is not one of presentation alone. From an English perspective, that is to say from the point of view of by far the largest section of the electorate, Labour's constitutional programme has been negative. It is seen, in so far as it is visible at all, as eliminating outdated impediments rather than creating new opportunities. The Scots want a parliament — they will no longer be *stopped* from having it. The European Convention on Human Rights is already the law of the land, British judges will no longer be *prevented* from adjudicating it. Going to the international court at Strasbourg was an impediment that the Human Rights Act will therefore *remove*. Freedom of information will likewise *remove an impediment* to our knowing what is going on. Hereditary peers are a self-evident anachronism. Labour will *get rid of them*. Londoners suffer from being the only European capital without a government, this incongruity will be *eliminated*. You can call it negative modernisation, or you can call it good housekeeping cleaning out after the previous owners, but from an English point of view Labour has not been seen as constructing new structures.

Its proposals for a new House of Lords will change this. Finally, Labour will no longer be telling us what it dislikes: it will be telling us what it wants Britain's constitutional structure and spirit *to be like*. It will be creating a new, governing institution of its own. Furthermore, this institution will touch almost every relationship of state sovereignty: the Church, the legislature, the monarchy, not to speak of the executive, the Law Lords and, as devolution proceeds, the relation of Westminster to the United Kingdom as a whole.

The House of Lords is at present a pretty powerless, symbolic institution whose main actual (or efficient[8]) role is to provide a space for government to amend its own legislation. But this so-called unimportance is deceptive. The Lords is also, to use a current phrase, an institution that 'brands Britain'. Its (dignified) symbolism means that it has a special importance in the public eye. It provides an image of what Britain *was*. A new upper house will provide an image of what Britain will become. Or rather, of what Labour wants Britain to become. Labour's decision on the Lords will be a 'defining moment'.[9]

The Government should not seek to preserve as much of the Lords as possible. If it does it will be justly criticised for being radical in talk while bending its knee in deeds. It should not look backwards to see how best it can keep what works well enough for it at the moment. Would a *genuinely* new, young, modern Government spend a lot of time keeping the House of Lords pretty much as it is with the addition of a few elected members? The answer should be 'no' — and on this question public sentiment is radical.

The Powers and Role of the Upper House

Technically, the House of Lords retains formidable powers that are a residue of its having been, historically, a full-blooded legislative chamber. In reality, the

[8] The distinction between the 'efficient' and 'dignified' role of civic institutions is derived from Walter Bagehot, *The English Constitution* (1867).
[9] See Anthony Barnett *The Defining Moment*, published by Charter 88, 1995.

current role and powers of the Lords are more limited and have been analysed in detail elsewhere.[10] They may be summarised as:

- *Scrutiny and revising:* it oversees up to 1,500 amendments to legislation every year, often at the government's instigation.
- *Deliberation:* it debates legislation as well as issues of importance where there is no proposed legislation. It also has specialist select committees.
- *Power of delay:* it can force the government to think again by delaying nonfinancial legislation for a year, although this power is hardly ever used.
- *Power to act as a constitutional check* in limited cases such as election law.

In a recent interview, the Lord Chancellor, Derry Irvine, suggested that the existing powers of the Lords are 'about right' for any future chamber.[11] But is it the case that the existing system in Westminster works so well that its only significant drawback is the method whereby members qualify for the second chamber? There is one respect in which Irvine's view is right. If an upper chamber was given or gained considerable new powers to legislate, or to delay financial legislation, or to prevent the passage of regular legislation, then it could act as a competitor to the House of Commons. Such an outcome is likely to be destructive. The American experience shows how competition between arms of the legislature can result in gridlock that then encourages covert and corrupt practises. To this extent then, if he means that the Commons should continue to be the supreme law

---

[10] Lynda Clark MP, *Reform of the Legislative Process*, Submission to the House of Commons Select Committee on the Modernisation of the House of Commons, 12 July 1997.
[11] Interview with Ian Hargreaves, *New Statesman*, 6 February 1998.

making body within the UK, Irvine has a strong case. Anyway, this view is already written into the Labour manifesto: 'The legislative powers of the House of Lords will remain unaltered'.

But it does not follow that all is well, either on the day-to-day level or at the deeper level of the underlying structure of political power in Britain. The relationship between the executive and the two houses of the legislature is unhealthy. The virtually nonexistent power of the Lords is not 'about right', for example, in circumstances where the Commons passes manifestly undemocratic laws. The second chamber should have the power to veto legislation that is constitutionally dangerous — provided the judgement on this is seen to be impartial. Also, it ought to have the power to return legislation to the Commons for it to be reconsidered if it is found to be manifestly likely to produce outcomes that the government says it wishes to avoid. Finally, it should be able to ensure that legislation is drafted in clear language that the public can comprehend.

In all these ways, the *powers of scrutiny* of the second chamber need to be enhanced. This role cannot be left to the Commons alone. Partly because it is inherently adversarial, partly because of the patronage system and the role of the whips, the Commons is at best arbitrary in its treatment of the detail of legislation. The British system needs a second chamber to exercise constructive scrutiny, to safeguard democracy and to help ensure the honest and clear exercise of power. To fulfil such a role, however, it needs to be capable of dispassionate rather than party-political oversight.

Thus, while the *strictly legislative* powers of the second chamber should indeed remain unaltered, and provided its composition can ensure that it is capable of being impartial, its powers to scrutinise and to check legislation should be increased in three ways. It should have the power to:

- insist that laws are drafted in language that is clear and understandable
- return legislation that, beyond reasonable doubt, will fail in its stated aim
- reject legislation that threatens the fundamental values of our constitution.

Each of these issues is considered below.

Language

Our elected representatives in the House of Commons should decide what laws are to be passed. But a second chamber can have authority to insist that these laws be expressed in clear English. Much of the legislation that the Commons produces is incomprehensible and shoddy. The main source for the improvement of this ought to be the Commons. If a second chamber had the *power* to insist that the Commons draft legislation so that its meaning is clear, this would also enhance the ability of MPs to make sure this happens. By acting with rather than against the grain of the Commons, a second chamber might help MPs in the Commons hold the executive to account.

Members of the public may not realise that the routine creation of law by the Commons can be dreadful. In a vivid submission to the House of Commons Select Committee on the Modernisation of the House of Commons, Lynda Clark MP, a new Labour member and an experienced lawyer, wrote:

> I take as my starting point that successful legislation should be accessible to both citizens and lawyers and clear in its meaning ... Parliament chooses to legislate in piecemeal fashion, amending principle statutes which are often many years out of date. On occasion the principle statute is amended almost out of existence ...

> Often a number of different statutes bear on the
> same subject matter with no attempt at any con-
> solidation ... too often the legislation which is
> produced by parliamentary counsel forms an
> impenetrable text for members of the House
> who then ... make it even more impenetrable ...
> Other countries which follow a civilian tradition
> manage to produce legislation in codified form
> which is comprehensible to its citizens.

It is difficult to ensure the rule of law in a democracy if people cannot find out what the law is and then
cannot understand it at all. This becomes more important as the amount of regulation increases. We need a
second chamber that will read the law on behalf of the
public to see if it is clear — with the power to demand
clarification if it is obscure.

Manifestly flawed legislation

A new upper house should have the power to return
legislation that is so obviously flawed that, after dispassionate consideration of the evidence from all
sides, it concludes *beyond reasonable doubt* that the legislation, or some part of it, will *result in an outcome at
odds with the government's stated intention.* In such a
case the second chamber should have the power to
ask the government to think again: either to be honest
about its aim or alter the proposed Bill.

For example, in 1988 the government insisted on
the abolition of free eye tests as a money-saving measure. Regular eye tests are the best way to pick up the
early onset of glaucoma, which can then be treated. If
it is not identified early it leads to blindness. The cost
of nursing and aiding the blind, especially when they
are ageing, is very high, and of course there is an
increase in suffering. It took a mobilisation of hereditary Tory peers under a three-line whip to pass the legislation. The predicted increase in glaucoma seems

to have occurred.[12] There is, therefore, a long-term
economic case for free eye tests. Obviously, a government is entitled to come to its own view. If the
elected government decides to abolish free eye tests
and acknowledges that this will increase blindness,
then it *should* have the power to do this if it can command the necessary majority in the Commons. A second chamber should not have the power to reject laws
that it dislikes. However, if the government wishes to
abolish free eye tests and at the same time *denies* that
this will increase blindness and if, then, a second
chamber finds no reasonable grounds for believing
this is so, then that chamber should have the power to
refuse to pass such legislation.

The benefit of the doubt must go to the government or its programme could be frustrated on capri-
cious grounds. And there are always unintended
consequences of legislation. Indeed, no one can ever
be sure that legislation will positively achieve its
stated aims. Nonetheless, it is possible, as in this
exceptional case, to be reasonably wise about a likely
side effect of legislation. One role for a second chamber is to have the exceptional power to oblige the government to level with the electorate when there is little
room for doubt about an outcome. In this way, the sec-

---

[12] *Losing Sight of Blindness,* RNIB, January 1997, documents the
rise of blindness since the abolition of free eye-tests. The
RNIB is now preparing a report on the costs of blindness. For
a discussion of the vote at the time, Anthony Barnett *New
Statesman* (2 December 1988) as it launched Charter 88,
'Today, we know that those who call each other "my noble
and gallant lord" have ensured that some hundreds or even
thousands of their British subjects will, in years to come,
suffer accentuated blindness. This is a small fact... The task of
a second chamber is to protect society from electoral tyranny.
But the House of Lords has reinforced it through the
mobilisation of hereditary peers.'

ond chamber will be protecting democracy by enforc-
ing an improved degree of honesty in government.

There are other examples of laws shown to be
flawed at the time they were passed. The pensions
debacle was preventable because cogent warnings
were made in Parliament by MPs when the Bill was in
its committee stage that accurately predicted how the
legislation could go wrong through mis-selling.[13] The
government did not listen because it had no need to do
so. A reformed second chamber should have the
authority to force a government to listen in similar circumstances. If it did, one result would be to strengthen
the constructive influence of MPs.

Unconstitutional legislation

Mostly the government in the Commons produces
democratically acceptable legislation — however
much one may agree or disagree with it in policy
terms. But to say this is like saying that a car is in good
working order when it does not go wrong. In the case
of the parliamentary vehicle we know that the engine
is chronically prone to breakdown during a second or
third term stint. Because we know this, it is something
that should be attended to while the vehicle is going in
for service.

When the poll tax was being considered the Home
Office warned that it might be 'a tax on voting', something that would drive people   from the electoral
register.[14] When Margaret Thatcher observed the nar-

---

[13] Andrew Marr, *Ruling Britannia*, 1995, pp.143-153, for an
account of Standing Committee B of the House of Commons,
4 February to 4 March 1986; ten pages that are essential
reading for anyone who thinks that Parliament's ability to
hold the executive to account is 'about right'.

[14] David Butler, Andrew Adonis and Tony Travers, *Failure in
British Government: the Politics of the Poll Tax*, Oxford 1994, pp.
78-79.

row outcome of the 1992 election she was quoted as saying ruefully that 'the poll tax worked after all'.[15] If for no other reason than the way it threatened political equality through being a tax on voter registration, the poll tax should have been ruled unconstitutional — as, indeed, it would have been in the United States.[16] A second chamber entrusted to protect basic or constitutional principles of fairness and political equity would almost certainly have refused to pass the poll tax into law. A renewed second chamber certainly ought to have this power.

In the major study of the tax, *Failure in British Government: the politics of the Poll Tax*, the authors find it incontrovertible that alongside personal errors:

> system failure was also to blame. The fundamental weakness stares out ... namely, the 'elective dictatorship' which gave the Government an almost completely free rein to carry through its poll tax plans. Two aspects of 'elective dictatorship' are evident from our study. The first is the absence of checks and balances faced by a government with a secure hold on the Commons ... second ... is the freedom of a government with a subservient parliament to rewrite the constitution at will.[17]

One can put it in terms of a rhetorical question. What is the point of going to all the trouble to reform the constitution and create a new second chamber if it leaves intact the same potential for system failure that permitted a disaster of the scale of the poll tax?

No system can be error-proof, obviously. Big mistakes can always be made — by mistake. But the poll tax was a defiant misjudgement that flew in the face of wisdom and advice that could not make itself heard

---

[15] *Sunday Telegraph,* 12 April 1992.
[16] See Godfrey Hodgson, *A Squinting Eye to Democracy,* Violations No 8, Charter 88, 1993.
[17] Butler and others, as above, pp. 302-3.

effectively thanks to the absence of effective checks on Britain's over-centralised system of power. The lack of any checks upon the government invited the madness. Or, to put it in more familiar terms, the absolute power invested in the executive corrupted its judgement. Corrupted, not in the sense that it was done for personal gain, but in the sense of *rotted, made soft and complacent*. It permitted the accumulation of errors that resulted in a constitutional scandal.

A second chamber should not frequently reject legislation on the grounds of constitutional impropriety. But if it did have such a power this would function to deter government from proposing such legislation. If Britain had possessed a second chamber which could have scrutinised the poll tax in a genuine non-partisan fashion with the power to safeguard constitutional fairness, the likelihood is that Margaret Thatcher's government would have come up with a better reform of local government taxation. Hindsight will not undo mistakes but it can help to prevent future misjudgements. The existence of an upper chamber that has the power to prevent abuses to constitutional fairness is likely to deter future governments from attempting such legislation.

It might be objected that because we do not have a written constitution it is impossible to give a second chamber the role of constitutional protector. Of course, having a written constitution would make such a role much easier and more transparent. However, on the use of referendums, the Leader of the Opposition has already called, in effect, for constitutional rules about how they should be held.[18] Across a number of other fronts pressure for codified constitu-

---

[18] William Hague, *Tradition and Change: Thinking Creatively about the Constitution*, Speech to Centre for Policy Studies, 24 February 1998.

tional regulation is bound to increase: as relations between the Westminster and other parliaments and assemblies in the UK become fraught, for example, or as judges give their views on the status of legislation, or because of the need for a statute of limitations vis-a-vis the European Union.

An 'Athenian' replacement of the Lords would doubtless add to this list of pressures for a modern constitution. Nonetheless, we do already have a constitution, even though it is unwritten. It is widely held that there are constitutional values, such as fairness or the rule of law, which everyone can understand. When ex-prime minister Lord Home chaired a review of the Lords for the Conservative Party in 1978, his report described the Lords as 'a constitutional long-stop'. It recommended limited reform with a mixture of elected members alongside its appointed ones, and suggested that its functions should include, 'the provision of some measure of constitutional protection'.[19] A deliberative assembly of 'ordinary' people can be equally entrusted to safeguard Britain's uncodified principles. Indeed, they may well be safer in such hands.

To conclude, the existing powers of the Lords should be retained and enhanced only in a limited way to give the reformed chamber the power to:

- reject legislation that undermines the principles of constitutional democracy
- return non-fiscal legislation that it believes will not achieve the objectives the government claims and to insist that the government reformulates either its aims or its legislation
- insist that legislation be drafted in a way that citizens can understand.

[19] *The House of Lords, Tire Report of the Conservative Review Committee*, 1978.

Such a chamber might be called a 'House of Scrutiny'.

How a Chamber Selected by Lot Could Fulfil These Powers

Having described the powers that a reformed second chamber ought to have, powers that can be summed up as impartial and democratic scrutiny, we now propose that the best way to create such a second chamber would be by adopting a selection procedure that we have termed 'Athenian'. We will examine briefly possible lengths of service and the basis for selection of the proposed new 'Peers'. It is not our purpose to insist on one option: we are arguing for a period of *experimentation*. Should the will to introduce the Athenian solution exist, the best fashion to carry it out can be found. While we will describe in an ideal way something we believe to be practical, as pragmatic people we might approach our own proposal by initiating a range of pilot initiatives within the reformed second chamber over a five- to ten-year period, designed to test out options for new forms of participation in the process of scrutiny and to draw on lessons from experiments in direct democracy elsewhere.

Classical Athens was governed by, among other institutions, a Council (boule) of 500 citizens. They were selected by lot, but not entirely at random. Athens was divided into 139 demes or local wards where the lottery choice for boule members was made from citizens who put themselves forward. Each deme had a strict quota of boule members in proportion to their citizen population. This would indicate that the Athenians were keen to ensure the fair representation of all areas. Athens was a slave society that excluded women from citizenship. It operated devices such as ostracism that we would regard as repugnant. It was far from enjoying a framework of basic, human rights. It is not any part of our purpose to idealise it. But it is interesting to note that a governing council or citizen jury can be organised so that it ensures participation from different types of people, a high degree of deliberation, and a belief in the legitimacy of its decisions due to the way the council/jury is composed.[20]

Two measures could be taken in the random selection of members for a British second chamber to make them representative. Half the members can be women and all the members, men and women, can be selected on a regional basis proportionate to the populations of the regions. Say, for example, that the new chamber was to have 300 jury members and London has 10 per cent of the population, then 30 members, fifteen men and fifteen women, would be selected at random from Londoners. By ensuring equality of gender and fairness by region, the representative character of such a jury selection will be enhanced.

Immediately, obvious questions come to mind. What if people do not wish to serve, how long would they serve for, how can gender balance be ensured, what if the individuals selected cannot read, or cannot read English? We will address these questions below. For the moment, we want to establish what the scrutiny and assessment of legislation might be like if undertaken by citizens selected by lot. The best way to do this is to imagine a piece of legislation going through the new House.

---

[20] James S. Fishkin the pioneer of deliberative polling has discussed Athenian procedures. See his *The Voice of the People: Public Opinion and Democracy*, Yale 1995 — Anthony Barnett benefited from a helpful discussion with him in London at the Channel 4 discussion of his techniques. Channel 4 has broadcast *Power and the People*, a series that uses his deliberative procedures.

Before we do this we need to give the new legislators a name. We suggest calling them 'Peers'. The first meaning of the word 'peer' in Chambers English Dictionary is 'equal'. This is the meaning we use when we say that those who go to court on a serious charge will be tried by 'a jury of their peers'. It has an egalitarian and inclusive sense that we will use to trump the aristocratic sense. As those selected to consider legislation will be peers in parliament, we will call them PPs.

too clever-clever

Now suppose, for example, that the legislation on the establishment of the independent Food Safety Agency is going before PPs in the new House of Peers. Let us say that 71 jurors have been selected to act as the deliberative body to scrutinise this legislation. Obviously there will be other bodies of jurors scrutinising other pieces of legislation. But the 71 will be dedicated to considering the FSA legislation from beginning to end. They will be its Peer Committee.

They meet for the first reading. At the initial reading through of the legislation they will seek to establish whether it is written in comprehensible language. (They might have it read to them in small groups.) And they may then ask for its meaning to be clarified. A government spokesperson will introduce the Bill and explain its origins and objectives and answer questions. Representatives from the opposing parties will state the nature of their objections. The PPs will not have the power to reject the legislation. Their behaviour and language will not be parliamentary or theatrical — their role will be one of constructive scrutiny — probing policy to comprehend it.

After the reading for meaning, the Bill will go to a general discussion among all the PPs then currently serving who will listen to a presentation from the government and opposition and then be free to raise their concerns and suggestions in a general debate.

At this point the Government might identify areas of special concern where it has a relatively open mind. In its remarkable White Paper on Freedom of Information, the Labour Government has signalled areas where it especially welcomes public comment. It sets out its basic proposals and purpose exceptionally well, but it also identifies aspects where it wishes to consult more before making up its mind — for example on whether there should be two levels of charges so that a commercial rate can be charged for commercial applications of information.[21] One of the drawbacks of the adversarial character of the Commons is that a government finds it hard to put a question like this to the House. The opposition spokesman will promptly rise. to denounce the government for being weak: 'It does not know what it thinks — well, we do!'. Whatever it is that the opposition decides it thinks, its backbenchers will have to follow. If the Government agrees it will seem feeble. If it does not, it may be wrong. In this familiar way policy gets trapped into party tram-lines. But there will be less difficulty in a Government stating that it will finally decide certain aspects of its legislation only when the arguments have been debated before the deliberative committee in the second chamber.

At the second reading of the Bill, the deliberative group of PPs could call before them experts to present their criticisms and praise of the Bill and suggest amendments and alterations that they believe will improve it, or oppose proposals made by others. The government will chose its experts and may include senior civil servants involved in the drafting to explain departmental thinking. Each political party should have the right to name its witnesses. The PPs should

---

[21] *Your Right to Know: The Government's Proposals for a Freedom of Information Act*, Cm3818 December 1997. p.13.

have the right to decide whether others who wish to appear before them should do so—in the case of the FSA this would presumably include farmers, chemical company representatives and the Consumers' Association. PPs should be able to ensure that witnesses can exchange and debate their points between each other in front of the committee.

For this process to work it can be seen that it will be essential for the political parties to nominate PPs of their own so that on each deliberative group of PPs there are political representatives who can ensure that the arguments that the parties wish to be made are put to the various witnesses. These permanent or party PPs should not have a vote. But they will play a vital role in taking back to the Government—and also to the opposition parties—proposals for amendments that arise out of the hearings. They will also transmit the 'feelings' and attitudes of PPs about the Bill. In this process the government will have the opportunity to amend its own legislation if it wishes.

At the end of the second reading, the PPs can vote on whether the Bill threatens any constitutional values. If the PPs decide that it does threaten basic constitutional values, then they will have to take that argument to the larger assembly of PPs and gain their support for this decision, with the Government's PPs able to participate fully in the debate. They may also vote on whether any part of it will lead, beyond reasonable doubt, to any outcomes that the Government states it does not wish to see. Here too, if the vote goes against the Government the decision needs to be taken to a full assembly of PPs.

When the legislation has passed its second, detailed stage and been amended by the government, it may return for final approval in the upper house for a second general debate among all the PPs, who will wish the legislation well and put down any markers for its future assessment.

A process such as this will rely upon the good judge- ment of regular people selected at random but repre- senting a fair cross-sample of the population geographically and an equal number of men and women. Will they be up to the job? This is the key question. Will they have the wisdom and responsibil- ity that is needed? All the evidence from the experi- ence of operating citizens' juries and deliberative assemblies suggest that they will, provided that their role is one of *scrutiny* and their responsibilities are clearly defined. As Anna Coote and Jo Lenaghan put it in their study of citizens' juries in action:

> It is clear from our pilots that ordinary citizens are willing to get involved in decision-making processes ... most jurors are reasonably well able to deal with quite complex issues and to scruti- nise and assimilate arguments and data. Their capacity to do so depends to a great extent upon the questions and agendas being prepared in an appropriate and manageable form.[22]

Citizen Peers would *not* be asked to be legislators in our proposal. Their role would be a more limited one than the governing Council of ancient Athens. The role for citizens suggested here is one that scrutinises and checks the House of Commons—which contin- ues to provide legislation and the executive. We live in a representative democracy. Everyone should want to vote directly for the people who make up the government and decide the laws, and also to be able to vote against them and remove them from office. Rep- resentative democracy is a clumsy instrument open to abuse and subject to manipulation, not least by the media. But it is also an enabling form of government that helps to ensure consent and provide legiti-

---

[22] Coote and Lenaghan, as above, p.88.

macy. It would be unacceptable to allow membership of our body of *legislators* to be decided by a
lottery.

The Athenian solution does not propose this. But no
government should have absolute power to pass
whatever it wishes into law. A second chamber is
needed to scrutinise power and hold it to account. A
cross-section of the population, given the time and
necessary help, are quite capable of providing the necessary scrutiny. Of course, some will say daft things
and some will be credulous. But on the whole politicians and journalists, the two main groups that presently hold the government to account, display at least
an average share of such failings. Given the opportunity, citizens can apply their own judgement and
experience to assess their government in a wise and
creative fashion.

Duration and Selection

Nominated or life PPs

In the course of the above sketch, we saw that there
would need to be nominated PPs (who will therefore
be akin to present life peers) to work alongside the
ones selected by lot. The main parties will need to be
able to appoint their own PPs across the range of policy, to act as their questioners in the deliberative sessions and as spokesmen and women in the second
chamber's overall debate of legislation. In addition,
each of the deliberative juries dedicated to specific
bills will need to be chaired by skilled, independent
individuals entrusted with overseeing the process of
scrutiny. They too could be non-voting PPs. Thus
while the actual judgements passed on the issues
raised by legislation will be made by representative
juries of citizens, they will not be operating in a vacuum disconnected from the priorities of the Commons

or from independent and experienced managers of due process. There would be a role for the equivalent of today's working peers and for working cross-benchers.

How long?

Our primary concern is to establish the viability of the *principle* of selecting citizens by lot for service as Parliamentary Peers. There are a variety of ways in which such a role could be carried out. One possibility is that PPs should become, so to speak, members of the political class for a four-year term, after a short training period. Such PPs would fill a second chamber of say 600 members with 150 new individuals selected every year. They would deal with the entire process of the upper house, with members specialising in specific pieces of legislation in deliberative groups. In this model such a chamber of PPs would mimic a traditional second chamber while being recruited differently.

An alternative approach would be to select citizens to be PPs for a specific deliberative 'jury' to oversee each Bill. PPs selected on this basis would not take on the role of being a PP as a continuous task or job but would rather fulfil their 'democratic jury service' only when their committee meets and prepares for its sessions, and when the full House meets for general debates while they are serving. Their total period of being such a PP would usually be less than a year.

Another option would be to appoint PPs for a year to oversee minor Bills while specialising in one or at most two pieces of legislation.

Thus, there could be a varying number of such deliberative juries in existence at any given time who come together for debates of the whole House. Or there could be a single chamber of PPs, with a quarter renewed annually; individuals would serve for four years. Or there could be a new, annual house of PPs selected each year.

Selection

As for selection, this would probably need to be a two-stage process. The first stage could consist of selecting at random a significantly large number of people from each region — say 1,000 per region. They would be selected by lot from the electoral register. They would then be asked if they would like their names to go forward to the next round. People should, of course, be paid for serving as a PP at least at the same rate as an MP. Their employers should be compensated. And the role should be celebrated so that people are inclined to say 'yes'. But those who are too ill, too busy or too uninterested must have the right to refuse. And those who cannot read English should have the option of free training for future service. Selection should be encouraged and facilitated, but this 'democratic service' should not have the same degree of obligation on people to serve as does jury service for a court of law.

Once selected, two second stage lists can be drawn up for each region, one of men and one of women, and the random selection for PPs would take place from the lists. In this way, if a selected PP is suddenly unable to serve for any reason a substitute can be easily selected.

The Advantages

On 24 February 1998, William Hague demanded that the Government set out how it would replace the Lords. He said that the opposition would oppose the abolition of hereditary peers unless an acceptable democratic alternative was proposed. There is a politics to this proclamation of Tory principle. It is already clear that the Conservatives will not allow themselves to be stuck defending the hereditary principle. Their aim is to trap Labour into designing an undemocratic alternative so that they can then seize the high ground. Thus Hague announced that his party is 'no longer wedded to evolutionary change', meaning that it will henceforth advocate non-evolutionary reforms for which 'democratic accountability' will be the guiding principle.

In the course of the speech, Hague announced that there are six criteria that the Conservatives require of a reformed second chamber. These are:

- that it must be better at scrutinising and revising legislation than the present one
- that a substantial independent element must remain
- that the prime minister's powers of patronage must not be increased
- that the members must be drawn from all parts of the United Kingdom
- that reform must be considered in the context of its effects on Parliament as a whole
- that the supreme authority of the House of Commons must remain intact.

The Athenian solution meets all six criteria. The only one that is somewhat challenged is the last. The Commons would no longer be so supreme that it could insist on legislation like the poll tax becoming law if the PPs found it to be unconstitutional. In this sense its actually existing supremacy would not be as unconstrained as at present. But 'intact' is a strange word to choose. Under the Athenian solution the supremacy of the Commons as the sole effective source of legislation would remain intact.

The Disadvantages of Other Systems

We have considered the disadvantages of a directly elected second chamber that would duplicate the Commons.[23] An indirectly elected chamber is likely to create a bureaucratic version of the same problem. Representatives would be in effect delegates, say of regional governments, as in the German *Bundesrat*. But in the UK we do not even have regional governments. And while it would be greatly to the benefit of the country if we did, they need to stem from consent not imposition — and there is not yet a regional politics to generate legitimate voice. A powerful argument for a regionally-based chamber is that it would encourage the growing development of regional and national devolution in a constructive fashion by providing an all-British space for the expression and possible resolution of difference. This would be a new role distinct from that of scrutiny and revision. It is not at all clear that a second chamber removed from real executive power could provide the necessary forum.[24]

Another alternative has been advocated by Lord Runciman: a House of Experts. He argues that it should be possible to appoint a top team of the experienced and wise 'particularly well qualified to perform the revising and advising functions'. University professorships and national sporting teams are filled by appointment, he argues, a reformed House of Lords

---

[23] Katharine Quarmby has argued for just such a 'big bang' creation of a directly elected Senate in a 1998 discussion paper for the IPPR.

[24] John Osborne of the Institute for Welsh Affairs has written a paper advocating such a regional model second chamber that draws on German and Spanish experience, presented to Charter 88 Council in 1996 and in more developed form to IPPR in 1998.

should be appointed in the same way.[25] A parallel proposal for a 'Senate of Interests' has been made by Jaques Arnold, the Conservative MP for Gravesham from 1987 to 1997.[26] Save us from government by such experts! Those expert enough in their field to become distinguished are often just the ones who are losing touch with current thinking after having built up a lifetime of vested interests and professional jealousy. And that is just within their own field of expertise. It is even more naïve to think that expertise in one field — say health — gives you the authority to scrutinise education policy. Such attributed importance may lull you into believing you are expert when you are not.

To put it another way, a leading expert in education will be no better at considering the pros and cons of the Food Standards Agency legislation than a single mother who probably does much more shopping than the expert. And when it comes to education policy itself, either the upper house experts are in agreement, in which case they have been poorly selected, or they are in disagreement, in which case the issues will still have to be decided by non-experts.

Of course there are genuinely wise, open-minded experts, although such virtue is more likely to arise from their character than from their expertise. Neither they nor their more one-sided colleagues will be excluded from policy making in the Athenian option. On the contrary, it builds expert discussion and assessment into the process of scrutiny through its deliberative hearings. At these, however, experts

---

[25] Letter to *The Times* 22 April 1996. Runciman adds, 'I have suggested the outline of a scheme on these lines to the leaders of both the major political parties, but to no discernible effect'.

[26] *Reform of the Lords: A Senate of Interests*, a proposal by Jacques Arnold.

will advocate their conflicting views before a dedicated jury of people who do not have an axe to grind, a party to support, or a region that has sent them there to fight its corner. We need less vested interests at the centre, not more.

The likely option: mixed fudge

The most likely option for a reformed Lords is one that keeps the fading glamour of its ermine and titles, retains the life peers, includes an elected element to provide a democratic veneer, and embraces a new method for future appointments. We call this the mixed fudge solution. Lord Irvine appeared to point in its direction when he said:

> It's difficult to see how without a very significant nominated element you can really ensure that the House of Lords is a house of all the talents, and a place in which people enter at a fairly high age, which may be thought a virtue because they bring a lifetime's experience. How compatible that is with election is another matter.[27]

There is a gap between what the Lord Chancellor seems to believe (his words do not commit him) and how the public perceive the present House of Lords. It is far from being 'a house of all the talents'. Most people who have had a successful life are not represented in it. The high age makes it closer to a retirement home than a place of contemporary wisdom. Prime ministers have used the Lords as an instrument of patronage that allows them to get old lags out the way and offer compensation for the frustration that most politicians claim to suffer. Many life peers have spent most of their working lives in the Palace of Westminster and become institutionalised by its culture of dependency. Their continued subsidy cannot be justified.

---

[27]   Interview with *New Statesman, as* above.

There is a case for a plurality of selection methods. Alongside PPs we see the need for appointed members to ensure that party interests are adequately voiced and due process observed. The active core of present life peers could thus foresee a role for themselves in the Athenian option.

The main problem with mixed fudge is not the inclusion of some appointed members of the second chamber but the desire to avoid the consequences of a more radical measure. To return to the point made at the start, Labour is uncertain what it wants Britain to be like. It is therefore attracted to modernising the country's appearance and leaving it at that. Such an approach is justified by so-called practical men in the name of pragmatism. It is one thing to argue for small adjustments if your real interest is to keep things as they are. However, the reform programme Labour has already unleashed, with new parliaments and assemblies, a Council of the British Isles and basic rights, is already comparable to that of 1832. And its policy towards Europe, where its declared desire is to 'share economic sovereignty', is even more revolutionary — for once the word is justified. Having committed itself to such giant strides forward it would be a shame if, when it came to the renewal of the Lords, New Labour reduced its steps to pigmy shuffles such as adding a few bishops from other faiths.

It is not the case that the alternative is a big bang with its inevitable victims. It is, indeed, best to proceed in a practical, step-by-step fashion. Provided that you know where you want to go — and are clear with the public about this. There are two kinds of pragmatism in politics. There is the kind of piecemeal approach for which Britain has been famous during this century, designed to preserve as many inherited privileges and as much executive prerogative as is practical. The other form of pragmatism sets ambitious goals and moves towards them in a practical way with care and preparation.

Britain needs a democratic second chamber. This should be the aim. It is a necessary modernisation and also a bold one. The Athenian proposal is one way to achieve it; a way that does not, as we have seen, suffer from the disadvantages of other proposals. If, nonetheless, it raises further constitutional problems this is because they are unavoidable thanks to the pre-democratic nature of the surrounding arrangements. To touch on two examples, no democratic upper house of any kind could, in the end, sensibly include the Bishops of the Church of England or the Law Lords in their present fashion.

An Athenian option — like any other genuinely democratic reform of the Lords — would bring disestablishment of the Church of England closer. It would also mean that the Law Lords would meet in their own name as the country's highest court. In fact, they do so already in all but name. The formal, public recognition of their status would increase calls to make their appointment more accountable.

A mixed fudge solution is apparently seen as an approach that can head off such demands for further change. By creating a renewed, more legitimate House of Lords, that plays the identical role as the present one, it is proposed that the Government oversee a classic example of British reform, of altering appearance to preserve the essence. Such, it seems, is the thinking.

We doubt very much if this approach will work. Not least because of the radical nature of other reforms already introduced. In his most considered speech on the constitution (quoted at the beginning of the pamphlet) John Smith, spoke of how constitutional reform is a 'continuous process'. Reform of the Lords should be approached in this spirit — one that welcomes and assists further change. Today, a reform of the upper

house that goes part of the way to making it democratic and then brakes to a halt will exacerbate, not
assuage, demand for further action. To repeat, this is
not to argue for a 'big bang' in which everything is
changed at once. A new constitutional settlement is
not a destination that can be arrived at overnight. But
reform that works will be reform that points *in the
direction* of a new constitutional settlement, that gener-
ates further public energy, enthusiasm and identification with such a modernisation, rather than seeking to
stifle further initiatives for a democratic outcome. In
the case of the Lords — and John Smith was unequivo-
cal that he wanted to see it 'replaced' — it is absurd to
think that a re-jigging of the elements will stifle effective calls for disestablishment, or for a formally
accountable judiciary, just to take our two examples.

Already, the heir to the throne has made a careful
declaration on television that he desires to be seen as a
defender of faith and not of *'the faith'* at his Coronation. He has explained that he dislikes the exclusive
character of the Coronation Oath because of his belief
'in the divinity of other religions'.[28] If only for this reason,
the present privileged form of the Establishment of the
Church of England is bound to be altered in some way.
So far as the Law Lords are concerned, William Hague
has already floated the possibility that the Conservative Party will anyway call for their appointment to be
subject to direct political oversight given the new
powers they are likely to gain from Labour's human
rights legislation.[29]

A 'mixed fudge' reform of the Lords, therefore, will
not stifle demands for further change simply because
it is itself designed to avoid provoking them. Instead,

---

[28] Jonathan Dimbleby, *The Prince of Wales*, London 1994, pp.
526-534, for a description of the care Prince Charles took over
his announcement and its possible ramifications.
[29] Speech on 24 February 1998, as cited.

because a reconstruction of the House of Lords without hereditaries will lead to a much less hallowed institution, it will permit and even encourage calls for further reforms without having any principled answer to them.

Thus mixed fudge will not provide a 'sensible' conclusion to a period of intense constitutional change. On the contrary it will be the worst of all worlds. it will deepen disbelief in the Government's radical intentions, it will arouse a louder demand for principled constitutional change, it will make the public more disillusioned with politics and it will not improve the way we are governed.

Conclusion

In its report, *Reform of the House of Lords*, the Constitution Unit surveys international alternatives and notes, 'perhaps more than any other part of the political system, second chambers reflect the history and character of the state'. The main forms of government today, such as parliamentary or presidential, are relatively few. The appendage of a second chamber varies a lot from polity to polity according to local traditions. In Britain, discussion of the Lords has often focused on the unique bond between it and British history. But when its replacement is advocated, the tendency is to look abroad for one model or another. This then allows the advocates of the status quo (or mixed fudge) to reinforce their argument as they denigrate proposals which fail to fit with the British way. So we should look to see what there is of worth in the existing House of Lords. In the modern context the core hereditary tradition has one virtue. It is not that hereditary peers were born to be better than us. Their prime quality, it appears, is that they were not born to be politicians. In this one sense they can be presented as being 'representative' because it makes them like the rest of us.

The proposal to experiment with an 'Athenian' solution is, we believe, a much better way to reproduce this quality. It is in tune with the modernising spirit of the times in our constitutional politics: there is a wave of enthusiasm for experimenting with new forms of participation at local and regional level, and our proposal for the second chamber should be seen as a contribution to this upsurge of ideas. The debate on the revitalisation of our democracy has not taken a dogmatic turn. No one wants a rigid or inflexible outcome imported from outside. The reform of the upper house we have proposed could ensure more dispassionate, independent oversight of legislation. It also strengthens the best aspect of the current relationship between the Lords and Commons.

Finally, we make the proposal in an experimental spirit, not as something that we think should be imposed overnight but as an ideal that can, with some trial and no doubt some error, be made to work. If it did, an Athenian option would provide continuity of a refreshing and genuinely democratic kind. The British constitution has long been an engine of change; now it is time for it to change itself.

Appendix: Participation and Meetings

Those in charge of British politics regularly call on the population to be more active, to pull their weight in society and to participate in its improvement. Douglas Hurd, for example, initiated a high profile campaign to persuade British subjects to become 'active citizens'. The new Government also wants us to participate, for example in the Dome, or rather 'The Millennium Experience'. In a speech to the Citizenship Foundation in January 1998, the Lord Chancellor made a particularly strong pitch for participation:

> The new Labour Government is working hard to transform the political landscape—but we cannot succeed without the support, and participation, of the People.

And he used the capital P. But 'The People', in the singular is unable to participate in anything. It is a top-down creation. And Lord Irvine continued in this tone:

> this Government has declared war on disillusionment and social exclusion. We call on all who care about Britain to help us win that war. There is no justification for sitting on the sidelines and watching other people make all the running. Democracy is not a spectator sport.[30]

Perhaps the Lord Chancellor's desire that we participate is well meant. But it is not hard to see why such pleas are experienced as an attempt at conscription. 'Participation' in this usage is a form of mobilisation rather than a proposal that inspires citizens to exercise their freedom and commitment. This is not to argue against participation. We·need to consider what it means more carefully and not use it as a cliché.

---

[30] Lord Irvine of Lairg, 'Creating a Nation of Real Citizens', Speech to the Citizenship Foundation, 27 January 1998.

Take, for example, the statement that 'Democracy is not a spectator sport'. Well, oddly enough, although the game is also for real, representative democracy is a form of spectator sport. It has been since the hustings were developed. It has become all the more so under modern conditions of media competition. Of course, it is not just a spectator sport. But it does now include elements of the big game. Furthermore, this is no bad thing, because it is also a form of participation. Spectators identify with a team and argue through its strength and weaknesses with a strong sense of ownership. They participate vicariously but nonetheless passionately in the game itself. Through being committed spectators, supporters experience a concentration of fate, chance, skill, opportunity, excellence, victory and defeat, all of which are part of the story of life. Spectator sport, in other words, is not just a passive activity.

As identification with sporting teams has become stronger, interest in and commitment to party politics has become weaker. Organised, tribal identification of the old kind is lessening. So too is belief in the commitment of politicians to ideas and arguments. The media intensifies the process. It concentrates on personalities and less and less on policies. It justifies this on the grounds that people are not interested in politics. But really, who can be interested in policies that are reduced to politicians slanging at each other? Thus the concentration on personalities, far from compensating for the loss of interest in public affairs, makes it worse as the whole process is hollowed out.

Perhaps this is too light-hearted a way of touching upon a serious problem, but one way to increase participation is to heighten vicarious identification; that is to say, identification *at a distance*, so that people take a greater interest in the disputes over policy itself. For this to happen, the political argument needs to be conducted in a form that people can identify with. Rather than in the parliamentary and media circus forms that turn them off.

There is a second, quite opposite form of participation. This is to actually play the game oneself. For most of us this will mean an amateur effort, enjoyable and not ambitious. One reason why football has such a hold on the popular imagination is that most of its followers, if not all, have kicked a ball around themselves.

In politics the traditional form of participation was not founded on very much actual playing of an amateur kind. The main form of participation was through meetings. This is a peculiar form of early modern behaviour. It is one that people find increasingly frustrating. When Pol Pot seized power in Cambodia he and his fellow Khmer Rouge set about purging the language of foreign words. But despite their fanaticism, they did not find a substitute for *Miting*. These were the dreadful sessions at which village populations were drilled into the 'correct' way of thinking, as the traditional form of the political meeting was driven to its fanatical conclusion.

The numbers that attend meetings are taken as a measure of participation—by the speakers and organisers. From the perspective of those who attend, however, they are all too often unsatisfactory events at which nothing happens—no new arguments are advanced, no minds are changed and there are no unexpected outcomes. One is reduced not enhanced by attendance. Most people prefer social gatherings or good arguments to such non-events. They prefer clear, effective and good decision making. Traditional meetings rarely lead to any of these things.

By contrast, a jury in a court of law is participating even though its members are largely spectators. This is because they have a specific task—to reach a verdict—to be undertaken with specific responsibilities, such as to grant the defendant the benefit of reasonable doubt. Because they have their own role, a jury *participates* in a trial.

To be offered a defined power in a decision making process is to be offered a chance to participate in it in a meaningful way. Calls to participate that do not offer such an opportunity of influence are increasingly hollow.

An Athenian solution for the replacement of the House of Lords could increase participation in three ways. Most obviously, those who are selected to scrutinise and vote on legislation will clearly be participants with a defined if modest degree of public power. Second, because they are chosen from among us, we the public will be able to identify with them and follow their debates and questioning. We will be able to identify vicariously, especially with those chosen from our locality, job or profession—and also because it might be our turn next. Third, the process of scrutiny, questioning and debating—including the questioning of politicians and the debating with them—could increase interest in policy and politics as the issues are brought out in a new context that everybody can relate to.

Chaps or Citizens? The White Paper of 2008 v The Athenian Option

We delayed completing this new edition of *The Athenian Option* in order to respond to a promised White Paper on the next stage of replacing the House of Lords which, we were reliably informed, would announce how a new chamber would be elected.

Our original 1998 pamphlet, published thanks to Ian Christie at Demos, came out of the blue. It did not engage with actual policy proposals. To be sure it was encouraged by the promise of a new reforming government and a commitment to abolish hereditary peers. Talk about a full-scale replacement of the House of Lords was in the air; we joined it from 'stage left'.

Then came the Royal Commission chaired by Lord Wakeham, and our experience of giving evidence before it, recorded here. This confirmed that our proposal was, while still beyond the pale, hovering within earshot of official discourse. (We were told that the editor of the *Daily Telegraph* had flirted with proposing the recruitment of regular citizens by lottery into the House of Lords, but dropped it when he heard that this was being proposed by the likes of us.)

Despite the odds we would like our proposal to be taken seriously. We share the hope of many reformers (in this and other contexts), that each improvement will open the way for further change. We are not wedded to 'making the best the enemy of the good'; we do not argue for sortition in an impossibilist spirit, confident that it will never happen, to show off our superior radicalism. Everyone is aware of how hard it is to actually democratise the central institutions of British power. So we looked forward to parliament's plans for electing the Lords. Here would be a chance to test our proposals against a fully-fledged alternative that had emerged out of a major House of Commons battle. An alternative backed by the might of experience, official drafting, a large research budget and the accumulated wisdom of many months of cross-party discussion. Now that a definite plan is being presented to the country it will be possible to ask: which way forward is the more practical and would do more for the progress of democracy in the UK—elections or the Athenian option?

At the end of July 2008 the White Paper was finally published by the Ministry of Justice, overseen by Jack Straw, its Secretary of State. Called *An Elected Second Chamber: Further reform of the House of Lords,* we will hereafter refer to it as the *White Paper.* It offers a great deal less than was promised, and what is does offer is often not wholly clear. Some forensic patience and careful probing into legerdemain is necessary to extract anything firm enough to compare and contrast with our own approach.

But our findings from our analysis of the *White Paper,* by contrast with the contents of the Paper itself, are straightforward enough. It seems to us that its approach is so uncompelling that it creates an opening for an altogether more refreshing solution. As we have mentioned in the introduction, sortition now has a considerable body of experience and analysis behind it. We know that it *could* work. We also know that a new upper chamber is going to be created in Westminster over the next few years. The chasm between the public and the political class is, to borrow a phrase, simultaneously deepening and widening. In terms of generating public interest, let alone allegiance, parliament needs to be rescued. Surely someone who has influence in one of the major parties has the imagination to consider 'What if....'

Before assessing the *White Paper* itself there are two distinctive aspects to the process which led up to it that are worth noting: its history and its 'all-party' character.

A Little History

The House of Commons voted to make the second chamber of the UK an elected assembly in March 2007. The vote came about after all three main UK parties had pledged some kind of Lords reform in their manifestos in the 2005 election. A year later, in June 2006, a cross-party group met and discussed reform regularly for eight months. A White Paper was then published and the Commons debate followed. Various options were presented to the House and MPs voted to endorse two of them: There was a majority of over 100 for a wholly elected second chamber, by 337 to 224. There was less support for the option of having an upper house that is 80 per cent elected and 20 per cent appointed, 305 to 267—a majority of nearly 40. All other options were rejected.

David Marquand and Patrick Dunleavy, among others, have emphasised the historic, watershed nature of this vote. Provided that Scotland does not shortly decide on independence in a referendum and

the United Kingdom holds together, it really does
seem likely that Britain will see a genuine *replacement*
of the Lords by a second chamber that is either 80 or
100 per cent elected — a second chamber that will have
to be called something new, a 'Senate' being the most
favoured term.

True, history will grind slowly. By our calculation it
will be around 2022 before all of the *White Paper's* proposed elected members will be in place, sitting alongside the remaining life peers, because the newcomers
will only be elected in three tranches, starting with the
general election after next (i.e. around 2014). In addition, the *White Paper* has various options for excluding
the present incumbents, and if the one apparently
favoured by Jack Straw is adopted, it will take until at
least 2040 before the last of the current life peers leaves
the chamber to go on to the upper house in the sky (or
warmer lodgings below).

Nonetheless, from within the Westminster bubble
itself, in terms of British history and tradition, electing
the second chamber seems like profound change. A
sense of this can be gained by reading Robin Cook's
memoir *The Point of Departure*. It recounts his two
years as Leader of the House: from June 2001, after
Blair sacked him from being Foreign Secretary (the
post he held for Labour's first term of office) to March
2003 when Cook resigned from the cabinet to oppose
the invasion of Iraq. Two themes dominate the book.
The most important is the Iraq war, while the second is
Cook's protracted efforts to turn the Lords into an
elected chamber. Reporting on his first meeting with
the Prime Minister in his new role, on 3rd July 2001,
Cook writes

> I put it to him that reform of the House of Lords
> will be his historic monument. He is playing for
> his place in history.[1]

What seems clear is that Cook regarded achieving an elected second chamber as being *his* 'historic monument'. At first Blair managed to string Cook along: after all, Blair was a moderniser so he surely wanted reform. Gradually Cook realised that the Prime Minister wanted no such thing and had created the Wakeham Committee to perpetuate a wholly appointed chamber with all the advantages of leverage and patronage, not to speak of the funding opportunities that it afforded him (always provided, as Blair once put it, that they are not part of a single transaction). In fact by proposing *some* elected members Wakeham, according to Derry Irvine, the then Lord Chancellor, 'let us all down'. Over the same dinner, Irvine went on to ask Cook (they had shared 'two bottles of wine and a whisky apiece'),

> But are there enough people of calibre out there
> to fill an elected House of Lords? [2]

Cook does not hide his consternation. He ploughed on. He gets a commitment for the creation of a joint committee and a free vote of MPs. With the question of whether the committee should have a deadline for its recommendation top of the agenda, Cook went into a meeting with the Prime Minister and the Lord Chancellor:

> We all know, although never say, that the divid-
> ing line in the room is between those who see the
> new plan as a way of making progress and those
> who see it as a way of halting progress.[3]

---

[1]   Robin Cook, *The Point of Departure: diaries from the front bench*, London, 2004, p. 14.

[2]   As above, p. 85.

[3]   As above, p. 148.

This is a most apt warning. It should be pinned above all 'new plans' for reform in Westminster and Whitehall.

Poor Robin Cook. He finally gets his debate, although the joint committee has come up with multiple options for parliament to consider, thus ensuring the debate would be as confusing as possible. At Prime Minister's Questions six days before, Blair answers a planted question:

> Tony slammed a big fat torpedo into our joint strategy on Lords Reform. He had an unerring aim and I was left sitting silently beside him for the rest of Question Time contemplating the wreck of democratic reform sinking beneath the horizon.

Cook describes how he had 'begged' Blair not to express a preference. Instead, the PM told the House:

> The key question of election is whether we want a revising chamber or a rival chamber. My view is we want a revising chamber.

Cook immediately understood that it was impossible to 'square the spirit of the free vote' with a Prime Minister telling his party what outcome he wanted.

> Blair's intervention brilliantly positioned a democratic second chamber as a threat to the Commons rather than a challenge to the Executive...[4]

The result of the free vote on 4 February 2003 was that all options were rejected, a farcical conclusion.

It was doubtless satisfactory for the great moderniser himself. Blair could continue to accumulate his 'Tony's cronies'. *All options rejected* is an apt historic monument, a symbol of his approach to reforming the central British state.

---

[4]   As above pp. 274-81.

Within a month, Iraq was invaded. However honourable, Cook's career came to an utterly frustrated
conclusion. In the published extracts from his diary of
The Blair Years, Alastair Campbell does not even deign
to include any references to the shabby fixing of Robin
Cook over Lords reform. Yet contempt for democracy
in Blair's No 10 surely connects the Iraq decision to the
crushing of Lords reform. Both widened the gap
between parliament and the voters. As all Cook's
efforts unravelled in the ridiculous Commons vote,
millions across the country were starting to prepare
for the largest demonstration ever seen on the streets
of Britain, on the 15 February. This time the mob
proved to be wiser than its masters.[5] It was a historic
turning point in the balance of authority and legitimacy between Britain's political leaders and those
who vote. The UK's 'political class' is still in denial
about the implications. Its central directorate got it
wrong. The public as a whole was wiser and more
far-sighted in its judgement than parliament, not to
speak of most of the press. Of course the media now
wishes us all to forget that Michael Howard and David
Cameron and Tony Blair and Gordon Brown and
David Miliband were all wrong about a defining issue
of going to war, when the thoughtful citizenry were
right. But at a deeper level it remains a profound fact
that has altered the balance of argument about introducing citizen participation into the scrutiny of
legislation.

We emphasise this point because constitutional
reform in the UK is all too often discussed either in
technical terms abstracted from the actual political

---

[5] See 'Democracy and openDemocracy', Isabel Hilton and
Anthony Barnett, *openDemocracy*, 12 October 2005,
http://www.opendemocracy.net/democracy-opening/bar
nett_hilton_2792.jsp

context or, by politicians with the 'unctuous compla-
cency' well described by Hugo Young in the article
republished here. Public opinion is on the march.
Robin Cook was a master parliamentarian and loved
to occupy what he described as a 'high office of state'.
Nonetheless, he retained a Scottish democratic intelli-
gence which gave him the capacity to perceive the
larger realities outside the pomp and privileges of
Whitehall. His conclusion is that British politics does
not suffer from the 'imaginary tussle between the
Lords and the Commons for primacy' that Blair
evoked. Rather, it faces two problems. First, in the
'struggle' between the executive and parliament the
latter ought to be a strong check on government but is
not. Second, there is a 'crumbling of public esteem' for
both parliament and government.[6]

In his view, creating an elected second chamber
would be a big step to resolving both these problems.
But will it? Where we agree with Robin Cook is that
the reform of the second chamber is an opportunity to
create a framework that will strengthen the Commons,
so that parliament as a whole has much more authority to check the executive. If this succeeds it should
help restore public belief in the political process. The
question is whether simply electing the second chamber will achieve this. The 2006 vote by the Commons
came after Cook died. His influence lived on to ensure
that parliament once again had a free vote on a list of
options. This time his 'historic' principle of an elected
second chamber was endorsed.

All-Party Support

The second aspect of the process that led up to the
White Paper which deserves notice is the cooperation

---

[6]   As above p. 280-81.

of all three main parties. This is rooted in the procedural nature of the change and Cook understandably went out of his way to create a cross-party alliance for reform. One would be wise to consider whether such collaboration is motivated by the spirit of democracy or a desire by the parties to further enhance (or perhaps one should say 'modernise') their control. Since the hereditary peers have been ejected from the Lords (apart from the remaining 92 who, oddly enough, are currently the only 'elected' members, because they are chosen by their fellow members of the historic peerage), Britain's upper house has become more independent minded.

Why were all three main parties meeting behind closed doors for months on end to try and agree on a shared approach? Their argument is that without this, and without a resulting co-ordinated commitment to a democratic second chamber in their manifestos, the Lords will vote down any proposal to abolish it. Certainly, it seems momentum is being created. But manifestos be damned. In these circumstances they have become a matter of convention and procedure. The cross-party investment in the detail seems better designed to ensure reform by inertia under the sheer weight of White Papers and their appendices, rather than by the encouragement of popular support for the transformation being engineered. This alone makes it unlikely that it will light a touchpaper for democracy, let alone create, thanks to its more representative nature, such a compelling centre of legitimacy that further reform will finally be forced upon the House of Commons itself.

What Should the Second Chamber Do?

In its Executive Summary, the *White Paper* looks at the powers of the House of Lords and states

> In its three main functions of scrutinising legis-
> lation, conducting investigations and holding
> Government to account, the second chamber
> should complement the work of the Commons.
> Irrespective of its membership, this should con-
> tinue to be the case in a reformed second
> chamber.

These functions are not discussed in the document
which simply states that all parties are agreed that
'there should be no change to the powers of a reformed
chamber'. In other words while shifting its membership to being predominantly elected, in terms of
power the objective is to keep everything unchanged.

But a widely identified problem with the current
system of British sovereignty is the way the government subordinates parliament to its will. For much of
the nineteenth century, government of an empire of
hundreds of millions relied heavily upon a small cabinet drawn from both houses within a weak party system. As the global reach of government shrank, its
ranks started to balloon while the influence of the cabinet diminished. In 2008 the cabinet is a ghost of its former self while the number of MPs with government
jobs has reached three figures, with a concomitant
growth of the 'pay-roll vote' in parliament.[7] On con-
tentious issues the Commons has become a 'ba-
zaar' — to quote the unchallenged description by
Diane Abbott MP in the recent Commons debate on
extending detention without charge to 42 days.

This system also operates inside the House of Lords.
It has its ministers and shadow ministers, its pay-roll
vote and aspirant pay-roll vote. It also initiates legislation and functions, as it has since the nineteenth century, as a chamber for the execution of government

---

[7] See Thomas Powell and Paul Lester, *Limitations on the number
of Ministers and the size of the Payroll vote*, House of Commons
Library, May 2008 (with thanks to Andrew Blick).

business. The executive's domination of the Lords is less complete than that of the Commons. This does not significantly take away from the fact—as well as the perception—that what matters today is *government*. Parliament is now seen as merely an extension of the government's writ causing only an occasional wrinkle in the smooth exercise of centralised power.

We need a second chamber that has sufficient authority independent of party politics to scrutinise and investigate what the government proposes. If the existing Lords, and on occasion the Commons, achieves this today it is only thanks to the qualities of exceptional individuals. A second chamber of elected members who have gained their place thanks to the party machines, many of them angling for jobs, is all too likely to diminish that chamber's spirit of independence. And this is before we come to the voting system.

An Elected Second Chamber

According to the strategy behind the *White Paper*, the winner of the coming general election will be responsible for creating an elected second chamber. At the moment the odds suggest this will be the Conservative Party. The *White Paper* states that the Conservatives 'favour' (so there is some flexibility),

> a First Past The Post system for elections to the second chamber. In particular, they favour using the 80 constituencies... leading to a total membership of 300 (of which 60 would be appointed), plus the Bishops.

First past the post in this context could well be described as 'reactionary modernisation'. But at least the Tory view is clear. Labour's is redolent of the heels-in-the-ground procrastination that Cook witnessed. As the *White Paper* puts it,

> The Government believes that further consider-
> ation should be given to the following voting
> systems options for elections to the second
> chamber:
>
> • a First Past The Post system;
>
> • an Alternative Vote system;
>
> • a Single Transferable Vote system; or
>
> • an open or semi-open list system.
>
> The choice of a voting system for elections to the
> second chamber is the subject of much discus-
> sion. It is a key decision about the way forward
> for a reformed second chamber and hence about
> the institutions of our democracy. The Govern-
> ment is therefore keen to facilitate an extensive
> and wide-ranging debate on this issue. Hence it
> would welcome views from all quarters.

How long is *that* going to take, if after all this time
Labour has come to absolutely no view at all? More
alarming, it has not even ruled out 'First Past The Post'
as its preferred voting system. No one has set out why
this matters more eloquently and forcefully than
David Marquand:

> PR elections to the Upper House—and it is
> surely inconceivable that it would be elected by
> First Past the Post—would mean that the Upper
> House was more legitimate than the Lower. I
> don't think such an absurd imbalance could last
> for long. Sooner or later (and I think sooner
> rather than later) PR for the upper house would
> force the Government and Opposition of the day
> to agree on PR, or at the very least AV, for the
> Commons. With every passing day the absur-
> dity of FPTP for the Commons becomes more
> glaring. We now have PR elections for London,
> Northern Ireland, Scotland and Wales: that
> already makes FPTP for the Westminster Com-
> mons a massive anomaly.
>
> The best way to get rid of the anomaly is to make
> it even more glaring—which PR elections for the
> upper house would do. To put the point in

another way, the most important single objective for democratic reform is PR. That would, at
a stroke, deprive the executive of an automatic
single-party majority; end the dreary game of
triangulation; liberate currently unrepresented
currents of opinion like the Greens; and enable a
politics of pluralism and negotiation to take root
in this country. A Senate elected by PR would be
really big step in that direction; it would be madness to throw that chance away.[8]

simpliste ✗

It is clear from the *White Paper* that no such 'really
big step' is on offer. While Jack Straw may have a
greater quotient of cunning than most, the Tories also
see that the fairer the second chamber's election system, the more this will reflect adversely on winner-
takes-all elections for the Commons which the two big
parties cherish for precisely the reason that Marquand
seeks their urgent overthrow.

But suppose there *is* a government after the next
election, perhaps one dependent on a coalition, that
does indeed lean towards some version of proportion-
ality in the electoral system for the new second
chamber. Will this have the effect that Marquand
envisages? It seems to us that the *White Paper* seeks to
put in place a series of defences in depth to prevent
this. First, there is the length of time envisaged for
reform to come about before the new chamber comes
into its own—at least 30 years. Second, there is the
multi-member geography of the constituency system
it proposes that will make its representative nature
opaque. Third, there is the staged nature of the voting,
which will ensure that it never represents opinion in
the country at any one time. Fourth, there is the commitment to a 20 per cent appointed element (plus some
Bishops) that is likely to ensure the new chamber is

a

b

c

d

[8]   See *openDemocracy/OurKingdom*, 14 July 2008, http://www.
opendemocracy.net/blog/ourkingdom-theme/2008/07/14
/sorting-out-the-lords

never perceived as being self-evidently 'more legitimate' than the Commons.

The constituencies will be very large. All parties are
looking at six-member constituencies returning a total
of between 300 and 400 members altogether (compared to around 650 in the Commons). The first two
members for each constituency will be elected in the
first general election after the reform becomes law, the
second two at the next general election and the final
two at the one after that, with all members serving just
one term across three UK general elections.

This means that it will only be some time in the
2020s that the third tranche of elected 'Senators' will
be created. Even then the option is left open that existing life peers will remain in place until they die (actu-
arial graphs are helpfully provided) haunting the
chamber through to 2040 and beyond.

The Government noted in its February 2007 White
Paper that:

> The current members have entered the House in
> the expectation that they will stay for life. Some
> will have given up careers and other roles to do
> so. It would be unfair to require them to leave in
> these circumstances.

But *even after* the current life peers have been swept
away, the proposed system will ensure that the elected
upper house is never representative of current opinion, because it will always be dominated by the
two-thirds elected four and eight years previously
plus the appointed fifth. We suspect that David
Marquand imagined that an upper house elected by a
fairer system than the Commons would be wholly
elected at the same time as the Commons (as in, for
example, Billy Bragg's 'secondary mandate' pro-

posal),[9] and in any case be seen as representing a self-evidently better balance of current opinion in the country. This will not be the case.

The authors of the *White Paper*, from all parties, do indeed appear to have used the 'new plan' of electing the second chamber to delay progress.

The Definition of a Chap

Finally, there are the 20 per cent of appointed members. Although this option got significantly less support when the Commons voted than the 100 per cent elected option, the *White Paper* flatly supports a 20 per cent appointed element. Here, then, is a chance to send into the Palace of Westminster regular folk from outside the establishment. And thereby address the most attractive aspect of the Athenian option, by including those who are not part of the political machine in the scrutiny of its outcome, to help bridge the gap between politicians and the public.

The section where the *White Paper* sets out the qualities its sees as necessary to qualify for the appointed 20 per cent, makes grimly entertaining reading. It says that:

> the key focus in assessing potential appointees should be their ability, willingness and commitment to take part in the full range of the work of the chamber

Meaning that they should be potential *legislators*. It agrees therefore that far from the appointed element introducing a breath of fresh air,

> the characteristics of distinguished former public servants are typically such that they would be extremely credible candidates for appointment to a reformed second chamber

---

[9]   The *Guardian*, 9 February 2004.

Aware of the need to demonstrate some spirit of reform, however, the Labour Government thinks that there should be:

> no *expectation* of membership of the reformed second chamber in the case of distinguished former public servants: each application would be considered on an individual basis. (Our emphasis)

While the Conservative Party on the other hand,

> considered that there was a case for an element of automaticity in the case of distinguished former public servants.

In a neat paragraph that reveals the degree of continuity with the present situation that is foreseen, the *White Paper* states,

> The Government would welcome views on whether there should be provision for appointments to a reformed second chamber specifically for the purposes of enabling a particular individual to become a Government Minister.

The *White Paper* emphasises the importance of the quality of 'independence' in any appointed members. What its authors seem to have in mind by this is authoritative mandarins who 'know what is best', such as former public servants and potential but unelected ministers.

No consideration whatsoever is given to whether or not appointed members might provide a counter-weight to the elitist nature of British political life. For example, it would seem to be what the Americans call a 'no brainer' that if 80 per cent of the chamber is to be elected and will therefore be members of the political parties, that the 'independent' appointed Senators should not also be party members. But this would mean that key back-room party supporters who are at present regularly rewarded with peerages would have to be eliminated from shaping the business of government via a place in the second chamber (current examples might be Lord Gould, Lord Rennard, Lord Ashcroft). So the *White Paper* goes out if its way to make sure that no one is eliminated from being qualified as an 'independent' appointee just because they have been part of the inner sanctums of political power. Here is how this particular circle is squared:

> there should not be a bar on those who have or who have had party-political affiliations or connections being considered. Those appointed to a reformed chamber should be, individually and collectively, those able to make the best contribution to its work. Any political affiliations should be disregarded when considering whether someone is suitable to serve and should not be the basis for either preferential or detrimental consideration. However, as the basis for appointment would be to provide an independent element, appointed members of a reformed second chamber would be expected to act independently from any political party.

So we are back to informal 'expectations' and a code of honour. And who decides who 'are able to make the best contribution'? It hardly needs to be said that it will be an appointments commission of people who are best able to judge this. But in the age of transparency, some criteria are also needed. The *White Paper* provides a profile of how to identify *a suitable chap* (using the term in its gender-neutral form). They are people who will:

- have a record of significance that demonstrates a range of experience, skills and competencies;
- be able to make an effective and significant contribution to the work of the House across a wide range of issues;
- have some understanding of the constitutional framework and the skills and qualities needed to be an effective member of the House;

- have the time available to make an effective contribution within the procedures of working practices of the House; and
- be able to demonstrate outstanding personal qualities, in particular integrity and independence.

In this way we can rest assured that appointed Senators will be 'one of them'.

Recall that sneak question, which the Government slipped in, about whether it should be allowed to appoint a person whom it wishes to make a minister. More than anything, this reveals that behind the fine words about 'independence' and 'scrutiny', our current politicians are thinking about the reformed second chamber as a way to extend their own party and administrative power, and to fill it with chaps like themselves.

What Should Happen?

Ralph Miliband, father of the famous brothers currently in the cabinet, once wrote that 'parliamentarism' in Britain "simultaneously enshrines the principle of popular inclusion *and* that of popular exclusion'.[10] The British tradition offers a democratic façade behind which there is an excluding reality that keeps voters at arms length. This tradition is healthy and alive in the *White Paper*. It appears to offer inclusion through the elemental procedure of the popular vote but its mechanisms—from its consideration of voting systems, to the time it foresees reform taking, to its criteria for the appointed members—are dedicated to reproducing the machinery of exclusion that marks the British way of government. We see no way forward here for reformers or democrats, whether from the left or right. The *White Paper* has been authored on

---

[10] Ralph Miliband, *Capitalist Democracy in Britain*, 1982, p. 39.

the other side of Robin Cook's dividing line. It is designed to put as firm a break on progress as can possibly be applied, in the circumstances.

The *White Paper* seeks to codify what are in effect the corrupt practices of the political class defending its closed shop of power and influence in Westminster and Whitehall.

Reformers who want to 'Carry On and Hope for the Best' may back its plans for elections. But they will find themselves participating in a Pinewood Studios-style revival that may be suggestive but is hardly priapic. Our advice to reformers, especially those who look to action on electing the Lords without any further debate about its role and powers, is that going down a blind alley with your eyes open will not stop it from being a cul de sac.

We challenge anyone to read the *White Paper* and the *Athenian Option* side by side to prefer in principle the course proposed by the *White Paper*. Of course *The Athenian Option* needs to be reinforced with international and UK wide research into the variety of deliberative exercises that have taken place. This could also provide more detailed accounts of the best possible size for 'juries' to assess legislation and the costs.

If the *Athenian Option* might be preferable because it seems more attractive in the 'abstract', is it practical? The way this question is usually asked assumes that it is not. But behind this assumption there is a greater one: that the existing system works and is only in need of limited improvement. Yet taken as a whole the British system of sovereignty is now a busted flush with many of its parts in need of replacement. As the saying goes, 'If it ain't broke, don't fix it!'. We agree: that's why we need to call in the builders.

We pose a simple challenge. We should build a second chamber whose role is to *strengthen* an elected

House of Commons, to help it propose laws in clear and readable English, that are scrutinised to assess both this and whether they will achieve what they are intended to do.

Using sortition to create representative juries of the people who can undertake this role in a serious deliberative fashion will add an element of direct democracy to our parliament. In his new study, *Democracy: Crisis and Renewal,* Paul Ginsborg, the outstanding historian of Italy, sets out the case for combining participatory democracy with representative democracy. Integrating sortition in the upper chamber with an elected House of Commons does just that.

How do we set about achieving this? When we gave evidence before the Wakeham commissioners Bill Morris asked us whether the fact that we expressed a desire to experiment to see how sortition could best work meant that we were uncertain about our approach. In its own way this is a very significant question. There is a widespread belief that political institutions and government generally must deliver certainty. This is a chimera. We need a spirit of experiment, enterprise and invention in politics just as we expect this in the economy. A spirit of openness in the *way* we govern ourselves is surely essential to the successful advance of democracy and a better way of ensuring that our historic traditions of liberty, independence, tolerance and self-government are renewed, however threadbare they have become.

The Royal Commission on the Reform of the House of Lords

Members: Baroness Dean, Lord Butler, Professor Dawn Oliver, Professor Anthony King, Bill Morris, Kenneth Munro, Lord Hurd, Sir Michael Wheeler-Booth, Ann Beynon, Gerald Kaufman MP, Lord Wakeham, Richard Harries (Bishop of Oxford)

Statement for the Royal Commission on the Reform of the House of Lords, 12 May 1999
by
Anthony Barnett and Peter Carty
authors of
The Athenian Solution

This brief statement welcomes the work of the Commission. We congratulate it on taking public evidence. Section I considers the historic task of the Commission and proposes some principles which we believe need to be followed. Section II considers what powers the new Chamber should exercise. Section III argues that the composition should include members drawn at random from the public and that this should be done in an open-minded, experimental and flexible manner. Sections II and III are based upon our Demos pamphlet, *The Athenian Option*, published in June 1998 and submitted to the Commission. Our presentation, therefore, is mainly concerned with powers and composition. These focus on one key function, that of scrutiny. Our argument can be summed up as follows. If the Government is right and the second chamber should not be a competitive legislative chamber, then its role must be to improve the legislation produced by the Commons. This means it must have enhanced powers to enforce such improvement. It will help such a House of Scrutiny if in part its composition is non-partisan, but this needs to be democratic if it is to win legitimacy in the eyes of the public.

I General

1. We welcome the removal of the core component and historic foundation of the House of Lords, the hereditary aristocracy. Few believe that the remaining appointed chamber will have legitimacy. The Government's decisive action has had the effect of abolishing the second chamber.

2. It falls to you to recommend how to replace Britain's second chamber. Even if you decide to reproduce it exactly as it was, it would still be different in a fundamental way. It will be a conscious, deliberated construction of an institution whose essential nature was that it evolved organically. The authority of the old Lords rested upon its claim to a natural, Burkian inheritance. Today, as your Consultation Paper describes, every aspect of the chamber, its functions, powers, procedures and composition, are being considered and decided. This task is unique in British constitutional history.

3. For the new second chamber to be regarded as legitimate over the long run, three basic principles need to be respected. The three principles are:

- No decisive executive patronage in appointing members
- The chamber be democratically representative
- The chamber have the power to reject extremely bad laws

4. In addition, there is a fundamental issue of process: voters need to be involved in the final shape of the chamber. This question is not in the Commission's formal brief but the legitimacy of the new chamber is. Because it will be the second half of our parliament, we, the voters of the 21st century, must have a say in its powers and composition. We request the Commission recommend that this happens. Similarly, we think any proposal that the new chamber be largely, let alone entirely, appointed is so contemptible as to be ridiculous. But our view would be influenced by research into public opinion. We hope that you yourselves take such soundings.

5. Our own formulations are deliberately open. The public might exercise its preference in a referendum or in other ways. There can be appointed members. There are different forms of democratic representation. 'Extremely bad laws' need to be defined. (But the public is unlikely to have respect for a Parliament so paralytic that it is powerless to stop legislation as bad as the poll tax even after a major reform.)

II *Powers*

6. Our Demos paper, *The Athenian Solution*, proposes that the new second house should be a chamber of scrutiny not one of legislation. It should oversee and not compete with the Commons, whose directly elected members are the country's legislators.

7. In terms of scrutiny it should exercise three powers which the present House of Lords does not enjoy:

- to insist that legislation is written in clear English and can be understood by anyone willing to give it a reasonable amount of time and concentration.

- to question the Government about the consequences of its legislation and seek to ensure that its answers are honest. If they are manifestly incredible it should have the power to return the legislation.

- to act as a constitutional check, or 'long-stop', as Lord Home's Commission put it in 1978, so as to safeguard fundamental rights, freedom and fairness.

8. At present, as it undertakes piecemeal improvement as well as scrutiny, the existence of the Lords functions to permit sloppy and careless legislation to pass through the Commons because the Government believes this can always be tidied up in the 'other place'. Thus the existence of a pliable second house encourages lax scrutiny and inadequate drafting in the first one. The new second chamber should have enough power to deter Government and Commons from proposing manifestly bad legislation.

III Composition

9. We are in a learning process so far as modern democracy is concerned. A flexible, open-minded, even experimental approach should be adopted towards the composition of the new chamber.

10. First with respect to the European Union. Second, with respect to the regions and nations of the UK, now that they have representative bodies of their own. Third, with respect to the coming 'knowledge economy'. This will alter profoundly the relationship between government and governed. And people will want an increased say over *how* this relationship changes.

11. In the foreseeable future a majority of the population will have higher education and an even larger
majority will be on the internet. The extraordinary
alteration in public perception of politics that began
with television will take new shapes. One response
already is a marked increase in the interest in politics
outside the tramlines of traditional party politics.
Apparently, up to 20 times more people are members
of special issue organisations than are affiliated to
political parties.

12. These changes mean that we cannot know the
shape of politics to come. The Commission should
ensure that Britain takes advantage of future uncer-
tainty. It should insist that the new chamber builds in
new methods of representation and is open to the public in new ways.

14. In particular, it should break the monopoly of
traditional politicians and elite representatives and
bring regular citizens into the process of scrutiny.

15. We do not propose, as some commentators who
did not read our Demos pamphlet claimed, that people should be taken from the street to become legislators. Legislation is a task for the elected. We propose
only that citizens help to assess legislation.

16. There is a considerable body of evidence which
shows that if a cross-section of the public, guided by
experienced moderators, are asked to put their preju-
dices aside and consider a problem, that they can
reach decisions at least as wise, sound and legitimate
as specialists, provided they hear the evidence and
argument of all sides, and are given the time to reflect,
discuss, and put their own questions.

17. We believe that members of the public drawn at
random in the way we suggest can assess whether legislation is understandable. They will be able to take a
fair view on the honesty of a government's justifica-

tion for its legislation. They can help judge whether legislation is unconstitutional.

18. At this early stage we support the arguments for a mixed chamber. We do not suggest that the new chamber should be made up immediately of a majority chosen at random on the 'Athenian' lines we describe, fifty-fifty men and women, proportional in numbers to the regions and nations. We do urge the Commission to recommend that such 'deliberative juries' are assembled on these lines to scrutinise specific pieces of legislation, so that prepared citizens will have the authority to question Ministers, MPs, officials and experts.

19. If the experiment is deemed a success by the public, its expansion should follow.

20. One of the qualities of British government has been its flexibility. This stemmed from its famous organic character mentioned at the start. One of the arguments against the kind of exercise the Commission itself is engaged in, is that it will 'lock' government into rigid patterns which become unsuitable over time. We believe that it is possible to build flexibility and a potential for change into the new second chamber. We urge the Commissioners to do so. In this spirit we recommend the inclusion of regular citizens into the process of legislative scrutiny.

                                        29 April 1999

**Royal Commission for the Reform of the
House of Lords
Transcript of Public Hearing**
London 12 May 1999, Session Three

Lord Wakeham: To help them to understand what's
going on I believe that everyone should have by now
received a copy of our Consultation Paper. If not cop-
ies are available at the back of the hall. It sets out our
Terms of Reference, the Membership of the Commission and the way in which we propose to approach our
task. It also poses challenging questions on the issues
raised by Lords Reform.

As the Consultation Paper makes clear we are keen
to get the widest possible range of views on matters
within our Terms of Reference. I am pleased to say that
we have received well over 500 Submissions so far,
which has got us off to a very good start. But we would
be able to take account of any Submissions received
before the end of June. So if you haven't put pen to
paper, there is still time to do so, but the earlier the
better from our point of view. In addition, can I
remind you to complete and return the questionnaires
which you were given to you when you registered.
This will give us a very useful perspective on people's
views. We will be holding Public Hearings throughout
the country between now and the end of July. Full
details can be obtained by telephoning (01772) 881888.
The purpose of these Public Hearings is to enable us to
probe and to test some of the written evidence which
we have received, to ensure that we fully understand
the arguments which are being made. It should be a
good discipline for those giving oral evidence to
explain their views in response to questions from the
Commission.

It is also important that these exchanges would be
taking place in public as part of a truly open and trans-

parent Consultation. We hope the hearings will stimulate public interest and I am certainly encouraged by
the numbers who have been here throughout the day.
Additionally there will be opportunities for those
attending Public Hearings to comment on what they
have heard. As you know, the press, cameras, and so
on have been here and how many are still here, I am
not quite sure, but my advice to anyone is just to
ignore them. Secondly, to say that those who have got
mobile phones, if they were able to put them off, it
might help us a little bit.

The way we work is like this. The Witnesses will be
invited to take the stand in turn, each will be asked
briefly to recapitulate the main points of their Written
Evidence, my colleagues on the Commission and I will
then ask them a number of questions. The Witnesses
for this evening's session will be Tony Benn MP, the
Earl of Halsbury and Anthony Barnett and Peter Carty
from Demos. Once all the Witnesses have finished
answering our questions, I will invite members of the
audience to express their own views on the issues. You
may therefore wish to make a note of any points which
will occur to you during the session so that you can
raise them at the end. And the final point that I'd like
to emphasise is that for Members of the Royal Commission at least, this is the very early stage in the information gathering process. We do not have settled
views on many of the issues under consideration. We
want to absorb the mass of written evidence which has
already arrived, and further material which is yet to
come in and to complete our program of Public Hearings before we take stock. The Public Hearing is therefore part of a genuine exploratory process. We hope
that we will all approach it and view it in that light and
contribute to the debate in that spirit...

Lord Wakeham: We move on now to the last Witnesses for today and that is Mr Barnett and Mr Carty from Demos and if they'd like to take the stand. I'm not sure which is which. Mr Barnett is a Senior Fellow of Birkbeck College and Mr Carty is a journalist and I wonder whether one of you would like to make a few opening remarks.

Mr Barnett: I would like to make a few opening remarks and then Mr Carty will make some additions. We appreciate very much the opportunity to appear before you on what is an historic day, not only because the Welsh Assembly and the Scottish Parliament meet for the first time, but also because this is the first occasion on which members of the public have been allowed, officially, to consider the fate of the House of Lords. I notice that we are meeting in the 'Coronet Room', and hope that this is not a bad omen.

Our proposal is that an Upper House dedicated to scrutiny and revision of legislation should include members of the public, selected by lot. We must vote for our law makers. In this [we] agree with Mr Tony Benn who has just spoken to us. But in reality the Lords is no longer a Legislative Chamber, and the role of scrutiny and revision which is its current function is a complementary one which can be carried out in a non-partisan fashion and a jury made up of regular citizens can add both authority and wisdom to this process. We do not propose that the entire Second Chamber be recruited by lot. The principle is radical and imaginative. Its use needs to be tested in a practical fashion. We argue for a flexible approach. In the first instance drawing groups from a list of citizens, 50% men, 50% women, who have been selected by lot and who have agreed to serve if called. Then each group, a relatively small one, should scrutinise one piece of legislation. To clarify the principles behind our thinking, we can say that we have one agreement and two disagreements with what we understand to be the Government's position. We agree that the Second Chamber should enhance, not compete, with the Commons. Therefore it should not be dominated by politicians elected on national slates. US-style gridlock will open the way to behind the scenes corruption. It doesn't follow, and here is our first disagreement, that the Upper House should not have more powers than those it currently exercises. The great drawback of the present British Constitution, is the over-mighty strength of the executive. The Commons is already far too weak. It is the inability of the Commons to check a determined executive which is the greatest problem faced by British democracy. A reformed Upper House must have additional powers so that it too, is not supine before the executive. For if it is powerless, this will simply confirm the weakness of the Commons. Instead it needs new powers designed to help it strengthen the Commons itself. There are three such powers in our view.

First it should have the power to ensure that legislation is written in clear English, this is quite a radical proposal. Second, it should have the power to judge whether the Government is manifestly incredible in its description of the consequences of its proposed legislation (and you can question us on what we mean by this). Third, it should have the power to safeguard the country from laws so unfair that they can be deemed unconstitutional. A classic example: the Poll Tax. If the House of Commons is doing its job, the Second Chamber should not need to exercise such powers, but by having them it will stiffen the resolve of MPs to do their job and ensure the Government is willing to listen to them.

Second, we also disagree with the proposal, we understand that the Government is making, that the House should be largely appointed. Especially if the appointed element, and here I think we disagree with the previous speaker, is designed to be representative of various professional bodies and interests, if there is one thing that you can do for your grandchildren it is to save them, and us, from pompous debates by the self-consciously important who have vested interests in their own area of expertise and no experience of exercising public judgement in other matters. We want 'People's Peers' but they must come from the people and not be chosen from above, by an official body. It is possible to have a strong non-partisan element in the Second Chamber, and for this to be and to be seen to be democratic and lively, as the use of citizens' juries and participative assemblies grows, their techniques will some day be introduced into national parliaments to complement representative democracy. Let the country which is among the last to retain the hereditary principle become the first to introduce the new principle of direct citizens' participation into its Parliament. Thank you.

Mr Carty: I would just like to add three brief points. Anthony and I came up with our proposals independently and I believe there's a lot of other people who are interested in this kind of idea. The paper is a result of two of us collaborating, but it would be wrong to assume our paper isn't part of a wider movement to apply ideas involving direct democracy in Government. The other point is that citizens' juries for example have already been used successfully in Local Government as part of the decision-making processes. Finally it is important to emphasise that we're not advocating Government by continuous plebiscite. We are not saying that our 'people's peers' should initiate legislation. We're not saying that essentially they would have a hugely different function from the present incumbents of the Upper Chamber.

Lord Wakeham: Thank you very much. Can I just start the ball rolling, by asking you this question. It may be very actively an advantage to your scheme which hadn't occurred to you, but it seems to me that if the scheme that you put forward is legislation initiated in the Commons, passes the Commons and then comes to the Upper House for scrutiny, and that's your system, what about the present position of a lot of legislation which starts in the Upper House and then goes to the Commons? If your system can't be made to work in reverse, then you would reduce substantially the amount of business that any Government could get through in any one year. I say that may be an advantage or a disadvantage depending on your point of view. But your system does seem to me to imply, starting in the Commons and going to the Lords.

Mr Barnett: It does imply that and it may well imply that there is less legislation although it would be about higher quality, if I may say that. But I think that the point that Mr Benn made, which is a very good one, that a lot of the Amendments and the processes that take place in the Lords are actually in fact Government, and in effect therefore House of Commons-initiated changes where the Government is using the Lords for its own legislative purposes. There is [in] effect only one, in a real sense we have a unicameral system, we have 650 MPs and the implication of what we are suggesting is that the House of Commons should be the main centre of legislation and should be able to organise itself to legislate.

Lord Wakeham: Yes but the fact is also that about half the Bills in each session start in the Lords and then go to the Commons and that would present a difficulty. But Bill Morris would you like to....

Bill Morris: Thank you Chairman. Mr Barnett, we find your proposals interesting and obviously we want to ask some questions to get more information from you. In your supplementary statement, I think its paragraph 18 you say, that at this early stage we support the arguments for a Mixed Chamber, that seems to me that some of the suggestions that you make, you may not be ready for yourself. Is that a reasonable assumption?

Mr Barnett: No not from my part. I think that if you said to me, well will this work, if we just go over to it, from where we are now, to a full scale selecting the entire House by lot, then I wouldn't be able to say to you, hand on heart, I'm absolutely confident that is what we can do. One question which Peter and I have debated quite a lot is, 'should you select people by lot, who in effect become Peers, over a number of years or would it be better if we selected them or if they were selected by lot to examine as a jury so to speak, one piece of legislation'. So we want to emphasise the experimental approach. We think that we should adopt a flexible approach to see how this works, to see whether people like this, to see whether people respond well to it, to see whether it does indeed capture the public imagination, before trying to then proceed to make this, so to speak, the majority of a Second Chamber. So this doesn't come from a lack of belief in it, but from the belief that you can actually make this thing work and grow and give it its space and give it a chance to see how it works.

Bill Morris: That obviously gives rise to some very practical questions. Questions like would Members of the Chamber be chosen from all the electorate? What about those who just don't want to serve and how long would people serve for? Those are some of the practical questions that you'd be obliged to answer before the thing could even be considered for legislation.

Mr Barnett: Well if you take, for example, if you say that you are trying to pass one piece of legislation and you'd need to experiment partly, would you have in effect a citizens' jury, a jury of 'people's peers' would it be 10 strong, would that be the best number? Would the best number be 50 strong to assess a really serious piece of legislation? Now if you've selected a group, let's say we're selecting 30 or 40, they've been selected by lot, they are willing to serve, they should be paid. They should be certainly paid at the same rate as an MP, if they're earning more than an MP they should get what their rate is paid. Their employer should be compensated for the period of absence, they have got then to look at the period of time that this legislation might be going through Parliament, let's say it is going through Parliament over the course of the year. They wouldn't need to be employed doing this for a full year, but a number of months of that year they would need to be able to go into preparation, they would need to be able to read the material, they would need then to be able to talk about it amongst themselves. For that period of time they should need to be given as much time as possible. They should get down to work and that is different from selecting people by lot who are then, so to speak, to become Peers to look at all legislation.

Bill Morris: You seem to have a healthy criticism of experts in the context of the paper. Do you feel that it's not necessary that Members of the Second Chamber should have some experts and some experience around?

Mr Carty: Maybe if I could answer that. I see no reason why ordinary members of the public, any members of the public usually has a considerable body of expertise that he or she could bring to bear. I think part of the thinking behind the proposal is that those ordinary members of the public, for one reason or another, are often excluded from the legislative process altogether.

Mr Barnett: Could I interrupt. Lord Hurd made the point earlier, that many people who used to be in the House of Commons had done practical jobs of various kinds before in their lives. Now if you select people like this process, as part of a Second House, they would indeed bring to bear a very wide range of different experiences and this doesn't mean that they shouldn't be questioning experts, I'm very strongly in favour of asking experts to give their advice and to give their views. But I think if they're giving their views to regular citizens, the regular citizens will be able to assess the validity of their views just as well as you or I.

Bill Morris: Could you tell us how the Bishops and the Law Lords would fit into your proposal?

Mr Barnett: No I think we're leaving that problem to you.

Lord Wakeham: Thank you very much. Professor King, would you like to ask a few questions.

Professor King: One is more to do with the tone of your original Demos pamphlet than with its substance. You say at one point 'it is said that there are three stages in the life of every important idea: first it's ignored, next its ridiculed, then it becomes accepted wisdom'. Now I have two problems with that statement. First is it's manifestly untrue, as an account of what happens to important ideas and secondly it seems to suggest that if an idea is ignored and/or ridiculed, that somehow by that fact it becomes important. I mean you're not implying that are you? There's a slight suggestion in this paragraph that if one actually dissented from your idea, it would merely prove that you are somehow an old fuddy duddy.

Mr Barnett: It doesn't have to imply that you are an old fuddy-duddy, but it doesn't mean that you're not an old fuddy-duddy.

Professor King: I thank you for that reassurance. On a much more down to earth level, you say at one point in the paper and you say in your oral presentation, that the newly-constituted Second Chamber should insist that laws are drafted in comprehensible English, that they should return legislation that, beyond reasonable doubt, will fail in its stated aim and it should reject legislation that threatens the fundamental values of our Constitution. Now it would be fun to pursue all three of those, but could I just pursue the unconstitutional legislation point because that is an issue that we are all seized of. You illustrate the general point with the case of the Poll Tax. Now I thought the Poll Tax was dotty from day one. I thought that it was dotty when it was abolished, I still think in retrospect that it was dotty, but that it was unconstitutional seems to me to be much [less] clear and I am not entirely sure who would decide and on what basis that a piece of ostensibly fiscal legislation like the Poll Tax should be unconstitutional.

Mr Barnett: Yes well I think this is a very, as you can imagine, a very interesting question. Let's just take one simple aspect of the Poll Tax. The Home Office sent a memo to the Cabinet, when it was under consideration as I think you know, saying that the existence of a Poll Tax would have the effect of making people not register to vote. So it had the effect and was known by the Government to have potential effect of driving people off the electoral register. After the 1992 election, which the Conservative Party won rather narrowly, in terms of the 20 seats that gave them the majority, the Sunday Telegraph quoted Mrs Thatcher, I think as she then was, Lady Thatcher as saying, 'the Poll Tax worked after all'. And she did not deny making this statement when it was published. So there is a clear argument for saying that one aspect of the Poll Tax was to drive, with simple basic political unfairness, that it was actually taking away from the population as a whole, the equal right to vote. And I think that it is reasonable to construe that argument, as I think it would have been in the United States formerly, as suggesting that that aspect, certainly that consequence of the legislation, would mean that you could argue it was unconstitutional. Now the problem about this is that we don't have a formal written Constitution, by which you can then make those judgements. But if one of the roles of a Chamber of scrutiny is to see that the way we are governed is secure, is to secure that, then I think you then have to say to that Chamber, well then are there certain principles of basic fairness which we could reasonably agree on our constitutional principles for our country. I think that that is one, and I think that if you gave that to a jury you would get a very safe and sound verdict.

Professor King: So is the answer to the first of my two questions that the House of Peers, in the form of a citizens' jury, would itself decide what fell under the Constitutional rubric?

Mr Barnett: I think that on this issue, and this is where you do certainly need to have, in my own view guidance or perhaps appointed people that would help to focus the citizens' jury, or a participative body of this sort, is what the evidence appears to show, is that when people are given clear questions, issues are raised which they must then focus on and look at that they can come to a constructive view. So if this argument is put, perhaps by experts like yourself about the Poll Tax, that in this case, the consequences would be to drive people off the Electoral Register, and that surely does mean it should be considered unconstitutional, that issue would have to be debated as such and they would then come to a view on that.

Professor King: Okay. My next question concerns the issue that Bill Morris raised a few moments ago, about how the 'citizens juries' because that is in effect what they are, would be chosen. Now you suggest that they should be chosen by lot and there is I think confusion in a lot of people's minds between a random sample and a sample that constitutes a representative cross-section of the population. Precisely because a group is chosen at random, it may well turn out to be not at all representative. Now the section in your paper about selection is very short and rather tantalising on this point and I was genuinely not at all sure how you would set up these 'citizens' juries'.

Mr Carty: Well the basic idea would be to firstly have Regional Catchments consisting of parts of the Electoral Register, stratified by region and then the only other demarcation we would introduce would be by gender. So the citizens selected from a particular area would definitely be 50:50 split between men and women, but apart from that at the moment our proposal would be that it would be random within a geographical area.

Professor King: But they could randomly turn out to be all under the age of 22, all over the age of 75, all strong supporters of the Conservative Party. If what you're after is a group of people who represent a larger population, then I can assure you and there are statistical textbooks that will assure you at greater length, that stratifying by only two variables and then drawing lots, especially with such small numbers of people, is almost guaranteed not to produce what I think you think you want.

Mr Barnett: Yes, I think this is, you know, maybe we can bow somewhat to your expertise on this, but I think the sense that people have got an equal chance whether they are black or white, whatever their religion, whatever the complexities of their compositional identity, that they have as equal chance as anybody else, is an important part of people identifying with those who are chosen by random. So there is an attractive element to the randomness but it is important, and this was drawn from, which struck me very strongly in terms of the way the Athenians drew up their own jury of 201, they drew them equally from the 12 tribes, as I understand it, not being an expert in this, and that therefore it was also representative as well as random. They had the two elements that were involved in that. There is a risk in randomness that if you look at the present House of Commons or the present House of Lords, with all respect, there's a risk in all political processes.

Professor King: I can see the Chairman glaring at me, so I won't ask another question, I'll just make a point. Which is that one of the things that worried me both about the paper and about your oral presentation is the suggestion that we should make recommendations for a new House of Lords which would be highly experimental and subject to frequent change: if one way of doing things didn't work we'd have another. I suppose I feel, and I imagine most of my colleagues feel, that we should be trying to get it broadly right the first time; that if what we are dealing with is the country's Constitution, we shouldn't treat is as though it was some kind of adventure playground in which one was trying out a number of ideas which might or might not work. Can I just sort of lodge that concern.

Mr Barnett: May I respond to that point?

Lord Wakeham: Sure, please do.

Mr Barnett: I think that this attitude is gravely mistaken and Baroness Dean made the point about the low turnouts in the sense that there is in the public at the moment a sense of alienation from the political process. But the other side of this coin is, and only recently we have seen this, that actually it was public interest groups who generated an enormous public response over genetically modified food that forced the entire political class to turn on its head. The Government and all of its advisors and so on, said this was safe, and public opinion led not by elected politicians, but by other groups using many of the modern techniques of communication, transformed both public opinion and then political policy. And that showed very considerable and a new degree of interest in politics of a different kind in the public. Now I think in these circumstances, we don't know what democracy is going to be like in 20 or 30 years and I think it would be quite wrong, with all respect to your great wisdom and ability, I don't think that you are able to draw up a Constitution now which settles matters for the next 30, 40 or 50 years. Certainly not if you are looking at the House of Lords, in isolation from other aspects of a fast moving Constitution on Europe and domestically. So I think that an element of flexibility into the way the new Upper Chamber should grow is something that you could certainly argue for. Not at all in a childish fashion but in a very serious and sober one. Peter, Do you want to add anything?

Mr Carty: Well I'd just make the final point that we have a more highly educated general population than ever before, there is cynicism about the legislative process and really it is difficult now, I feel, to argue against the idea that an element of direct democracy should be experimented with to some extent within the new Upper Chamber.

Lord Wakeham: Thank you very much. You certainly made your points with clarity and I think we understood them. We appreciate your coming and appreciate your evidence and of course we will consider it very carefully. Thank you very much indeed.

Seven members of the public who had come along to hear the evidence had a chance to comment; one supports the Athenian Option. Here is the complete section of the transcript.

Lord Wakeham: Now we come to the last part of the day's session which is to give an opportunity for anybody who wants to, to add a comment. I think what we'll do is if I make it clear that we will run this for 15 minutes and as many people who can speak as shortly as possible, we'll get as many in as we can. I think the gentleman at the front here.

Philip Daniels, the Catholic Union: You have our memorandum before you and I wanted to refer to a point which was made this morning about the danger of so interpreting the paragraphs in your paper and in the White Paper about the representation of organised religion as to produce a spirit of sectarianism. Well clearly we wouldn't want that. The Catholic Union has existed since about 1829 in some form or other following the Catholic Relief Act and it was necessary because it was very difficult to get Catholic Members into the House of Commons, because of the prejudice against Roman Catholics standing for anything. Indeed, 100 years after 1829, we only had 10 Members. By that time the Irish had gone, so this is the problem. But I don't think that we would want you to consider extending the concept of Lords Spiritual to include representatives of all the organised religions including the oriental religions, and so on. Because Lords Spiritual really aren't spiritual Lords. The Lords Spiritual are there to look after that corporation called the Church of England which has a very special place in the Constitution and I don't want to say anything about that. But they don't apply anywhere else in the four countries represented in the House of Commons and I think what we would look for is some way in which people of principle and of religious belief can get into both Houses on their merits and on their faith and that in a revised Upper House there would still be a cross-bench and they would be eligible and chosen through whatever means you choose, to become Members of the Upper House. Representative, your paper talks about not on a personal basis but representative of. Now we've heard something about representation today, is it representative of or representative on behalf of, but I haven't yet been able to work out a system, perhaps you can, how you can have something which fits into our normal procedures in this country and which could lead to the appearance in a revised Upper House of representatives of organised religion. Not people simply nominated by a large number of bodies, I think there are 33 in the Council of Churches of Britain and Ireland, and then you've got to think of the Jews, the Muslims, the Hindus and so on. We think that the place for religious people, well religious conviction, is still the Upper House, and they should come through the Cross Benches.

(Unknown): Thank you very much Lord Chairman. I speak entirely personally but earlier this year I made a three part series called 'Inside the Lords' for the BBC. I think it is hard to argue against any form of direct election for a future House of Lords, but I know that it will, in the end be always possible that you'll go down the route of some sort of nomination. I plead with you that you will make only one method of nomination to a new Second House. I think what may be a problem in the years ahead, is there are different forms of nomination or indirect election, to get to the House of Lords. One of the problems at the moment is that it is the different forms of people being there, is in itself divisive. If say you go down the path of having indirectly

elected people from the Scottish Parliament and nominated people from another area of life and another
form of nomination for another people, I do think that
people will be competitive amongst themselves, as to
whether their own nomination to the Chamber is more
valid than someone else's. So I hope that whatever
method you choose is a unifying method.

Helen Seaford: I just wanted to follow up the point
that Tony Benn made, which related to something I
said.

Lord Wakeham: Sorry I didn't recognise you. I think
probably it's only fair to let others have a go.

Keith Nilsen: My name's Keith Nilsen. I'd just like to
support the idea of voting by lot, broadly put forward
by Anthony Barnett but to focus attention on three
points. The first is the rising level of education
amongst the general population, which we're talking
about a century in terms of Constitutional reform and
you should think expansively in those terms. What
will the general population look like educationally in
100 years' time. The second is that with the end of the
Cold War and the, if you like triumph of liberal
democracy and capitalism over its main competing
ideology of socialism, there is a tendency for sameness
in politics, that differences become increasingly
blurred. There was a position put forward in a famous
book by Francis Fukiyama about the end of ideology
in the next century. Now one function or one consequence of that could be a drift toward corporatism and
the anti-democratic consequences of that. For example, I would cite the introduction of GM foods against
the consent of the general population as one example
of the drift toward corporatism. Thirdly there's the
problem of the increasing technology of surveillance
in society. I bring to your attention the recent case of
employers actually putting video cameras in toilets in

work places, there is a general sociological theory of surveyors and the history of surveyors and I think that in the next century, with the increase in sophistication of weapons technology and surveillance technology it is a serious factor to take into account. Against the background of those three points I would put to you that the introduction of voting by lot as a complementary component of the Reform of the Lords, not an exclusive one by any means but a complementary component, should be viewed as a necessary support, reinforcement, of the separation of powers of argument. Which as you know is fundamental to the whole doctrine of liberalism and the defence of Human Rights. So that's the point I wanted to make.

Lord Wakeham: Thank you very much.

Alex Samuels, Lawyer: We live in a political society, indeed a party political society, and all of us are here including you and your colleagues Chairman, because one political party has perceived the present system as politically unfair to them. If you speak of Government policy legislation, you're talking about political issues. Non-political nominees often sit very uneasily with elected striving politicians. The Bishops and the Law Lords in the House of Lords are of course somewhat inhibited as one might expect, and you find at local Government level that non-elected members of police committees and education committees, etc, again often find it very uncomfortable and inappropriate. Interest groups can always apply to give their evidence to Select Committees and so on in the normal way. If you think of the function of the Second Chamber calling a Government to account, scrutinising policy, scrutinising bills those are all political issues, so Chairman I would urge you and your colleagues, not simply to compromise on a mix, please don't ignore or seek to disguise the political realities, the party politi-

cal realities, of the society in which we live. Indeed a
very healthy society. Thank you.

Mary Honeyball: I am [a] candidate for the European
Parliament Elections. I'd like to make a few points
about direct elections to the Second Chamber. I mean
some of which have been covered but I think actually
could do with reiterating. The first was the one that
Lord Hurd talked about, about the issue of competition between the Commons and what that means and
how that would be resolved and all the questions
around that. And also the elections, if elections were to
be held at a different time from elections to the Commons and the question of turnout in elections and the
way that low turnouts undermine democracy which I
think is actually very relevant, since we've actually
had local Government elections where the turnout
was about 26%. I do think that's an issue which we
need to think about in general, but specifically if we
are thinking at all about further direct elections to any
institutions and there are other questions which arise.
Specifically if we were to have a directly elected Second Chamber actually how long that would sit for.
There have been suggestions that it would be three
Commons terms which could be anything between
9-15 years. Which, if you think about what that would
mean in reality, we could see a Second Chamber sitting from 1985 to the year 2000 which would mean
several General Elections and several changes in Government and obviously a lot that would need to be
considered if we were ever to consider going down
that route.

The last point I want to make is about legitimacy and if
there were to be a mix of elected Members of the Second Chamber and those who were nominated and
appointed how that relationship would work and
whether the elected Members might actually feel that

they had more legitimacy because they were elected over and above those who were appointed. Again that could cause problems. So I think there are some very thorny issues here which I hope the Royal Commission would take account of.

Mary O'Brien: I am particularly concerned that we may go to a wholly appointed Chamber if I read the Government's latest statements correctly. I noticed about a year ago, I think, Margaret Jay saying something like, anything's better than a Hereditary Peerage. I did write back at that point that I think that this is a very dangerous way of looking at our problems. From my own vantage point, perspective, as a rather modest member of the science technology workers in this country, the idea that the appointed Peers be selected through a Commission or directly by Government, fills me with horror. Because I notice the jockeying for position amongst the people who want to be influential in legislative circles throughout their careers. They are by no means the wisest of our councils in the learned societies and in the institutions, Chartered Institutions, or whatever as Lord Halsbury was speaking. I think this is a very dangerous precedent. We've got to be awfully careful that we get the best people from the professions, whether technical or non-technical. I don't at the moment see how to do it, but a wholly-elected Second Chamber I think is a very dangerous way to go, let alone being by the methods of there being selected through the Chartered Institutions and so forth.

(Unknown): Thank you. There have been many wonderful and charming speeches, but with due respect I wonder if the esteemed Commission might wonder whether its really necessary to re-invent this particular wheel.

Lord Wakeham: Thank you very much. That seems to be a very felicitous remark on which to close the sessions for today. Thank you very much for attending. Thank you very much to my colleagues for being here. I think that we have had a very good day and I appreciate all your help. Thank you.

Appendix II

Press Reactions
to the publication of the
original pamphlet

**It Could Be Lord You: For the duties are
delightful and the privileges great**
The Times, Leading Article, 30 May 1998

A politicised version of the National Lottery should
select the members of a reformed 'people's' House of
Lords. As we report today, Demos, the fashionable
think-tank, will make this speculative proposal in a
report due to be published next week.

There are incidental merits in its suggestion. The
first democracy did indeed select its jurors and some
of its magistrates by mechanical lottery machines,
though the franchise was limited. Sortition (election
by raffle) can be seen as a more democratic process
than being born with a title inherited from an ancestor
who slept with a king, or came over to conquer with
William, or knew Lloyd George. A genuine lottery
would produce a more representative sample of modern Britain than the partisan lottery of lists of superannuated politicians, or the expensive tombola of
contributors to party funds, or Buggins's lucky dip of
office-holders and other professional representatives.

But there are also demerits in picking new peers by the tumble of the balls. Under the Lords' and commoners' law of averages, the people's ermine will fall on inconvenient as well as random or deserving shoulders. Crofters in Lewis and family solicitors in Penzance might resent having to commute to London — and missing the weekend train home because of a three-line people's whip.

In the *Wasps*, the predecessor of *Have I Got News for You?*, Aristophanes sent up the populist delusions of election by lottery. In it only the elderly retired can afford to be elected. They may think that they are enjoying the pleasures and benefits of exercising power irresponsibly. But in fact they are being manipulated by cynical professional politicians and spin-doctors. The chance of being a self-important lottery legislator becomes addictive and corrupting.

So there will have to be safeguards if peers are ever to be elected by lot. Otherwise there will be ugly scenes over the breakfast table when the news of ennoblement arrives. As in the common National Lottery, the winners of peerages should be allowed to opt for no publicity. There must be a rule to prevent ambitious politicians such as Lord Archer of Weston-super-Mare from buying 100 tickets in their lordships' lottery. The Anthea Turner figure hostessing the draw on television must perform in ermine and with dignity, because, with all their faults, the British love their House of Peers. And the consolation prize for those who just fail to become people's peers must be a job at Demos.

Is Labour Too Old-fashioned for Athens?
Anthony Barnett, *The Times*, 30 May 1998

'We must modernise,' the Government cries out, as if it is being radical. Perhaps it is — within the milieu of the media, Westminster, and its bodyguard of spin-doctors. In the real world, however, an already modern country lives and breathes. Will the two worlds meet? The coming reform of the Lords provides a test case. If Blair fails it, we can draw the curtain — or as one wit put it, the wallpaper — over 'new' Labour.

I should declare an interest. In my book *This Time* (Vintage), I suggest that there has been a fundamental shift in public mood that makes it realistic for Britain to adopt a written constitution. Yet constitutions need their general character to be debated. Otherwise they wither and die. And the old one has died. As William Hague ruefully admitted, the Conservative Party, guardian of the narcoleptic order, became a victim of its rigor mortis: 'We had allowed the language,' he complained, 'to become so abstract and unfamiliar that phrases such as "sovereignty", "the supremacy of Parliament", "the rule of law", even the word "consti-tution" itself, are literally meaningless to most people.'

Recent opinion polls show that the concepts have not become meaningless. Rather, what has ceased to be relevant is the special 'British meaning' these terms were given by the traditional context of hierarchy and deference. In 1993, the Rowntree Trust commissioned a MORI poll that showed 79 per cent support for a written constitution to 'provide clear legal rules' for ministers and civil servants. That astounding result was treated as a blip. Now a similar poll has just been published by NOP. It reveals 85 per cent support for a written constitution.

This is a Mussolini level of endorsement. Indeed, many a dictator's plebiscite has scored less. But who has led the public in this direction? The politicians tell each other that 'the people are not ready' for such a drastic measure. Since the general election no organ of extensive public influence has advocated a written constitution in Britain, except perhaps *The Mail on Sunday*. Once a cause of *The Guardian* and *The Observer*, these papers seem to regard it as yesterday's fashion. It is never mentioned on television, apparently because it is less 'sexy' than debates about the Queen. Labour does not call for a written constitution. The Liberal Democrats say they 'always do' then lapse into silence. Mr Hague considered a constitutional convention, but dropped the idea.

Could the media and political elite come round to public opinion? Gordon Brown now favours a written constitution, it is said. Tony Blair does not rule it out, apparently. Over the next few months, they and their colleagues will confront an issue that brings the larger picture in to focus — the reform of the Lords after the abolition of its hereditary element. The House of Lords may seem unimportant because it is largely symbolic. But, to use a current phrase, its symbolism branded Britain. The House of Lords provides an image of what Britain was. In its reform of the second chamber, therefore, Labour will be telling us what it wants Britain to become.

There are genuine problems with most proposals for reform of the Lords, such as an elected or a regional-based chamber. Often they lead to political gridlock, which as America shows, opens the way to corruption. The Government would be right to reject such measures, which anyway belong to the mid-century. The aim should not be limited to 'catching up', as if the other countries have solved the problems of modern government. On the contrary, democracy everywhere stands in need of revitalisation. Reform of the Lords should be seized as a chance to be moving ahead.

Inspired by the inventiveness of classical Athens, a colleague and I have proposed a representative Upper House selected largely by lot like a jury (while retaining some appointed 'Peoples Peers'). None would be legislators; that is the role of elected politicians. Instead, the ordinary citizens in the Upper House could check and complement the House of Commons through scrutiny of legislation, ensuring for example, that is is written in clear and comprehensible English. Recently, Mr Hague set down the six Tory conditions for the renewal of the Lords, presumably in the hope that no reform could meet them. The Athenian option does so triumphantly.

Experiments with citizens' juries and other deliberative methods of participatory democracy have been widely welcomed for local government. A second chamber developed on similar lines need be neither exotic nor impractical. The last state to cling to aristocratic rulers could become the first to apply modern citizen scrutiny to its parliament.

It seems all too likely, however,that the Government will declare that 'enough is enough' and that no further constitutional radicalism is required. New Labour will become 'good old' Labour, as it declares the profound wisdom of our constitutional mores, thus closing the door on a new settlement.

The alternative is a process that will include, naturally, a written constitution that can articulate the relations between the decentralised parts of the United Kingdom and check the executive. Lords reform could open the way to a new, overall approach. Far from regarding this as a revolution, we now know that 85 per cent of the public will raise an eyebrow and ask 'what took you so long?'

Athenian Solution to Lords Reform
The Times, Letters to the Editor, 31 May 1998

From Mr Peter Carty

My co-author Anthony Barnett and I much enjoyed your witty leading article of May 30 on our Demos paper, *The Athenian Solution*, which advances radical reform for the House of Lords.

However, in case your readers have been misled about our proposals, which centre on selection of members of a new upper chamber by lot (sortition), we are not proposing retention of aristocratic titles for members of a new Upper House. We would like to see a new breed of peers in Parliament (PPs), or people's peers.

Such 'PPs' would not be subject to party whips. so the chances of manipulation by 'cynical professional politicians and spin-doctors' would be limited. And we are not proposing that a reformed upper chamber should have legislative powers: we are saying that it should scrutinise new statutes and have a power of veto in very specific and rare circumstances.

So perhaps your readers can relax and actually look forward to a call to participate in direct democracy.

PETER CARTY
54 Godfrey House, Bath Street, ECIV 9ES

From Dr P.A. Cartledge

Sortition, as the Ancient Athenians perceived, and as the earliest attested example of Western political theory enjoined, is the most democratic procedure available for selecting office-holders: it randomises selection, it maximises the chances of all eligible persons being selected, it encourages the largest number of those eligible to put their names forward for selection, and—not least—it presumes that all those eligible not only can but also should assume the relevant office.

Moreover, it can be adapted for use both in a system of direct democratic government, such as that of Ancient Athens, and in a modern representative system such as our own. The lot, and the provision of political pay, were the twin engines of Ancient Greek democracy. We have long been used to the latter. Introduction of the former is long overdue.

PAUL CARTLEDGE
(Reader in Greek History)
Clare College, Cambridge CB2 1TL

From Dr Adrian Seville

Your leader refers to the idea of drawing lots to select representatives for a reformed Upper House.

In 1576, the Doge of Genoa, Andrea Doria, instituted a local government reform whereby in each year the five retiring members of the ruling colleges would be replaced by five selected by drawing lots from the pool of candidates. The method chosen was the extraction of numbered balls from a single urn (known as *Il Seminario*) containing 120 in total, corresponding to the candidates, each identified by a particular number.

These chance events were ideal material for side bets: betting on the outcome of election to office was already common, but the new method gave some assurance of randomness and hence of fairness. Betting on the numbers became hugely popular and, with a later reduction in the number of candidates, was the origin of the form of the lottery still in use today in Italy and elsewhere in continental Europe: the extraction of five numbers from a total of 90. Indeed, it can be argued that this was also the forerunner of our own modern lottery.

It has to be said that Doria's reform had the unintentional effect of focusing attention on the process of betting rather than on the democratic choice of candidates. Still, times change.

ADRIAN SEVILLE
(Academic Registrar)
The City University, Northampton Square, ECIV OH

From Mr Martin Wainwright

Choosing Lords by lottery would have the merit defined by Alexis de Tocqueville (*Democracy in America*, 1835), in his study of the randomly chosen court jury as a political rather than legal institution.

Referring to juries as a free school in citizenship which is always open, de Tocqueville described how jury service makes all men feel that they have duties towards society and that they take a share in its government. The jury is both the most efficient way of establishing the people's rule and the most efficient way of teaching them how to rule.

This is one reason why the National Lottery Charities Board — appropriately — is about to choose a number of new members of its advisory panels in London and Yorkshire by the random system used to select juries. As the first extension of the system from the courts to quangoland, the experiment may be worth watching.

MARTIN WAINWRIGHT
(Chair, Yorkshire and Humber Regional Advisory
Panel, National Lottery Charities Board)
Cragg Mount, Woodlands Drive, Rawdon, Leeds

Drawbacks to Choosing Lords by Lot
The Times, Letters to the Editor, 3 June 1998

From Dr Peter Jones

Sir, It is good to see that, with their proposals for appointing a House of Lords by lot (letters, June 3), the daringly radical thinkers on Demos have finally caught up with *The Spectator* ('Ancient & modern', August 9, 1997).

They might like to brood on the fact that in ancient Athens the serious experts (those running the military and the exchequer) were not appointed by lot (Athenians were not daft) but elected.

Since the serious experts in today's Government are not MPs — who gaily switch from exchequer to education to health to Home Office almost by the second — but civil servants, perhaps we should extend Athenian principles to the Commons and appoint MPs by lot, civil servants by vote.

PETER JONES
(Founder, Friends of Classics)
28 Akenside Terrace, Newcastle upon Tyne NE2 ITN

From Mr Francis Bennion

The suggestion by Demos that members of our second House of Parliament should be chosen like a jury from ordinary citizens is naive. We need more knowledgeable legislators than that.

Anthony Barnett (article, 'Is Labour too old-fashioned for Athens?', June 3) says these ordinary citizens could check and complement the House of Commons through scrutiny of legislation, ensuring that it is written in clear and comprehensible English. With respect, this is tommy rot and moonshine.

Having spent half a century in the legislative field, I can say that effective scrutiny of Bills requires great skill and experience. So does turning them into plain English.

The Inland Revenue's skilled tax-law rewrite team, set up in 1996, already aims to put our tax law into plain English. In their plans for 1998–99, just published, they admit to finding it heavy going:

> Our first full year of rewrite work saw less progress than we had hoped ... As the work progressed it quickly became clear that our original targets were unattainable ... our task is even more complex, difficult and time-consuming than we first thought it would be ... almost every line of the existing legislation throws up awkward questions.

Scarcely a task for ordinary citizens.

FRANCIS BENNION
5 Old Nursery View, Kennington, Oxford OXI 5NT

From Dr Roger Gard

Those who recommend 'the Athenian solution' to Lords reform should remember that the democracy in question was deplored by the greatest minds of the time, most notably by Plato and Thucydides.

It seems to vanish from their view that Athenian democracy was based in slavery and the denial of rights to women, waged disastrous war, killed Socrates, and was the prelude to the takeover of the city by Macedon and then Rome. Only the cultural prestige generated by the above-mentioned thinkers and others can account for anyone recalling the period at all.

The search for a solution to this question might surely be more fruitfully conducted by looking at the virtues, as opposed to the oft-stressed vices, of our evolved older system—such as the traditions of honour and disinterestedness, the ethic of public service and of political careers divorced from personal ambition, the variety of good sense and talents assembled neither by election, patronage, or pure chance.

Try to recreate these by all means; but why look back longingly to the first great age of demagoguery?

ROGER GARD
Maiden Newton House Dorchester, Dorset DT2 OAA

From Mr A. R. Hawkes

Sir, I fully support Demos's suggestion that members of Parliament's second chamber should be selected by random method.

The simplest and cheapest lottery is that of accident of birth, and we have that already in the Lords.

A. R. HAWKES
Birchwood, Sutherland Road, Longsdon,
Stoke-on-Trent ST9 9Q

This is not Lords reform at all: it is a conspiracy of deluded rubbish
Hugo Young, *Guardian*, 9 June 1998

The reform of the House of Lords is all about power. What does this place exist to do? To fight, or to ponce about? To endorse or to challenge? To enrich democracy, or extend the life of the second chamber as a post-modern fig leaf for the excesses of the first? The Government is not prepared to give a clear answer to these questions. That's why Lord Richard, the leader of the Lords, devoted the Cabinet's first big speech on the subject yesterday not to the power but the people. Who , shall sit there? It is the easy, but wholly distracting, issue.

Hereditary peers have no place in a legislature, and Lord Richard spent a long time saying so. He sounded like a man who thought he was uttering a sentiment of the profoundest radicalism. That argument, however, has been won, which is already an achievement. It is possible to construct a scenario where the old buffers play their own power-game, They could decline to comply with their expulsion and, having nothing more to lose, scorch their inheritance and block the Government's programme. Though some life peers might become death peers, with Labour's worthies forced into months of all-night sessions to get the measures through, this is an option. But the Tories would have a hard time making it sound in, any way legitimate. I don't think it will happen.

After the people, however, there is the power, and, as to that, Lord Richard's opaqueness was a disguise for what promises to be abject conservatism. Don't press us on the second stage of reform, he urged. One thing at a time. Let us create our nominated interim quango, though this must 'be regarded as legitimate', and its method of selection therefore modified. But, whatever then happened, the Lords 'should exercise no more than its present powers'. Its power 'will remain unaltered'. For it makes 'an important contribution'. It is 'an essential part' of the legislature. His lordship said he could have extolled many more of the second chamber's virtues, except that this might imply that the first chamber 'is not doing its job properly' — a charge, we're meant smirkingly to understand, no peer would dare to level.

Such rolling unctuousness gives a taste of things to come. It was a catalogue of complacent fictions. The Lords, as presently powered, has very little function. Unless an election beckons, as in the rare case of the Police Bill last year, it has no leverage. It is not essential, or even important. Its work on Europe, touted as the peak of its scrutinising diligence, is, though competent enough, a nullity. Brussels, like Whitehall, offers a patronising glance and carries on regardless. The fabled expertise of the second chamber, though often impressive, is evacuated into the empty air: admired by its exponents, greeted with mutual sycophancy, but of no importance to a government with a massive democratic majority.

The power, therefore, must come first. Are these evacuations ever to be allowed to count? Will the Lords be made into a body the government is forced, on moderately rare occasions, to listen to? Or will the conspiracy of deluded rubbish peddled by Lord Richard, which says how wonderful the Lords is and always will be as long as it has 'a different class of member', continue to satisfy 'reformers'?

Real reform would look something like this. The chamber would lose all its existing members, inherited and life. A new membership would be partly nominated, to meet the need for cross-bench expertise, but mostly elected, to supply minimal legitimacy. Both categories would be there for a fixed term, and the nominees could not have another. An electoral cycle would be constructed, with perhaps a third of the seats being vacated every three years of a nine-year term, to ensure a different pattern from the Commons: The new chamber, from which the designation 'Lord' would disappear, would be more legitimate than now without being able to challenge the greater legitimacy of the Commons.

It would also have somewhat, but not hugely, greater powers. In other words, it could revise Bills better, bringing better weaponry to bear against such enormities as the present Data Protection Bill—far from alone—which has already had 200 on-the-hoof amendments from the Government itself. The Commons, with a massive majority of ambitious loyalists under iron command, is an almost useless scrutineer. But, as well as more revising, the new body would have special powers to protect the constitution and human rights. Without this, there's nothing to stop another government, for example, from emulating the most neglected vileness of the last lot, the conniving by Prime Minister Major and Lord Chancellor Mackay to amend the 1688 Bill of Rights at the sole behest of that parliamentary hero, Mr Neil Hamilton.

Lords reform is a subject replete with cranks and bores. That is what the anti-reformers, among whom Lord Richard and Lord Irvine are evidently preparing to count themselves, depend on. It produces such puerilities as the latest offering from Demos, which says the legislative task is so serious that it should be handed to people chosen by lottery. The scheme outlined above, taken from what is still the most compact and rational reform proposal, by Jeremy Mitchell and Anne Davies (IPPR, 1993), is a more serious challenge to the claim, by Blair and Richard, that they want a Lords that is 'more democratic and representative'.

So far, they haven't tried. The opposite tendency, packing in the nominees, is well under way. The annual count of life peers has risen from eight in 1988 to no fewer than 91 in 1997. This caused no fuss. I haven't seen the number in print. More will follow this month, as the super-quango, shorn of the birthright members, is readied for service, its interim status defended by Lord Richard on the basis of a promise about the future which will acquire credibility only when some public shape is put on it. But that, in turn, depends on attitude. Is this new, reformed thing to be a theatre where clubmen posture and place-men are rewarded? Where accountability is a giant pretence, and revision merely a congenial performance? Or will it be designed to make government more careful, more apprehensive, and daily more intimate with the public interest? If not, the new second chamber will be an updated excrescence, worse than the old, and the best argument for burdening the public purse with only single-chamber government.

Overall, not v. well written. Obvious intro to the spec. cuts in the UK HoL,

Makes non-ply virus & conduct comdns

But

Authors' Response

9 June 1998

Dear Guardian,

Hugo Young needs to read before he writes. He dismisses our Demos pamphlet *The Athenian Option* because it, 'says the legislative task is so serious that it should be handed to people chosen by lottery'. We propose nothing of the sort. If the role of the second chamber is to be limited to scrutiny, then this could be carried out by citizens' juries alongside appointed members (equivalent to life peers). Such an assembly could be 50 per cent women and drawn proportionately from the regions. We point out, with emphasises in the original: 'Citizen Peers would *not* be asked to be legislators…It would be unacceptable to allow membership of our body of *legislators* to be decided by lottery'.

Young insists on a second chamber on the German model. We argue that, 'Instead of trying to catch up with other countries, Britain should use the opportunity offered by constitutional reform to move ahead and experiment with new forms of democracy'. The last state in the world to cling to a hereditary parliament could become the first to introduce direct democracy within its portals. What Young regards a 'puerile' today, the world might see as an example of the creativity and inventiveness of the British people — once they have discarded the influence of their paternalistic elite.

Anthony Barnett
& Peter Carty
c/o 9 Bridewell Place
London EC4V 6AP

Sortition and Public Policy

General Editor: Barbara Goodwin, University of East Anglia

A major new series on the use of randomisation in education, politics and other public policy areas

The Political Potential of Sortition: A study of the random selection of citizens for public office *by Oliver Dowlen*

The central feature of every true lottery is that all rational evaluation is deliberately excluded. Once this principle is grasped, the author argues, we can begin to understand exactly what benefits sortition can bring to the political community. The book includes a study of the use of sortition in ancient Athens and in late medieval and renaissance Italy. It also includes commentary on the contributions to sortition made by Machiavelli, Guicciardini, Harrington and Paine; an account of the history of the randomly-selected jury; and new research into lesser-known examples from England, America and revolutionary France. The DPhil thesis on which this book was based won the Sir Ernest Barker Prize in Political Theory for 2007 from the Political Studies Association.

300 pp., £30 / $58, 978-1845401375 (cloth), Aug. 2008

The Nature and Uses of Lotteries

Thomas Gataker (ed. Conall Boyle)

Thomas Gataker was a disputatious Puritan divine. His *The Nature and Uses of Lotteries* (1627) was the first systematic exposition of a modern view of lotteries, not just as a form of gambling, but as a fair method of division. Gataker approved of these uses, but condemned divination and sorcery using random signs or spells. This important treatise is often referred to, but is generally inaccessible due to its rarity and old-style of language. The text of this edition has been fully modernised, with notes on important sources used by Gataker and includes a new introduction and index.

'A well-reasoned and curious book, teeming with quaint learning.' **William Lecky** (1865)

300 pp., £17.95 / $34.90, 978-1845401177 (pbk.), Aug. 2008

Justice By Lottery *by Barbara Goodwin*

This book is about the virtues and social justice of random distribution. The first chapter is a utopian fragment about a future country, Aleatoria, where everything, including political power, jobs and money, is distributed by lottery. The rest of the book is devoted to considering the idea of the lottery in terms of the conventional components and assumptions of theories of justice, and to reviewing the possible applications of lottery distribution in contemporary society – including education and political representation. Revised second edition.

'*Justice by Lottery* will richly repay close reading.' *Mind*

'Imaginative and provocative'. **Jonathan Riley**, *Ethics*

'Weighs in as the year's most dangerous political book. It should provide a sensation.' *New Statesman*

250 pp., £17.95 / $34.90, 978-1845400255 (pbk; 2nd edition)

The following two essays, printed back to back in a single volume, offer complementary solutions to the democratic deficit in Britain and the USA

Sutherland, *A People's Parliament* / Callenbach & Phillips, *A Citizen Legislature*, 350 pp., £14.95 / $29.90, 978-1845401085 (pbk.); £30 / $58 978-1845401382 (cloth), Aug. 2008

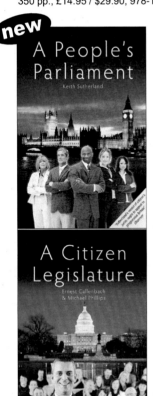

new

A People's Parliament
Keith Sutherland

In his book *The Party's Over: Blueprint for a Very English Revolution* (2004), Keith Sutherland questioned the role of the party in the post-ideological age and concluded that it would be better for government ministers to be appointed by headhunters and held to account by a people's parliament selected by lot. This completely revised and updated edition includes a study of the recent literature on deliberative polling.

'Sutherland's model of citizen's juries ought to have much greater appeal to progressive Britain.' **Tim Luckhurst**, *Observer*

'An extremely valuable contribution.' **Graham Allen MP**, *Tribune*

'A political essay in the best tradition – shrewd, erudite, polemical, partisan, mischievous and highly topical.' *Contemporary Political Theory*

A Citizen Legislature
Ernest Callenbach & Michael Phillips (intro. Peter Stone)

The American founders proposed that their legislature should be 'an exact portrait, in miniature, of the people at large'. Whether or not this was true at the time, the exponential growth of the population, skyrocketing campaign funding, the power of pressure groups, the grease of the pork-barrel and the dominance of charisma and demagoguery means that the US Constitution could now better be described as a kleptocracy. This pioneering essay proposes selecting Congressional members by random lot (leaving the Senate and Presidency unchanged) to 'restore a direct, powerful voice in Washington to the whole of America'. Originally published in 1985, this new edition includes an introduction by political scientist Peter Stone.

The Athenian Option: An idea whose time is coming
Anthony Barnett and Peter Carty

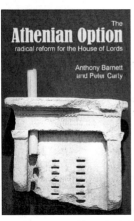

Before New Labour came to power and when even the prospect of reform of Britain's House of Lords was regarded with scepticism, Anthony Barnett and Peter Carty developed the idea of selecting part of a new upper house by lot: creating a jury or juries, that are representative of the population as a whole while being selected at random, to assess legislation. This new edition of the original proposal includes an account of the reception of the idea, their evidence before the Commission on the Lords established by Tony Blair, and a response to the great advances in citizen-based deliberation that have taken place since the mid-1990s. It concludes with a new appeal to adopt their approach as efforts to reform the Lords continue. Anthony Barnett was the first director of Charter 88 and is the founder of openDemocracy.net; Peter Carty is a journalist and writer.

112 pp., £8.95 / $17.90, 978-1845401399 (pbk.); £25 / $40 978-1845401405 (cloth), Aug. 2008